PURE MATHEMATICS

1. ALGEBRA

SECOND EDITION

ANTHONY NICOLAIDES

B.Sc. (Eng.), C. Eng. M.I.E.E.
SENIOR LECTURER

P.A.S.S. PUBLICATIONS

PRIVATE ACADEMIC & SCIENTIFIC STUDIES LTD

©   A. NICOLAIDES 1991, 1995

First Published in Great Britain 1991 by

Private Academic & Scientific Studies Limited

ISBN 1 872684 25 4

SECOND EDITION 1995

Titles by the same author in the GCE A series.

1. Algebra.

2. Trigonometry.

3. Complex Numbers.

4. Differential Calculus and Applications.

5. Cartesian and Polar Curve Sketching.

6.   Coordinate Geometry in two Dimensions.

7.   Integral Calculus and Applications.

8.   Vectors in two and three dimensions.

9.   Determinants and Matrices.

10.   Combinations. Permutations Probabilities.

PURE MATHEMATICS:
THE COMPLETE WORKS
GCE A LEVEL

Printed and bound in Great Britain by Hartnolls Limited, Bodmin, Cornwall

PREFACE

This book, which is part of the GCE A level series in Pure Mathematics covers the specialised topic of Algebra.

The GCE A level series in Pure Mathematics is comprised of ten books, covering the syllabuses of most examining boards. The books are designed to assist the student wishing to master the subject of Pure Mathematics. The series is easy to follow with minimum help. It can be easily adopted by a student who wishes to study it in the comforts of his home at his pace without having to attend classes formally; it is ideal for the working person who wishes to enhance his knowledge and qualification. Algebra book, like all the books in the series, is divided into two parts. In Part I, the theory is comprehensively dealt with, together with many worked examples and exercises. A step by step approach is adopted in all the worked examples. Part II of the book, a special and unique feature acts as a problem solver for all the exercises set at the end of each chapter in Part I.

This book develops the basic concepts and skills that are essential for the GCE A level in Pure Mathematics.

I am grateful to Mr. Myat Thaw Kaung, an excellent ex-student of mine, who typeset the manuscript superbly with great care on a desktop publishing system.

I am also grateful to Mr. Alex Yau for checking thoroughly this book.

I am also grateful to Mr. Constantin for drawing the diagrams in this book.

The GCE A is equivalent to the new advanced GNVQ level III.

Thanks are due to the following examining bodies who have kindly allowed me to use questions from their past examination papers.

Cambridge	C
Associated Examining Board	AEB
The University of London School Examinations	UL

The University of London School Examinations Board and The Associated Examining Board accept no responsibility whatsoever for the accuracy of working in the answers given.

Revised and improved edition

A. Nicolaides

1. ALGEBRA

CONTENTS

7. INDICES

Positive, negative, zero indices.

$$a^m \times a^n = a^{m+n}, \qquad a^m \div a^n = a^{m-n} \text{ superpowers } \left(a^m\right)^n = a^{mn},$$
$$\left(\left(\left(a^m\right)^n\right)^p\right)^q = a^{mnpq}.$$

A surd number. Rational and irrational numbers. $N^{m/n} = \sqrt[n]{N^m}$.
Root notation. Exponential functions.

8. LOGARITHMS

Definition. Rules of logarithms and proofs. $\log AB = \log A + \log B$

$$\log A^n = n \log A \qquad \log \frac{A}{B} = \log A - \log B.$$

Change of base. Solution of simultaneous equations.

9. EXPONENTIAL AND LOGARITHMIC FUNCTIONS.

Exponential Functions. Logarithmic functions. Graphs.

10. ARITHMETIC PROGRESSIONS

Arithmetic series, common difference, last term and sum of n terms.
Arithmetic means.

11. GEOMETRIC PROGRESSIONS

Common ratio, last term. Geometric means. Sum of n terms.
Convergent and divergent series.

Sum of an infinite geometric series. Applications.
Compound interest. Mortgage repayments.

12. THE BINOMIAL THEOREM

The binomial expansions for positive integers.

The combinational notation ^nC_r or $\binom{n}{r}$. Negative and fractional

indices. Pascal's triangle. The factorial notation.
Proof of the binomial theorem by mathematical induction.

Use of binomial expansions for approximate calculations.
Expansion of logarithmic functions. Expansion of trigonometic
functions. Expansion of exponential function.

13. THE SIGMA NOTATION AND SERIES 1-I/152

Σ the sigma notation.

Convergency. Divergency. Comparison test.
Derivation of summation of series.

$$\sum_{r=1}^{n} r, \sum_{r=1}^{n} r^2, \sum_{r=1}^{n} r^3, \sum_{r=1}^{n} r^4.$$

D'Alembert's ratio test. Testing for convergent and divergent series.

14. NON LINEAR TO LINEAR LAWS 1-I/167

$y = ax^2 + b,$ $\qquad y = \dfrac{a}{x} + b,$ $\qquad yx = bx + c$

$y^2 = ax^2 + b$ $\qquad y = ax^{2/3} + b,$ $\qquad y = ab^x,$ $\qquad y = ax^n$

$T = T_o e^{\mu\theta}, y = \dfrac{A}{x^n}, V = kl^n.$

ALGEBRAIC OPERATIONS

ADDITION

$$a + b = b + a$$

addend + augend = augend + addend = sum.

SUBTRACTIONS

$$a - b = \text{difference} \qquad a = \text{minuend}$$

minuend − subtrahend = difference $\qquad b$ = subtrahend.

MULTIPLICATION

$$a \times b = \text{product} \qquad a = \text{multiplicand}$$

multiplicand × multiplier = product $\qquad b$ = multiplier.

DIVISION

$$\frac{a}{b} = \textit{quotient} \qquad a = \text{divident}$$

$$\frac{\text{divident}}{\text{divisor}} = \text{quotient} \qquad b = \text{divisor.}$$

COMMUTATIVE LAW

$$a + b = b + a$$
$$a \times b = b \times a$$

ASSOCIATIVE LAW

$$(a + b) + c = a + (b + c)$$
$$(a \times b) \times c = a \times (b \times c).$$

DISTRIBUTIVE LAW

$$a \times (b + c) = a \times b + a \times c$$
$$(a + b) \times c = a \times c + b \times c.$$

DIRECTED NUMBERS

$$(-) \times (-) = (+) \qquad (-) \text{ minus sign}$$
$$(-) \times (+) = (-) \qquad (+) \text{ plus sign}$$
$$(+) \times (-) = (-) \qquad (\times) \text{ times}$$
$$(+) \times (+) = (+) \qquad (\div) \text{ divided by}$$

$$\frac{(-)}{(-)} = \frac{(+)}{(+)} = (+)$$

$$\frac{(+)}{(-)} = \frac{(-)}{(+)} = (-)$$

1. ALGEBRA

1. REMAINDER AND FACTOR THEOREMS

LONG DIVISION OF POLYNOMIALS

Divide $3x^3 - 2x^2 + x - 1$ by $x + 1$ and find the remainder

$$
\begin{array}{r}
3x^2 - 5x + 6 \\
x + 1 \overline{\smash{\big)}\ 3x^3 - 2x^2 + x - 1} \\
\underline{3x^3 + 3x^2} \\
-5x^2 + x - 1 \\
\underline{-5x^2 - 5x} \\
6x + 1 \\
\underline{6x + 6} \\
-7
\end{array}
$$

x into $3x^3$ goes $3x^2$, $3x^2$ times x is $3x^3$ and $3x^2$ times 1 is $3x^2$ subtract $3x^3 + 3x^2$ from $3x^3 - 2x^2 + x - 1$ gives $-5x^2 + x - 1$, x into $-5x^2$ goes $-5x$, $-5x$ times x is $-5x^2$ and $-5x$ times 1 is $-5x$, subtract $-5x^2 - 5x$ from $-5x^2 + x - 1$ gives $6x - 1$, x into $6x$ goes 6, 6 times x is $6x$ and 6 times 1 is 6, subtract $6x + 6$ from $6x - 1$, gives -7 which is the remainder of the long division.

Therefore $\dfrac{3x^3 - 2x^2 + x - 1}{x + 1} = 3x^2 - 5x + 6 + \dfrac{7}{x + 1}$.

Dividing a polynomial of degree three by a polynomial of degree one, gives a quotient of degree two, $3x^2 - 5x + 6$, and a remainder -7.

Let us try another example.

Find the remainder by dividing $5x^2 - 7x + 9$ by $x - 3$, by long division method.

$$
\begin{array}{r}
5x + 8 \\
x - 3 \overline{\smash{\big)}\ 5x^2 - 7x} \\
\underline{5x^2 - 15x} \\
8x + 9 \\
\underline{8x - 24} \\
33
\end{array}
$$

x into $5x^2$ goes $5x$, $5x$ times x is $5x^2$ and $5x$ times (-3) is $-15x$; subtract $5x^2 - 15x$ from $5x^2 - 7x + 9$ gives $8x + 9$, x into $8x$ goes 8, 8 times x is $8x$ and 8 times (-3) is -24; subtract $8x - 24$ from $8x + 9$ gives 33 which is the remainder.

$$\frac{5x^2 - 7x + 9}{x - 3} = 5x + 8 + \frac{33}{x - 3}.$$

FUNCTION NOTATION

$y = 3x^3 - x^2 + 5x - 5$ denotes that y is a function of x, x is an independent variable and y is a dependent variable. This expression can be denoted as

$$f(x) = 3x^3 - x^2 + 5x - 5$$

where $f(x)$ indicates that the function of f depends on and <u>not</u> that f is multiplied by (x).

Another function can be expressed by other letters such as $Q(x) = 5x^2 - 7x + 1$, here the function Q which is different from the function f, depends also on the value of (x).

Other examples of functions are:-

$g(t) = 3\sin t - 5\cos t$, g is a function of t, $p(Z) = 5Z^2 - \sin Z + e^z$,
p is a function of Z. However, a function of x is generally denoted as $f(x)$.

If $f(x) = 3x^3 - x^2 + 5x - 5$, then what does $f(0)$, $f(-1)$, $f(1)$ mean?
$f(0) = -5$, x is replaced by zero

$f(-1) = 3(-1)^3 - (-1)^2 + 5(-1) - 5 = -3 - 1 - 5 - 5 = -14$
x is replaced by -1

$f(1) = 3(1)^3 - 1^2 + 5(1) - 5 = 3 - 1 + 5 - 5 = 2$
x is replaced by 1.

POLYNOMIAL

$f(x) = 3x - 1$	first degree or linear
$f(x) = 2x^2 - 2x + 1$	second degree or quadratic
$f(x) = 3x^3 - x^2 + 5x - 5$	third degree or cubic
$f(x) = 4x^4 - 3x^3 + 2x^2 - x + 7$	fourth degree or quartic

are examples of several functions of x and generally

$f(x) = a_n x^n + a_{n-1} x^{n-1} + a_{n-2} x^{n-2} + \dots$ is a polynomial of nth degree.

All the above functions are polynomials, that is, function that consist of many terms such as $3x^4$, $5x^2$, $3x$. $5x^0$ or generally ax^n where 'a' is a multiple of an integral power of x.

WORKED EXAMPLE 1

A polynomial $f(x) = 5x^4 - 3x^3 + x^2 - x + 5$, find f(0), f(1), f(- 2).

SOLUTION 1

$f(0) = 5(0) - 3(0) + 0 - 0 + 5 = 5$

$f(1) = 5(1)^4 - 3(1)^3 + (1)^2 - (1) + 5 = 7$

$f(- 2) = 5(- 2)^4 - 3(- 2)^3 + (- 2)^2 - (- 2) + 5 = 80 + 24 + 4 + 2 + 5 = 115.$

WORKED EXAMPLE 2

Write down the values of g(0), f(- 1), p(a).

(i) $g(t) = 3\sin t - 5t^2 - 1$ (ii) $f(x) = 3x^2 - 5x + 1$

(iii) $p(y) = y^3 - y^2 + y - a.$

SOLUTION 2

(i) $g(0) = 3(0) - 5(0) - 1 = - 1$

(ii) $f(- 1) = 3(- 1)^2 - 5(- 1) + 1 = 3 + 5 + 1 = 9$

(iii) $p(a) = a^3 - a^2 + a - a = a^3 - a^2.$

THE REMAINDER THEOREM

If a polynomial $f(x)$ is divided by a linear expression $x - a$, the quotient is another function of one degree less than $f(x)$ such as $Q(x)$ and the remainder R is also one degree less than that of the divisor, $(x - a)$.

$$\frac{\text{divident}}{\text{divisor}} = \text{quotient} + \frac{\text{remainder}}{\text{divisor}}$$

$$\frac{f(x)}{x - a} = Q(x) + \frac{R}{x - a} \quad \dots (1)$$

multiplying each term of equation (1) by $x - a$, we have $f(x) \equiv Q(x)(x - a) + R$ which is an identity.

If $x = a$, then $f(a) = Q(a)(a - a) + R$, therefore $\boxed{R = f(a)}$

The remainder theorem tells us how to find the remainder quickly when a polynomial such as $f(x)$ is divided by a linear function such as $x - a$. The remainder is found by making $x - a = 0$ or $x = a$ is replaced in the function $f(x)$.

At the beginning of this chapter, the remainder was found by performing the long division which resulted in the tedious working.

If x is a polynomial of third degree and it is divided by a linear function, the quotient is of second degree and the remainder is one degree less than that of the divisior, a constant in this case.

WORKED EXAMPLE 3

Find the remainders if $f(x) = 3x^3 - 2x^2 + x - 1$ is divided by (i) $x - 1$, (ii) $x + 1$.

SOLUTION 3

(i) $R = f(1) = 3(1)^3 - 2(1)^2 + 1 - 1 = 3 - 2 + 1 - 1 = 1$

(ii) $R = f(-1) = 3(-1)^3 - 2(-1)^2 + 1(-1) - 1 = -3 - 2 - 1 - 1 = -7$

By long division

$$
\begin{array}{r}
3x^2 + x + 2 \\
x - 1 \, \overline{\smash{\big)}\, 3x^3 - 2x^2 + x - 1} \\
\underline{3x^3 - 3x^2} \\
x^2 + x - 1 \\
\underline{x^2 - x} \\
2x - 1 \\
\underline{2x - 2} \\
1
\end{array}
\qquad
\begin{array}{r}
3x^2 - 5x + 6 \\
x + 1 \, \overline{\smash{\big)}\, 3x^3 - 2x^2 + x - 1} \\
\underline{3x^3 + 3x^2} \\
-5x^2 + x - 1 \\
\underline{-5x^2 - 5x} \\
6x - 1 \\
\underline{6x + 6} \\
-7
\end{array}
$$

The remainder is 1.   The remainder is -7

WORKED EXAMPLE 4

If $f(x) = -x^3 + 2x^2 - 3x + 4$ obtain the remainders when $f(x)$ is divided by

(i) $x + 1$ (ii) $(x - 1)$ (iii) $x^2 - 1$.

SOLUTION 4

(i) $R = f(-1) = -(-1)^3 + 2(-1)^2 - 3(-1) + 4 = 1 + 2 + 3 + 4 = 10$

(ii) $R = f(1) = -1 + 2 - 3 + 4 = 2$

(iii) $\dfrac{f(x)}{x^2 - 1} = Q(x) + \dfrac{R(x)}{x^2 - 1}$

   $f(x) \equiv Q(x)(x^2 - 1) + R(x)$

   This is an identity, if $x = 1$ $f(1) = R(1)$.

   If $x = -1$, $f(-1) = R(-1)$, but $R(x) = ax + b$ is a polynomial of degree one

   $R(1) = a + b = f(1) = 2$ $R(-1) = -a + b = f(-1) = 10$

solving these simultaneous equations

$$a + b = 2$$
$$-a + b = 10$$
$$\overline{2b = 12}$$

$$\boxed{b = 6}$$

$$a = 2 - 6 = -4$$

$$\boxed{a = -4}$$

and therefore $R(x) = -4x + 6$ is the remainder checking this result by long division

$$
\begin{array}{r}
-x + 2 \\
x^2 - 1 \enclose{longdiv}{-x^3 + 2x^2 - 3x + 4} \\
-x^3 + 0x^2 + x \\
\hline
2x^2 - 4x + 4 \\
2x^2 + 0x - 2 \\
\hline
-4x + 6 \text{ the remainder}
\end{array}
$$

WORKED EXAMPLE 5

If $f(x) = x^5 + 3x^4 - 2x^3 + x^2 - 1$, obtain the remainder when $f(x)$ is divided by

(i) $x + 3$ (ii) $x - 3$ and   (iii) $x^2 - 9$.

SOLUTION 5

(i) $R = f(-3) = (-3)^5 + 3(-3)^4 - 2(-3)^3 + (-3)^2 - 1$

$\qquad\qquad = -243 + 243 + 54 + 9 - 1 = 62$

(ii) $R = f(3) = (3)^5 + 3(3)^4 - 2(3)^3 + (3)^2 - 1 = 243 + 243 - 54 + 9 - 1$

$\qquad\qquad = 440$

(iii) $R(x) = ax + b$ $\qquad R(-3) = f(-3) = -3a + b = 62$ ... (1)

$\qquad\qquad\qquad\qquad\quad R(3) = f(3) = 3a + b = 440$ ... (2)

adding equations (1) and (2) $2b = 502$

$$\boxed{b = 251}$$

substituting b into (2), $3a = 440 - 251 = 189$ $a = 63$.

The remainder therefore is $63x + 251 = R(x)$.

Therefore, from the above examples, we can establish a more general theorem.

$$\frac{f(x)}{(x - a)(x - b)} = Q(x) + \frac{R(x)}{(x - a)(x - b)}$$

$f(x) \equiv Q(x)(x - a)(x - b) + R(x)$, if $R(x) = Ax + B$.

If $x = a$, $f(a) = R(a) = Aa + B$ ... (1)

If $x = b$, $f(b) = R(b) = Ab + B$ ... (2)

Therefore, the remainder $R(x) = \dfrac{f(a) - f(b)}{a - b} x + \dfrac{af(b) - b = f(a)}{a - b}$

since $f(a) - f(b) = Aa - Ab$ or $A = \dfrac{f(a) - f(b)}{a - b}$

$b\, f(a) = Aab + Bb$ $a(b) = Aab + Ba$

$af(b) - bf(a) = B(a - b)$ or $B = \dfrac{af(b) - bf(a)}{a - b}$

THE FACTOR THEOREM

If f(x) is exactly divisible by $x - a$ then the remainder is zero

$$\frac{f(x)}{x - a} = Q(x) + \frac{0}{x - a} \qquad f(x) \equiv Q(x)(x - a)$$

If $x = a$ $\qquad$ $f(a) = Q(a)(a - a) = 0$

therefore $\boxed{f(a) = 0}$

WORKED EXAMPLE 6

Factorise the following expressions:-

(i) $a^3 + b^3$ $\qquad$ (ii) $a^2 - b^2$ $\qquad$ (iii) $a^3 - b^3$ $\qquad$ (iv) $8x^3 - 27y^3$ $\qquad$ (v) $x^4 - y^4$.

SOLUTION 6

(i) $\quad a^3 + b^3$ $\quad$ if $a = -b$, $(-b)^3 + b^3 = 0$

therefore, $a + b$ is a factor of $a^3 + b^3$ and by long division

$$
\begin{array}{r}
a^2 - ab + b^2 \\
a + b \overline{\big)\, a^3 + 0 + 0 + b^3} \\
a^3 + a^2 b \\
\hline
-a^2 b + 0 + b^3 \\
-a^2 b - ab^2 \\
\hline
ab^2 + b^3 \\
ab^2 + b^3 \\
\hline
0 \ (\text{remainder})
\end{array}
$$

therefore $\boxed{a^3 + b^3 = (a + b)\left(a^2 - ab + b^2\right)}$

(ii) $\quad a^2 - b^2$, if $a = b$, $b^2 - b^2 = 0$ and

therefore, $a - b$ is a factor of $a^2 - b^2$ and by long division

$$\begin{array}{r} a + b \\ a - b \enclose{longdiv}{a^2 + 0 - b^2} \\ a^2 - ab \\ \hline ab - b^2 \\ ab - b^2 \\ \hline 0 \text{ (remainder)} \end{array}$$

therefore $\boxed{a^2 - b^2 = (a - b)(a + b)}$

(iii) $a^3 - b^3$, if $a = b$, $b^3 - b^3 = 0$ and

therefore, $a - b$ is a factor of $a^3 - b^3$ and by long division

$$\begin{array}{r} a^2 + ab + b^2 \\ a + b \enclose{longdiv}{a^3 + 0 + 0 - b^3} \\ a^3 - a^2 b \\ \hline a^2 b + 0 - b^3 \\ a^2 b - ab^2 \\ \hline ab^2 - b^3 \\ ab^2 - b^3 \\ \hline 0 \text{ (remainder)} \end{array}$$

therefore $\boxed{a^3 - b^3 = (a - b)(a^2 + ab + b^2)}$

(iv) $8x^3 - 27y^3$.

If $2x = 3y$, then $(2x)^3 = (3y)^3$, $27y^3 = 0$ and therefore $(2x - 3y)$ is a factor of $8x^3 - 27y^3$ and by long division

$$\begin{array}{r} 4x^2 - 6xy + 9y^2 \\ 2x - 3y \enclose{longdiv}{8x^3 - 27y^3} \\ 8x^3 - 12x^2 y \\ \hline 12x^2 y - 17y^3 \\ 12x^2 y - 18xy^2 \\ \hline 18xy^2 - 27y^3 \\ 18xy^2 - 27y^3 \\ \hline 0 \text{ remainder} \end{array}$$

therefore $\boxed{8x^3 - 27y^3 \equiv (2x - 3y)(4x^2 + 6xy + 9y^2)}$

(v) $x^4 - y^4$.

If $x = y$, $y^4 - y^4 = 0$, therefore $x - y$ is a factor of $x^4 - y^4$.

If $x = -y$, $(-y)^4 - y^4 = 0$, therefore, $x + y$ is also another factor of $x^4 - y^4$

and $(x - y)(x + y) = x^2 - y^2$ is a factor of $x^4 - y^4$ and by long division

$$
\begin{array}{r}
x^2 + y^2 \\
x^2 - y^2 \enclose{longdiv}{x^4 - y^4} \\
x^4 - x^2 y^2 \\
\hline
x^2 y^2 - y^4 \\
x^2 y^2 - y^4 \\
\hline
\end{array}
$$

0 (remainder)

Therefore $x^4 - y^4 = \left(x^2 - y^2\right)\left(x^2 + y^2\right)$

$$\boxed{x^4 - y^4 \equiv (x - y)(x + y)\left(x^2 + y^2\right)}$$

SOLUTION OF CUBIC AND QUARTIC EQUATIONS

Solve $(x + 1)(x - 1)(x + 2) = 0$ the solution is easy and it is $x = -1$ or $x = 1$ or $x = -2$, since $x + 1 = 0$ or $x - 1 = 0$ or $x + 2 = 0$.

Multiply out $(x + 1)(x - 1)(x + 2) = (x^2 - 1)(x + 2) = x^3 - x + 2x^2 - 2$
$$= x^3 + 2x^2 - x - 2.$$

Solve the equation $x^3 + 2x^2 - x - 2 = 0$.

In solving this cubic equation, we try by the trial and error method to find a value of x that makes this equation zero. The trial solutions in this context must be simple, such as $0, \pm 1, \pm 2, \pm 3$ or $\pm \dfrac{1}{2}$.

Let $x = 1$, then f(1) $= 1^3 + 2(1)^2 - 1 - 2 = 1 + 2 - 1 - 2 = 0$, therefore, $x - 1$ is a factor.

Let $x = -1$, then f(-1) $= (-1)^3 + 2(-1)^2 - (-1) - 2 = -1 + 2 + 1 - 2 = 0$, therefore $x + 1$ is another factor.

Let $x = -2$, then $f(-2) = (-2)^3 + 2(-2)^2 - (-2) - 2 = -8 + 8 + 2 - 2 = 0$
and $x + 2$ is also a factor.

Therefore, $x^3 + 2x^2 - x - 2$ is completely factorised to $(x + 1)(x - 1)(x + 2)$
$x^3 + 2x^2 - x - 2 \equiv (x + 1)(x - 1)(x + 2)$.

WORKED EXAMPLE 7

Factorise the following functions:-

(i) $x^3 - x^2 - 4x + 4$ (ii) $x^3 - x^2 - 2x$ (iii) $2x^3 - 3x^2 - 3x + 2$.

SOLUTION 7

(i) $f(x) = x^3 - x^2 - 4x + 4$

     $f(1) = 1 - 1 - 4 + 4 = 0$ therefore $x - 1$ is a factor.

     $f(2) = 8 - 4 - 8 + 4 = 0$ therefore $x - 2$ is another factor.

     $f(-1) = (-1)^3 - (1)^2 - 4(-1) + 4 = -1 - 1 + 4 + 4 = 6$
     $x + 1$ is <u>not</u> a factor.

     $f(-2) = (-2)^3 - (-2)^2 - 4(-2) + 4 = -8 - 4 + 8 + 4 = 0$
     $x + 2$ is another factor,

     therefore, $f(x) = x^3 - x^2 - 4x + 4 = (x - 1)(x - 2)(x + 2)$.

(ii) $f(x) = x^3 - x^2 - 2x$

     $f(0) = 0$ therfore x is a factor

     $f(1) = 1 - 1 - 2 = -2$, $x - 1$ is <u>not</u> a factor

     $f(-1) = (-1)^3 - (-1)^2 - 2(-1) = -1 - 1 + 2 = 0$, $x + 1$ is a factor

     $f(2) = (2)^3 - (2)^2 - 2(2) = 8 - 4 - 4 = 0$, $x - 2$ is a factor.

     therefore, $f(x) = x^3 - x^2 - 2x = x(x - 2)(x + 1)$.

(iii) $f(x) = 2x^3 - 3x^2 - 3x + 2$

     $f(1) = 2 - 3 - 3 + 2 = -2$, $(x - 1)$ is not a factor

     $f(-1) = 2(-1)^3 - 3(-1)^2 - 3(-1) + 2 = -2 - 3 + 3 + 2 = 0$
     $x + 1$ is a factor

     $f(-2) = 2(-2)^3 - 3(-2)^2 - 3(-2) + 2 = 2(-8) - 12 + 6 + 2 = -20$
     $x + 2$ is not a factor

$f(0) = 2(0) - 3(0) - 3(0) + 2 = 2$, x is not a factor

Since $f(0) > 0$ and $f(1) < 0$, there must have a point between 0 and 1, which will make $f(x) = 0$.

$$f\left(\frac{1}{2}\right) = 2\left(\frac{1}{8}\right) - 3\left(\frac{1}{4}\right) - 3\left(\frac{1}{2}\right) + 2 = \frac{1}{4} - \frac{3}{4} - \frac{3}{2} + 2 = 0$$

$x - \dfrac{1}{2} = 0$ or $2x - 1$ is a factor, therefore

$$f(x) = (2x - 1)(x + 1)(x - 2)$$

WORKED EXAMPLE 8

Factorise the following functions:-

(i) $x^3 + 1$ (ii) $3x^3 + 2x^2 + 4x + 5$ (iii) $x^4 + 2x^3 - 13x^2 - 14x + 24$

SOLUTION 8

(i) $f(x) = x^3 + 1$

   $f(-1) = (-1)^3 + 1 = 0$, $x + 1$ is a factor and by long division

$$
\begin{array}{r}
x^2 - x + 1 \\
x + 1 \; {\overline{\smash{\big)}\, x^3 + 1}} \\
\underline{x^3 + x^2} \\
-x^2 + 1 \\
\underline{-x^2 - x} \\
x + 1 \\
\underline{x + 1} \\
0 \text{ (remainder)}
\end{array}
$$

   $f(x) = x^3 + 1 = (x + 1)(x^2 - x + 1)$ the quadratic factor has no other linear factors since $D = (-1)^2 - 4(1) = 1 - 4 = -3$, the discriminant is negative.

(ii) $f(x) = 3x^3 + 2x^2 + 4x + 5$

   $f(-1) = 3(-1)^2 + 2(-1)^2 + 4(-1) + 5 = -3 + 2 - 4 + 5 = 0$
   $x + 1$ is a factor

   $f(1) = 3 + 2 + 4 + 5 = 14$ $x - 1$ is not a factor

$f(2) = 24 + 8 + 8 + 5 = 45 \qquad x - 2$ is not a factor

$f(-2) = -24 + 8 + 5 = 19 \qquad x + 2$ is not a factor.

The trial solutions are becoming tedious, since $x + 1$ is a factor, we can find the quadratic factor by long division.

$$
\begin{array}{r}
3x^2 - x + 5 \\
x + 1 \enclose{longdiv}{3x^3 + 2x^2 + 4x + 5} \\
3x^3 + 3x^2 \\
\hline
-x^2 + 4x + 5 \\
-x^2 - x \\
\hline
5x + 5 \\
5x + 5 \\
\hline
0 \text{ (remainder)}
\end{array}
$$

therefore $f(x) = (x + 1)(3x^2 - x + 5)$ the quadratic factor has no linear factors since, $D = (-1)^2 - 4(3)(5) = +1 - 60 = -59$, the discriminant is negative.

(iii) $f(x) = x^4 + 2x^3 - 13x^2 - 14x + 24$

$f(1) = 1 + 2 - 13 - 14 + 24 = 0,\ x - 1$ is factor

$f(-1) = 1 - 2 - 13 + 14 + 24 = 24,\ x + 1$ is not a factor

$f(2) = 16 + 16 - 52 - 28 + 24 = -24,\ x - 2$ is not a factor

$f(-2) = 16 - 16 - 52 + 28 + 24 = 0,\ x + 2$ is a factor

$x - 1$ and $x + 2$ are factors so far and by long division we have

$$
\begin{array}{r}
x^2 + x - 12 \\
x^2 + x - 2 \enclose{longdiv}{x^4 + 2x^3 - 13x^2 - 14x + 24} \\
x^4 + x^3 - 2x^2 \\
\hline
x^3 - 11x^2 - 14x + 24 \\
x^3 - x^2 - 2x \\
\hline
-12x^2 - 12x + 24 \\
-12x^2 - 12x + 24 \\
\hline
0 \text{ (remainder)}
\end{array}
$$

$f(x) = (x - 1)(x + 2)(x^2 + x - 12)$

$x^2 + x - 12$ factorises $\qquad x^2 + 4x - 3x - 12 = (x + 4) - 3(x + 4)$

$$= (x - 3)(x + 4).$$

$\therefore\ f(x) = (x - 1)(x + 2)(x - 3)(x + 4).$

EXERCISES 1

1. Divide the following polynomials by the linear functions shown adjacently by long division and hence find the remainders

   (i) $-x^4 - 3x^3 - x^2 - 7x - x - 2$ by $x + 3$

   (ii) $x^3 + x^2 + x + 1$ by $x - 2$

   (iii) $-x^3 + x^2 - x + 1$ by $x - 2$.

2. Find the remainders of the polynomials shown in question 1 when divided by the linear expressions shown adjacently using the remainder theorem.

3. Solve the following equations:-

   (i) $x^3 + 2x^2 - 5x - 6 = 0$ (ii) $x^3 - 3x^2 - 4x + 12 = 0$

   (iii) $x^4 - a^4 = 0$ (iv) $x^3 - 3x^2 + x + 2 = 0$

   (vi) $6x^3 + x^2 - x = 0$

4. Find the remainder when $x^{25} + x^{35}$ is divided by $(x - 1)$.

5. Find the remainder when $x^7 - x^5$ is divided by $(x + 1)$.

6. Find the value of a if $x - 3$ is a factor of $x^3 + x^2 + ax + 7$.

7. Find the values of a and b if $-5x^3 + ax^2 + 7x - b$ is exactly divisible by $x - 2$ and also by $x - 1$.

8. When $ax^2 + bx + c$ is divided by x the remainder is 1; when divided by $x - 1$ the remainder is 2 and when divided by $x + 2$ the remainder is -9. Find a, b and c.

9. One factor of $ax^2 + bx + c$ is $x - 1$, find the other factor, if $a = 4$ and $c = 1$.

10. One root of $x^3 - 2x^2 + x + c$, is 2, find the other roots and state if they are real or complex.

11. If the polynomial $x^3 + ax^2 + bx - 5 = f(x)$ is divided by $x - 1$ the remainder is 3, when $f(x)$ is divided by $x + 1$ the remainder is 4. Determine a and b.

12. Find the values of a and b of $f(x)$ in the exercise 11, such that $f(x)$ is divisible by $(x + 2)$, and has a remainder of 50, if it is divided by $x - 1$.

13. If $f(x) \equiv ax^2 + bx + c$ is divided by $(x + 1)$, $(x - 1)$, $(x + 2)$ the remainders are respectively: $- 1, 4, 9$. Find a, b and c.

14. A quadratic equation is given by $f(x) = ax^2 + bx + c$, find a, b and c such that $f(x)$ is exactly divisible by $(x - 1)$ and has remainders 5 and $- 7$ when divided by $(x + 1)$ and $(x - 2)$ respectively.

   Determine $P(x) \equiv (ax^2 + bx + c)(dx + 1)^2$, where d is constant, given that, on division by $(x + 2)^2$, the remainder is $25x + 197$.

15. When $f(x) = x^4 + ax^3 + bx^2 + cx + 1$ is divided by $x^2 + 3x - 4$ the remainder is $- 30x + 20$ and when divided by $x^2 - 6x + 5$ the remainder is $20x - 30$. Find the values of a, b, c and d. Solve $f(x) = 0$.

16. When a polynomial $F(x)$ is divided by $x - 3$ the remainder is 1, and when it is divided by $x + 1$ the remainder is $- 15$. When it is divided by $(x - 3)(x + 1)$ the remainder is $ax + b$. Find the values of a and b.

17. When $P(x) = x^3 + ax^2 + bx + c$ is divided by $x^2 + 4x + 4$ the remainder is $2x + 3$. Given that $x + 1$ is a factor of $P(x)$, determine the values of a, b and c.

18. Prove the remainder and factor theorems.

19. When $F(x) = x^3 + ax^2 + bx + c$ is divided by $x - 1$ the remainder is 27 and when divided by $x^2 - 4$ the remainder is $- 30$. Find the values of a, b and c.

20. When $x^3 + ax^2 + bx + c$ is divided by $x + 4$, the remainder is 5. If $x^2 - 9$ is a factor of the polynomial, find the values of a, b and c.

2. PARTIAL FRACTIONS

IDENTITIES

What is the difference between an identity and an equation?

Let us first consider an equation $3x = 2$, this equation has the solution $x = \dfrac{2}{3}$ and therefore it is only satisfied if we substitute $x = \dfrac{2}{3}$ in the equation $3x = 2$, $3\left(\dfrac{2}{3}\right) = 2$. Another example, consider the equation $x^2 = 1$, which is satisfied only by the two values $x = \pm 1$, that is, if $x = 1$, $(1)^2 = 1$ and if $x = -1$, $(-1)^2 = 1$. But $x^2 - 1 \equiv (x - 1)(x + 1)$, which is read at $x^2 - 1$ is identically equal to $(x - 1)(x + 1)$.

This identity, for any value of x, the L.H.S. (Left Hand Side) is equal to the R.H.S. (Right Hand Side).

L.H.S. $= x^2 - 1$ R.H.S. $= (x - 1)(x + 1)$.

If $x = 2$, L.H.S. $= 3$ R.H.S. $= (2 - 1)(2 + 1) = 1 \times 3 = 3$.

If $x = 1$, L.H.S. $= 0$ R.H.S. $= 0$.

WORKED EXAMPLE 9

Find the values of the constants A and B such that $3x - 1 \equiv A(x + 3) + B(x - 1)$.

SOLUTION 9

$3x - 1 \equiv A(x + 3) + B(x - 1)$
$3x - 1 \equiv Ax + 3A + Bx - B = (A + B)x + 3A - B.$

Equating coefficients, we have:-

$3 = A + B$ ... (1) the coefficients of x
$-1 = 3A - B$ ... (2) the coefficients of x^0 or the constant terms and solving these equations, by adding (1) and (2) $4A = 2$

$$\boxed{A = \frac{1}{2}}$$

then substitute $A = \dfrac{1}{2}$ in (1), $3 = \dfrac{1}{2} + B$ or $\boxed{B = \dfrac{5}{2}}$

Alternatively.

The values of the constants A and B may be found easily by the <u>cover up rule</u>, in other words, the value of x that will make $A(x + 3) = 0$, that is, $x = -3$ and the value of x that will make $B(x - 1) = 0$, that is, $x = 1$.

If $x = -3$, $B = \dfrac{3(-3) - 1}{-3 - 1} = \dfrac{-10}{-4} = \dfrac{5}{2}$ $\qquad \boxed{B = \dfrac{5}{2}}$

If $x = 1$, $A = \dfrac{3(1) - (1)}{1 + 3} = \dfrac{2}{4} = \dfrac{1}{2}$ $\qquad \boxed{A = \dfrac{1}{2}}$

WORKED EXAMPLE 10

Find the values of the constants A, B and C such that
$$3x^2 - 7x + 9 \equiv A(x + 1)(x + 3) + B(x + 2)(x + 3) + C(x + 1)(x + 2).$$

SOLUTION 10

$$3x^2 - 7x + 9 \equiv A(x + 1)(x + 3) + B(x + 2)(x + 3) + C(x + 1)(x + 2).$$

METHOD I Employing the method of **equating coefficients**

$$3x^2 - 7x + 9 \equiv A(x^2 + 4x + 3) + B(x^2 + 5x + 6) + C(x^2 + 3x + 2)$$

$$3x^2 - 7x + 9 \equiv (A + B + C)x^2 + (4A + 5B + 3C)x + (3A + 6B + 2C).$$

The coefficients of x^2

$$A + B + C = 3 \; ... \; (1)$$

The coefficients of x

$$4A + 5B + 3C = -7 \; ... \; (2)$$

the coefficients of x^0 or the constants

$$3A + 6B + 2C = 9 \; ... \; (3)$$

To find A, B and C, we solve equations (1), (2) and (3). Eliminate A from (1) and (2)

$$4 \times (1) \qquad 4A + 4B + 4C = 12 \ \dots \ (4)$$
$$-1 \times (2) \qquad -4A - 5B - 3C = 7 \quad \dots \ (5)$$

Adding (4) and (5)

$$-B + C = 19 \quad \dots \ (8)$$

Eliminate A from (2) and (3)

$$3 \times (2) \qquad 12A + 15B + 9C = -21 \ \dots \ (6)$$
$$-4 \times (3) \qquad -12A - 24B - 8C = -36 \quad \dots \ (7)$$

Adding (6) and (7), $\qquad -9B + C = -57 \qquad \dots \ (9)$

subtracting (9) from (8)

$$8B = 19 + 57 \qquad B = \frac{76}{8} = \frac{19}{2} \qquad \boxed{B = \frac{19}{2}}$$

substituting this value in (8)

$$C = 19 + B = 19 + \frac{19}{2} \Rightarrow \qquad \boxed{C = \frac{57}{2}}$$

From (1) $A + B + C = 3$, $A = 3 - \dfrac{19}{2} - \dfrac{57}{2} = -35.$

Therefore, $A = -35$, $B = B = \dfrac{19}{2}$, $C = \dfrac{57}{2}$.

As it can be seen, the above calculation is rather tedious and long.

METHOD II

THE COVER UP RULE

$$3x^2 - 7x + 9 \equiv A(x + 1)(x + 3) + B(x + 2)(x + 3) + C(x + 1)(x + 2).$$

If $x = -1$, $3(-1)^2 - 7(-1) + 9 = A(-1 + 1)(-1 + 3) + B(-1 + 2)(-1 + 3) +$
$$C(-1 + 1)(-1 + 2)$$

$$\boxed{B = \frac{19}{2}}$$

If $x = -2$, $3(-2)^2 - 7(-2) + 9 = A(-2+1)(-2+3) + B(-2+2)(-2+3) +$
$$C(-2+1)(-2+2)$$

$$35 = A(-1)\,1 + B.\,0 + C.\,0$$

$$\boxed{A = -35}$$

If $x = -3$, $3(-3)^2 - 7(-3) + 9 \equiv A(-3+1)(-3+3) + B(-3+2)(-3+3) +$
$$C(-3+1)(-3+2)$$

$$57 = 0 + 0 + C(-2)(-1)$$

$$\boxed{C = \frac{57}{2}}$$

This method is neater and quicker and should be utilised in most cases if not always.

TO EXPRESS PARTIAL FRACTIONS INTO A SINGLE FRACTION

WORKED EXAMPLE 11

Express $\dfrac{1}{1+x} + \dfrac{3}{1-x}$ as a single fraction.

SOLUTION 11

$$\frac{1}{1+x} + \frac{3}{1-x} = \frac{(1-x) + 3(1+x)}{(1+x)(1-x)} = \frac{1-x+3+3x}{(1+x)(1-x)} = \frac{2x+4}{1-x^2}.$$

The LCM (least Common Multiple) is $(1+x)(1-x)$.

WORKED EXAMPLE 12

Express $-\dfrac{1}{x} + \dfrac{1}{x-1} - \dfrac{5}{x+2}$ as a single fraction.

SOLUTION 12

$$-\frac{1}{x} + \frac{1}{x-1} - \frac{5}{x+2} = \frac{-(x-1)(x+2) + x(x+2) - 5(x-1)\,x}{x(x-1)(x+2)}$$

The LCM is $x(x - 1)(x + 2)$

$$-\frac{1}{x} + \frac{1}{x - 1} - \frac{5}{x + 2} = \frac{-x^2 + x - 2x + 2 + x^2 + 2x - 5x^2 + 5x}{x(x - 1)(x + 2)}$$

$$= \frac{-5x^2 + 6x + 2}{x(x - 1)(x + 2)}.$$

EXPRESS IN PARTIAL FRACTIONS DENOMINATORS WITH ONLY LINEAR FACTORS

WORKED EXAMPLE 13

Express $\dfrac{x - 1}{(x - 2)(x - 1)}$ into partial fractions:-

By the methods of (a) equating coefficients (b) cover up rule.

SOLUTION 13

Let the single fraction be decomposed into partial fractions as shown:-

$$\frac{x - 1}{(x - 2)(x + 1)} \equiv \frac{A}{x - 2} + \frac{B}{x + 1}$$

(a)   Equating coefficients method.
Express the R.H.S. as a single fraction.

$$\frac{x - 1}{(x - 2)(x + 1)} \equiv \frac{A(x + 1) + B(x - 2)}{(x - 2)(x + 1)}.$$

Since the denominators are equal, then

$$x - 1 \equiv A(x + 1) + B(x - 2), \qquad x - 1 \equiv (A + B)x + A - 2B.$$

The coefficient of x on the L.H.S. is equal to the coefficient of x on the R.H.S. and the constant on the L.H.S. is equal the constant on the R.H.S.

Therefore, $1 = A + B$ ... (1) $-1 = A - 2B$ ... (2)

$$2 = 3B \text{ or } B = \frac{2}{3} \qquad 1 = A + \frac{2}{3} \text{ or } A = \frac{1}{3}.$$

$$\boxed{\frac{x - 1}{(x - 2)(x + 1)} \equiv \frac{1/3}{x - 2} + \frac{2/3}{x + 1}}$$

(b) Cover up rule method.

Let $\dfrac{x - 1}{(x - 2)(x + 1)} \equiv \dfrac{A}{x - 2} + \dfrac{B}{x + 1}$

$x - 1 \equiv A(x + 1) + B(x - 2)$

The cover up rule method is very convenient and it will be used extensively.

What makes $A(x + 1) = 0$, $x = -1$, therefore $x = -1$,
covers up $A(x + 1)$ **i.e.** it makes it $-1 - 1 \equiv A(-1 + 1) + B(-1 - 2)$

$-2 = 0 - 3B$, $B = \dfrac{2}{3}$.

If $x = 2$ $2 - 1 \equiv A(2 + 1) + B(2 - 2) \equiv 3A$ $A = \dfrac{1}{3}$.

Therefore $\dfrac{x - 1}{(x - 2)(x + 1)} \equiv \dfrac{1}{3(x - 2)} + \dfrac{2}{3(x + 1)}$.

The second method, the cover up rule is the easiest of the two methods.

WORKED EXAMPLE 14

Decompose $\dfrac{x + 5}{(x + 3)(x - 2)}$ into partial fractions.

SOLUTION 14

Let $\dfrac{x + 5}{(x + 3)(x - 2)} \equiv \dfrac{A}{x + 3} + \dfrac{B}{x - 2}$

$\dfrac{x + 5}{(x + 3)(x - 2)} \equiv \dfrac{A(x - 2) + B(x + 3)}{(x + 3)(x - 2)}$

$x + 5 \equiv A(x - 2) + B(x + 3)$.

If $x = 2$, $2 + 5 \equiv A(2 - 2) + B(2 + 3)$ $7 = 5B$

$$\boxed{B = \dfrac{7}{5}}$$

If $x = -3$, $-3 + 5 \equiv A(-3 - 2) + B(-3 + 3)$ $2 \equiv -5A$

$$\boxed{A = -\frac{2}{5}}$$

Therefore $\dfrac{x + 5}{(x + 3)(x - 2)} \equiv \dfrac{-2/5}{x + 3} + \dfrac{7/5}{x - 2}$

Let us check the answer of this example.

Express $\dfrac{-2/5}{x + 3} + \dfrac{7/5}{x - 2}$ into a single fraction

$$\frac{-2/5}{x + 3} + \frac{7/5}{x - 2} = \frac{(-2/5)(x - 2) + (7/5)(x + 3)}{(x + 3)(x - 2)}$$

$$\frac{-2/5}{x + 3} + \frac{7/5}{x - 2} = \frac{-2/5x + 4/5 + 7x/5 + 21/5}{(x + 3)(x - 2)} = \frac{x + 5}{(x + 3)(x - 2)}.$$

It is correct.

It is recommended to check the answer of the partial fractions so that we are certain that it is correct.

IMPROPER FRACTION INTO PARTIAL FRACTIONS

A proper fraction is one whose numerator is of one degree less than that of the denominator.

An improper fraction is one whose numerator is of degree equal to, or greater than, that of the denominator.

WORKED EXAMPLE 15

Express $\dfrac{x^2}{225 - x^2}$ into partial fractions.

SOLUTION 15

The numerator has a polynomial with highest degree of two and the denominator has a polynomial with highest degree of two. Since the highest degrees of the numerator and denominator are equal, we divide the numerator by the denominator.

$$\begin{array}{r} -1 \\ 225 - x^2 \enclose{longdiv}{x^2 } \\ \underline{x^2 - 225} \\ 225 \end{array}$$

Therefore $\dfrac{x^2}{225 - x^2} = -1 + \dfrac{225}{225 - x^2}$

Instead of performing the long division

$$\frac{x^2}{225 - x^2} = -\frac{-(225 - x^2) + 225}{225 - x^2} = -\frac{1}{1} + \frac{225}{225 - x^2} \rightarrow -1 + \frac{225}{225 - x^2}.$$

Let $\dfrac{225}{(15 - x)(15 + x)} \equiv \dfrac{A}{15 - x} + \dfrac{B}{15 + x} \qquad 225 \equiv A(15 + x) + B(15 - x).$

If $x = 15,$ $\quad 225 = 30A,$ $\qquad A = \dfrac{15}{2}.$

If $x = -15,$ $\quad 225 = 30B,$ $\qquad B = \dfrac{15}{2}$ $\qquad \dfrac{x^2}{225 - x^2} = -1 + \dfrac{15/2}{15 - x} + \dfrac{15/2}{15 + x}.$

WORKED EXAMPLE 16

Decompose $\dfrac{6x^3 - 7x^2 - 7x + 7}{(x - 1)(2x - 3)}$ into partial fractions.

SOLUTION 16

Since the highest degree of the numerator is three and that of the denominator is two, we perform first the division.

$$\begin{array}{r} 3x + 4 \\ 2x^2 - 5x + 3 \enclose{longdiv}{6x^3 - 7x^2 - 7x + 7} \\ \underline{6x^3 - 15x^2 + 6x } \\ 8x^2 - 13x + 7 \\ \underline{8x^2 - 20x + 12} \\ 7x - 5 \end{array}$$

$$\frac{6x^3 - 7x^2 - 7x + 7}{(x - 1)(2x - 3)} \equiv 3x + 4 + \frac{7x - 5}{(x - 1)(2x - 3)}$$

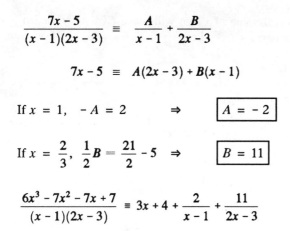

$$\frac{7x-5}{(x-1)(2x-3)} \equiv \frac{A}{x-1} + \frac{B}{2x-3}$$

$$7x-5 \equiv A(2x-3) + B(x-1)$$

If $x = 1$, $\quad -A = 2 \qquad \Rightarrow \qquad \boxed{A = -2}$

If $x = \dfrac{2}{3}$, $\quad \dfrac{1}{2}B = \dfrac{21}{2} - 5 \Rightarrow \qquad \boxed{B = 11}$

$$\frac{6x^3 - 7x^2 - 7x + 7}{(x-1)(2x-3)} \equiv 3x + 4 + \frac{2}{x-1} + \frac{11}{2x-3}$$

EXPRESS IN PARTIAL FRACTIONS DENOMINATORS WITH A QUADRATIC FACTOR

WORKED EXAMPLE 17

Decompose $\dfrac{3x}{(x^2+4)(x+3)}$ into partial fractions.

SOLUTION 17

Let $\dfrac{3x}{(x^2+4)(x+3)} \equiv \dfrac{Ax+B}{x^2+4} + \dfrac{C}{x+3}$

Observe the technique in expressing single fractions into partial factions. If the factor is quadratic, such as $x^2 + 4$, the numerator is a polynomial of one degree.

One degree less than that of the denominator, $Ax + B$, and the numerator for the factor $x + 3$ is merely a constant, C.

$$\frac{3x}{(x^2+4)(x+3)} \equiv \frac{Ax+B}{x^2+4} + \frac{C}{x+3}$$

$$3x \equiv (Ax+B)(x+3) + C(x^2+4)$$

If $x = -3$, $\quad 3(-3) = [A(-3) + B](-3+3) + C((-3)^2 + 4)$

$$-9 = 13C \qquad C = -\frac{9}{13}.$$

For the cover up rule, there is no real value of x that will make $C(x^2 + 4)$ vanish, therefore, try any other simple value except -3. Let $x = 0$ $0 = B3 + C4$ or

$$3B = -4C = +\frac{4 \times 9}{13} \text{ or } B = \frac{12}{13}.$$

Let $x = 1$

$3 = (A + B)(1 + 3) + C5$ then $3 = 4A + 4B + 5C$

$$3 = 4A + 4\left(\frac{12}{13}\right) + 5\left(\frac{9}{13}\right) \quad \text{then } 3 = 4A + \frac{48}{13} - \frac{45}{13}$$

$39 = 52A + 48 - 45$ or $36 = 52A$, $A = \dfrac{9}{13}$.

Therefore, $\dfrac{3x}{(x^2 + 4)(x + 3)} \equiv \dfrac{\frac{9}{13}x + \frac{12}{13}}{x^2 + 4} + \dfrac{-\frac{9}{13}}{x + 3}$

$$\boxed{\dfrac{3x}{(x^2 + 4)(x + 3)} \equiv \dfrac{9x + 12}{13(x^2 + 4)} - \dfrac{9}{13(x + 3)}}$$

EXPRESS IN PARTIAL FRACTIONS
DENOMINATORS WITH A REPEATED FACTOR

WORKED EXAMPLE 18

Decompose $\dfrac{1}{(1 + x)^2 (2 + x)}$.

SOLUTION 18

$$\dfrac{1}{(1 + x)^2 (2 + x)} \equiv \dfrac{A}{1 + x} + \dfrac{B}{(1 + x)^2} + \dfrac{C}{2 + x}.$$

When the factor in the denominator is a repeated factor, like in this case, $(1 + x)^2$,

there are two partial fractions $\dfrac{A}{1 + x}$ and $\dfrac{B}{(1 + x)^2}$, if the repeated is $(1 + x)^4$, there

are four partial fractions such as $\dfrac{A}{1 + x}$, $\dfrac{B}{1 + x^2}$, $\dfrac{C}{(1 + x)^3}$ and $\dfrac{D}{(1 + x)^4}$.

$$\frac{1}{(1 + x)^2(2 + x)} \equiv \frac{A}{1 + x} + \frac{B}{(1 + x)^2} + \frac{C}{2 + x}$$

$$\frac{1}{(1 + x)^2(2 + x)} \equiv \frac{A(1 + x)(2 + x) + B(2 + x) + C(1 + x)^2}{(1 + x)^2(2 + x)}$$

$$1 \equiv A(1 + x)(2 + x) + B(2 + x) + C(1 + x)^2$$

If $x = -1$, $\boxed{B = 1}$

If $x = -2$, $\boxed{C = 1}$

If $x = 0$, $1 = 2A + 2B + C$

$$1 = 2A + 2 + 1$$

$$2A = -2$$

$$A = -1$$

check that

$$\frac{1}{(1 + x)^2(2 + x)} \equiv \frac{-1}{1 + x} + \frac{1}{(1 + x)^2} + \frac{1}{2 + x}$$

$$\text{R.H.S.} \equiv \frac{-(1 + x)(2 + x) + 2 + x + (1 + x)^2}{(1 + x)^2(2 + x)}$$

$$\equiv \frac{-2 - x - 2x - x^2 + 2 + x + 1 + 2x + x^2}{(1 + x)^2(2 + x)}$$

$$\equiv \frac{1}{(1 + x)^2(2 + x)} \equiv \text{L.H.S.}$$

WORKED EXAMPLE 19

Express $\dfrac{3x^3 + 6x^2 + 6x + 2}{(x + 1)^3(2x + 1)}$ in partial fractions.

SOLUTION 19

$$\frac{3x^3 + 6x^2 + 6x + 2}{(x + 1)^3(2x + 1)} \equiv \frac{A}{x + 1} + \frac{B}{(x + 1)^2} + \frac{C}{(x + 1)^3} + \frac{D}{2x + 1}$$

$$\frac{3x^2 + 6x^2 + 6x + 2}{(x + 1)^3(2x + 1)} \equiv \frac{A(x + 1)^2(2x + 1) + B(x + 1)(2x + 1) + C(2x + 1) + D(x + 1)^3}{(x + 1)^3(2x + 1)}$$

$$3x^3 + 6x^2 + 6x + 2 \equiv A(x + 1)^2(2x + 1) + B(x + 1)(2x + 1) + C(2x + 1) + D(1 + x)^3.$$

If $x = -1$, $3(-1)^3 + 6(-1)^2 + 6(-1) + 2 = C(-2 + 1)$

$$-3 + 6 - 6 + 2 = -C \qquad \boxed{C = 1}$$

If $x = 0$. $2 = A + B + 1 + D \Rightarrow \boxed{A + B + D = 1}$ ... (1)

If $x = 1$, $3 + 6 + 6 + 2 = 12A + 6B + 3 + 8D$ $\boxed{12A + 6B + 8D = 14}$ ... (2)

If $x = -\dfrac{1}{2}$, $3\left(-\dfrac{1}{2}\right)^3 + 6\left(-\dfrac{1}{2}\right)^2 + 6\left(-\dfrac{1}{2}\right) + 2 = D\left(1 - \dfrac{1}{2}\right)^3$

$$-\frac{3}{8} + \frac{3}{2} - 3 + 2 = D\frac{1}{8} \Rightarrow \boxed{D = 1}$$

Substituting $D = 1$ in equations (1) and (2)

$A + B = 0 \Rightarrow A = -B$ $\qquad$ $12A + 6B = 6 \Rightarrow 2A + B = 1$ $\qquad$ $-B = 1$

$\boxed{B = -1}$ and $\boxed{A = 1}$

Therefore, $\dfrac{3x^3 + 6x^2 + 6x + 2}{(x + 1)^3(2x + 1)} = \dfrac{1}{x + 1} - \dfrac{1}{(x + 1)^2} + \dfrac{1}{(x + 1)^3} + \dfrac{1}{2x + 1}$.

EXERCISES 2

Express each of the following as a single fraction:-

1. $-\dfrac{1}{3-x} + \dfrac{5}{3+x}$

2. $\dfrac{1}{1} - \dfrac{1}{5}$

3. $\dfrac{3}{x+3} + \dfrac{5}{x-4}$

4. $\dfrac{2}{x} - \dfrac{3}{x+3}$

5. $\dfrac{1}{x^2} - \dfrac{1}{x+2}$

6. $\dfrac{1}{x} + \dfrac{2}{x+1} + \dfrac{3}{x+3}$

7. $\dfrac{1}{2} - \dfrac{1}{3} + \dfrac{1}{5}$

8. $\dfrac{x+1}{x-3} + \dfrac{1}{x+2} - \dfrac{3}{x-5}$

9. $1 - \dfrac{1}{x+1}$

10. $1 + \dfrac{x}{x+2}$

11. $\dfrac{x+1}{x-1} + \dfrac{3}{x}$

12. $\dfrac{1}{(x+1)^3} - \dfrac{1}{(x+1)^2} + \dfrac{1}{(x+1)} + \dfrac{1}{2x+1}$

13. $\dfrac{1}{(x^2+1)} + \dfrac{1}{x-1}$

14. $\dfrac{1}{2x-1} - \dfrac{1}{2x^2-3}$

15. $\dfrac{1}{(x+2)} + \dfrac{1}{(x+2)^2} - \dfrac{1}{x^2-5}$.

Express the following single fractions into the corresponding partial fractions:-

16. $\dfrac{x+7}{(x-3)(x+4)}$

17. $\dfrac{2x+1}{(x-1)(x+2)}$

18. $\dfrac{2x + 5}{(2x + 1)(3x - 1)}$

19. $\dfrac{x^2 + x - 5}{(x + 2)(x + 3)}$

20. $\dfrac{3x^2 - x - 7}{(x - 1)(x + 3)}$

21. $\dfrac{x^3}{(x + 4)(x - 5)}$

22. $\dfrac{x + 3}{x^2 - 49}$

23. $\dfrac{2x - 1}{81 - x^2}$

24. $\dfrac{3x + 7}{x^2 - 36}$

25. $\dfrac{x^2 - 3x + 5}{(x + 1)(x - 2)(x + 3)}$

26. $\dfrac{5x^2 + 25x - 7}{(x + 3)(x + 5)(x - 7)}$

27. $\dfrac{6(2 - x)}{(3 - x)(3 + x)}$

28. $\dfrac{6 - x}{x(x + 3)}$

29. $\dfrac{6x^2 + 13x + 3}{x(x + 1)(x + 3)}$

30. $\dfrac{x^3 - 3x^2 - 11x + 30}{(x + 2)(x - 3)(x - 5)}$

31. $\dfrac{x}{x + 1}$

32. $\dfrac{2(x + 1)}{x + 2}$

3. QUADRATIC FUNCTIONS

The General quadratic function in one variable.

A quadratic function, $f(x) = ax^2 + bx + c$ is a curve which has either a minimum or a maximum as shown in Fig. 1-I/1 and Fig. 1-I/2.

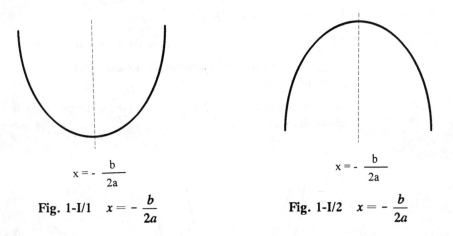

$$x = - \frac{b}{2a}$$

Fig. 1-I/1 $x = - \dfrac{b}{2a}$

$$x = - \frac{b}{2a}$$

Fig. 1-I/2 $x = - \dfrac{b}{2a}$

The minimum or the maximum occur when $x = -\dfrac{b}{2a}$, this can be proved as follows:-

$$f(x) = ax^2 + bx + c = a\left[x^2 + \frac{bx}{a} + \frac{c}{a}\right] = a\left[\left(x + \frac{b}{2a}\right)^2 - \frac{b^2}{4a^2} + \frac{c}{a}\right]$$

by completing the squares, that is, $x^2 + \dfrac{bx}{a} = \left(x + \dfrac{b}{2a}\right)^2 - \dfrac{b^2}{4a^2}$,

check this by expanding the binomial

$$\left(x + \frac{b}{2a}\right)^2 - \frac{b^2}{4a^2} = x^2 + \frac{bx}{a} + \frac{b^2}{4a^2} - \frac{b^2}{4a^2} = x^2 + \frac{b}{a}x.$$

$$f(x) = a\left[\left(x + \frac{b}{2a}\right)^2 - \frac{b^2}{4a^2} + \frac{c}{a}\right] = a\left[\left(x + \frac{b}{2a}\right)^2 - \frac{b^2 - 4ac}{4a^2}\right].$$

$$= a\left(x + \frac{b}{2a}\right)^2 - \frac{b^2 - 4ac}{4a} = ak - \frac{b^2 - 4ac}{4a}$$

where k is always positive since the binomial is squared.

If $a > 0$, that is, a is positive, then $ak > 0$, the minimum value of the function $f(x)$,

$$f(x)_{min} = -\frac{b^2 - 4\,ac}{4a}, \text{ which occurs when } k = 0, \text{ or } x = -\frac{b}{2a}.$$

$$f(x)_{min} = -\frac{D}{4a} \text{ where } D = b^2 - 4ac \text{ is the discriminant.}$$

There are three conditions to consider for D.

When $D = 0$, $f(x)_{min} = 0$ and the curve touches the x-axis, when $D > 0$,

$f(x)_{min} < 0$ and the curve intersects the x-axis, and has its minimum below the x-axis.

When $D < 0$, $f(x)_{min} > 0$ and the curve lies above the x-axis, the minimum lies above the x-axis,

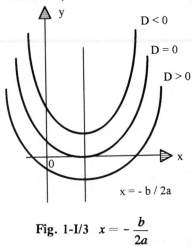

Fig. 1-I/3 $x = -\dfrac{b}{2a}$

The minima of these curves occur at $x = -\dfrac{b}{2a}$.

If $a < 0$, that is, a is negative, then $ak < 0$, and the maximum value of the function

$$f(x), \; f(x)_{max} = -\frac{b^2 - 4ac}{4a}, \text{ which occurs when } k = 0, \text{ or } \left(x + \frac{b}{2a}\right)^2 = 0, \text{ or}$$

$$x = -\frac{b}{2a} . \; f(x)_{max} = -\frac{D}{4a} \text{ where } D = b^2 - 4ac \text{ is the discriminant. There are three}$$

conditions to consider again for D.

When $D = 0$, $f(x)_{max} = 0$ and the curve touches the x-axis, when

       $D > 0$, $f(x)_{max} > 0$ and the curve intersects the x-axis, and has its maximum above the x-axis and when $D < 0$, $f(x)_{max} < 0$, and the curve lies below the x-axis.

The maxima of these curves occur again at $x = -\dfrac{b}{2a}$.

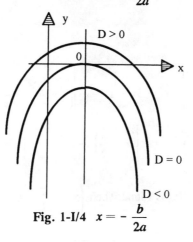

Fig. 1-I/4 $x = -\dfrac{b}{2a}$

WORKED EXAMPLE 20

Find the minimum value of the quadratic expression $f(x) = x^2 - x - 1$.

SOLUTION 20

$$f(x) = x^2 - x - 1 = \left(x - \frac{1}{2}\right)^2 - \frac{1}{4} - 1 = \left(x - \frac{1}{2}\right)^2 - \frac{5}{4}$$

since $\left(x - \dfrac{1}{2}\right)^2 \geq 0$ for all values of x, the minimum values of $f(x)$ is $-\dfrac{5}{4}$, when

$$\left(x - \frac{1}{2}\right)^2 = 0 \text{ or } x = \frac{1}{2} \quad f(0) = -1, \quad f(x)_{min} = -\frac{5}{4} \text{ when } x = -\frac{b}{2a} = -\frac{(-1)}{2 \times 1} = \frac{1}{2}.$$

$(0, -1)$

$(1/2, -5/4)$

Fig. 1-I/5

WORKED EXAMPLE 21

Find the maximum value of the quadratic function $f(x) = -x^2 - 3x + 1$.

SOLUTION 21

$$f(x) = -x^2 - 3x + 1 = -(x^2 + 3x - 1) = -\left[\left(x + \frac{3}{2}\right)^2 - \frac{9}{4} - 1\right]$$

$$= -\left[\left(x + \frac{3}{2}\right)^2 - \frac{9+4}{4}\right] = -\left[\left(x + \frac{3}{2}\right)^2 - \frac{13}{4}\right] = -\left(x + \frac{3}{2}\right)^2 + \frac{13}{4}.$$

The maximum value of $f(x)$ is found when $\left(x + \frac{3}{2}\right)^2 = 0$, $f(x)$ max $= \frac{13}{4}$, and it

occurs when $x = -\frac{3}{2} = -\frac{b}{2a} = -\frac{-3}{2(-1)} = -\frac{3}{2}$.

ALTERNATIVELY

The general quadratic function in one variable.

$f(x) = ax^2 + bx + c$ is a quadratic function in one variable. Differentiating this expression with respect to x $f'(x) = 2ax + b$.

The turning point, or the stationary value or the maximum and minimum points are found by making the gradient zero, $f'(x) = 0$ $2ax + b = 0$ for turning points

therefore at $\boxed{x = -\dfrac{b}{2a}}$ there is either a maximum or minimum.

Differentiating again $f''(x) = 2a$.

If a is positive the function has a minimum, if a is negative the function has a maximum.

$$\frac{d}{dx}\left(\frac{dy}{dx}\right) = \text{change of the gradient} = \frac{d^2y}{dx^2}.$$

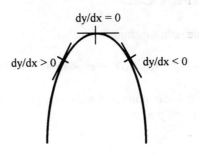

Fig. 1-I/6

The second derivative indicates the change of the gradient. For a maximum, $\dfrac{d^2y}{dx^2} < 0$ as shown above in the diagram.

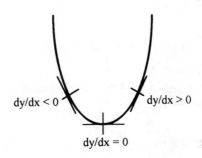

Fig. 1-I/7

Consider a minimum, before the minimum the gradient is negative, at the minimum the gradient is zero and after the minimum on the right, the gradient is positive

$\dfrac{d}{dx}\left(\dfrac{dy}{dx}\right)$ = the rate of change of the gradient is positive, therefore

$\dfrac{d^2y}{dx^2} > 0$ for a minimum.

So far, we can conclude the following (i) if $a > 0$ in the general quadratic function, the function has a minimum and this occurs at $x = -\dfrac{b}{2a}$

(ii)   If $a < 0$ in the general quadratic function, the function has a maximum and this occurs again at $x = -\dfrac{b}{2a}$.

To sketch a quadratic function.

WORKED EXAMPLE 22

Sketch the following quadratic functions:-

(i) $f(x) = -3x^2 + 5x - 7$ (ii) $f(x) = x^2 - 4x + 3$ (iii) $f(x) = x^2 - 6x + 8$.

Find the coordinates of the maximum and minimum points and the coordinates when the curves intersect the x and y axes.

SOLUTION 22

(i) $f(x) = -3x^2 + 5x - 7$.

The function has a maximum since $a = -3 < 0$ and it occurs at

$$x = -\frac{b}{2a} = -\frac{(5)}{2(-3)} = \frac{5}{6}.$$

Let us also examine if the function cuts the x-axis.

Examine the discriminant $D = b^2 - 4ac$
$D = 5^2 - 4(-3)(-7) = 25 - 84 = -59$, therefore $D < 0$ and the curve does not intersect or touch the x-axis.

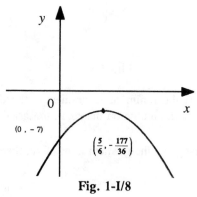

Fig. 1-I/8

$$f\left(\frac{5}{6}\right) = -3\left(\frac{5}{6}\right)^2 + 5\left(\frac{5}{6}\right) - 7 = -\frac{75}{36} + \frac{25}{6} - 7 = \frac{-75 + 150 - 252}{36} = -\frac{177}{36}.$$

The coordinates of the maximum point are $\left(\frac{5}{6}, \frac{-177}{36}\right)$.

(ii)   The function has a minimum since $a = 1 > 0$ and it occurs at

$$x = -\frac{b}{2a} = -\frac{(-4)}{2 \times 1} = 2 \qquad D = (-4)^2 - 4 \times 3 \times 1 = 16 - 12 = 4 > 0,$$

the function has real values since it intersects the x-axis when $f(x) = 0$.

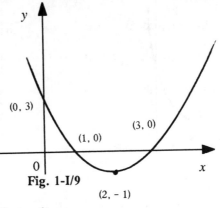

Fig. 1-I/9

$(2, -1)$

If $x = 2$, $f(2) = 4 - 8 + 3 = -1$.

The coordinates of the minimum point are $(2, -1)$. The curve intersects the x-axis when $x^2 - 4x + 3 = 0$ $x^2 - 3x - x + 3 = x(x - 3) - (x - 3) = 0$ or $(x - 3)(x - 1) = 0$ at $x = 1$ and $x = 3$ and cuts the y-axis at $f(0) = 3$.

(iii) $f(x) = x^2 - 6x + 8$. The function has a minimum $a = 1 > 0$ and it occurs at

$$-\frac{b}{2a} \quad D = (-6)^2 - 4 \times 8 \times 1 = 36 - 32 = 4 > 0,$$

the function intersect the x-axis when $f(x) = 0$, $(x - 2)(x - 4) = 0$ or $x = 2$ and $x = 4$ and $f(0) = 8$. If $x = 3$, $f(3) = 9 - 18 + 8 = -1$.

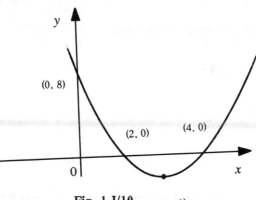

Fig. 1-I/10 $(3, -1)$

WORKED EXAMPLE 23

The following quadratic functions are shown in Fig. 1-I/11, Fig. 1-I/12, Fig. 1-I/13 and Fig. 1-I/14.

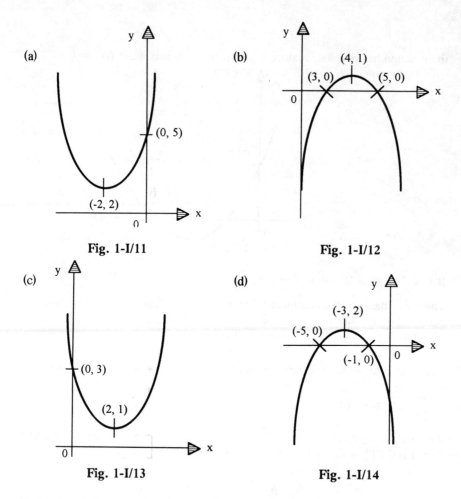

Fig. 1-I/11

Fig. 1-I/12

Fig. 1-I/13

Fig. 1-I/14

Write down the corresponding equations:-

SOLUTION 23

(a) $x = -\dfrac{b}{2a}$, $f(-2) = -2$, and $f(0) = 5$ $D < 0$ and the curve is minimum.

Let $ax^2 + bx + c = f(x)$, $f(0) = 5 = c$, $f(-2) = a(-2)^2 + b(-2) + 5 = 2$

$4a - 2b = -3$ but $\dfrac{-b}{2a} = -2 \Rightarrow b = 4a$, $4a - 2(4a) = -3$

$4a - 8a = -3 \Rightarrow -4a = -3 \Rightarrow a = \dfrac{3}{4}$, $b = 4a = 4\left(\dfrac{3}{4}\right) = 3$.

Therefore $\dfrac{3}{4}x^2 + 3x + 5 = f(x)$.

(b) The curve is maximum, therefore $a < 0$ $x = -\dfrac{b}{2a} = 4$ or $-b = 8a$

$f(3) = 0, f(5) = 0$ $f(4) = 1$

$f(x) = ax^2 + bx + c$ $f(4) = 16a + 4b + c = 1$ ... (i)

$f(3) = 9a + 3b + c = 0$ ... (ii) $f(5) = 25a + 5b + c = 0$ ... (iii)

(i) − (ii) $16a + 4b + c = 1$ (iv) − (v) $7a + b = 1$
$9a + 3b + c = 0$ $9a + b = -1$
$\overline{}$ $\overline{}$
$7a + b = 1$ ... (iv) $-2a = 2$

(iii) − (i) $16a + 4b + c = 1$ $\boxed{a = -1}$
$25a + 5b + c = 0$
$\overline{}$
$9a + b = -1$ ... (v)

$7a + b = 1$ $16a + 4b + c = 1$
$-7 + b = 1$ $-16 + 32 + c = 1$
$ b = 1 + 7$

$\boxed{b = 8}$ $\boxed{c = -15}$

$$f(x) = -x^2 + 8x - 15$$

(c) The curve is minimum, therefore $a > 0$

$f(0) = 3, f(2) = 1$ $D < 0$

$ax^2 + bx + c = f(x)$ $f(2) = 4a + 2b + 3 = 1$

$f(0) = 3, \boxed{c = 3}$ $4a + 2b = -2$
 $2a + b = -1$

$x = -\dfrac{b}{2a} = 2 \Rightarrow -b = 4a$ $-2a = -1$

$\boxed{b = -2}$ $\boxed{a = \dfrac{1}{2}}$

$2a - 4a = -1$ $f(x) = \dfrac{x^2}{2} - 2x + 3$

1-I/37

(d) f(– 3) = 2

  f(– 5) = 0

  f(– 1) = 0

  $f(x) = ax^2 + bx + c$

  $f(– 3) = 9a – 3b + c = 2$ ... (i)

  $f(– 5) = 25a – 5b + c = 0$ ... (ii)

  $f(– 1) = a – b + c = 0$ ... (iii)

  (iii) – (i) $16a – 2b = – 2$

       $8a – b = – 1$ ... (iv)

  (ii) – (iii) $24a – 4b = 0$

       $6a – b = 0$ ... (v)

  (iv) – (v) $2a = – 1$

$$\boxed{a = – \frac{1}{2}}$$

From (v), $b = 6a = 6\left(– \frac{1}{2}\right) = – 3$

$9a – 3b + c = 2$

$c = 2 – 9 + \dfrac{9}{2}$

$$\boxed{c = – \frac{5}{2}}$$

  $f(x) = – \dfrac{1}{2}x^2 – 3x – \dfrac{5}{2}.$

EXERCISES 3

1. If $f(x) = ax^2 + bx + c$, state the condition for the function $f(x)$ to be

    (i) maximum   (ii) minimum.

2. If $f(x) = ax^2 + bx + c$, state the value of x for which the function is either maximum or minimum.

3. Prove algebraically that the maximum or minimum of a quadratic function occurs when $x = -\dfrac{b}{2a}$.

4. Prove by calculus that the maximum or minimum of a quadratic function occurs when $x = \dfrac{b}{2a}$.

5. The curves show four quadratic functions:-

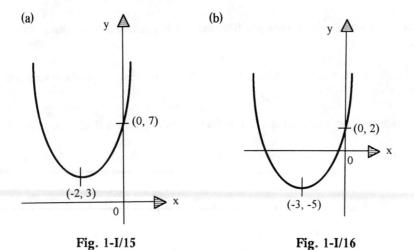

(a)

(0, 7)

(-2, 3)

Fig. 1-I/15

(b)

(0, 2)

(-3, -5)

Fig. 1-I/16

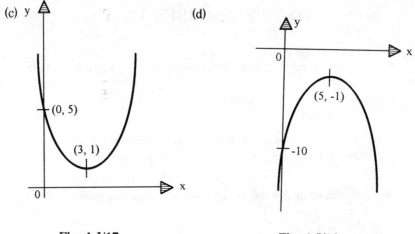

(c) y

(0, 5)

(3, 1)

0 x

(d) y

0 x

(5, -1)

-10

Fig. 1-I/17   **Fig. 1-I/18**

Find the quadratic equations that satisfy these conditions.

6. Sketch the following quadratic functions:-

   (i) $y = -x^2 + 4x - 1$ (ii) $y = -2x^2 + 5x + 7$

   (iii) $y = 3x^2 - 2x - 4$ (iv) $y = 5x^2 + 2x - 2.$

7. Sketch the graph of a quadratic function if a is positive and the discriminant is zero.

8. Sketch the graph of a quadratic function if a is positive and the discriminant is positive.

9. Sketch the graph of a quadratic function if a is negative and $b^2 - 4a\,c > 0$.

10. Sketch the graph of a quadratic function if a is negative and the discriminant is zero.

11. Sketch the graph of a quadratic function if a is positive and the discriminant is negative.

12. Sketch the graph of a quadratic function if a is negative and the discriminant is negative.

13. Find the greatest value of k for which $3x^2 + 5x + k + 1 = 0$ has real and unequal roots.

14. State the conditions for which the quadratic function has (i) equal and real roots (ii) imaginary roots (iii) unequal and real roots.

4. THE ROOTS OF THE QUADRATIC EQUATION

Let S be the sum of the roots, $S = \alpha + \beta$

$$S = \frac{-b}{2a} + \frac{\sqrt{b^2 - 4ac}}{2a} - \frac{b}{2a} - \frac{\sqrt{b^2 - 4ac}}{2a} = -\frac{b}{a}$$

$$\boxed{S = \alpha + \beta = -\frac{b}{a}}$$

Let P be the product of the roots, $P = \alpha\beta$

$$P = \alpha\beta = \left(-\frac{b + \sqrt{b^2 - 4ac}}{2a}\right)\left(\frac{-b - \sqrt{b^2 - 4ac}}{2a}\right)$$

$$= \left(-\frac{b}{2a}\right)^2 - \left(\frac{\sqrt{b^2 - 4ac}}{2a}\right)^2 \text{ using}$$

$$(a + b)(a - b) = a^2 - b^2 \qquad P = \alpha\beta = \frac{b^2}{4a^2} - \frac{b^2 - 4ac}{4a^2} = \frac{c}{a}$$

$$\boxed{P = \alpha\beta = \frac{c}{a}}$$

To find the sum and product of the roots there is a neater method.

$$x^2 + \frac{bx}{a} + \frac{c}{a} = 0.$$

If $x = \alpha$ and $x = \beta$ are the roots of the quadratic equation then $x - \alpha = 0$ and $x - \beta = 0$ and $(x - \alpha)(x - \beta) = 0$ therefore

$$x^2 + \frac{bx}{a} + \frac{c}{a} = (x - \alpha)(x - \beta) = x^2 - (\alpha + \beta)x + \alpha\beta$$

Equating the coefficients of x and constant term $\frac{b}{a} = -(\alpha + \beta)$ and $\frac{c}{a} = \alpha\beta$ therefore

$$S = -\frac{b}{a} = \alpha + \beta \text{ and } P = \alpha\beta = \frac{c}{a}.$$

The quadratic equation can be written as

$$\boxed{x^2 - (\alpha + \beta)x + \alpha\beta = 0}$$

The Roots of the Quadratic Equation

To prove that the roots of the quadratic equation $ax^2 + bx + c = 0$ are

$$\alpha = \frac{-b + \sqrt{b^2 - 4ac}}{2a} \quad \text{and} \quad \beta = \frac{-b - \sqrt{b^2 - 4ac}}{2a}.$$

$ax^2 + bx + c = 0$ dividing each term by a, provided that $a \neq 0$ $\quad x^2 + \dfrac{bx}{a} + \dfrac{c}{a} = 0$

completing the squares $\quad x^2 + \dfrac{b}{a}x = \left(x + \dfrac{b}{2a}\right)^2 - \dfrac{b^2}{4a^2} = x^2 + 2x\dfrac{b}{2a} + \dfrac{b^2}{4\,a^2} - \dfrac{b^2}{4\,a^2}$

therefore $\quad \left(x + \dfrac{b}{2a}\right)^2 - \dfrac{b^2}{4\,a^2} + \dfrac{c}{a} = 0$

$\left(x + \dfrac{b}{2a}\right)^2 = \dfrac{b^2}{4\,a^2} - \dfrac{c}{a} = \dfrac{b^2}{4\,a^2} - \dfrac{4\,ac}{4\,a^2} \qquad \left(x + \dfrac{b}{2a}\right)^2 = \dfrac{b^2 - 4\,ac}{4\,a^2}$

taking the square root on both sides $\quad x + \dfrac{b}{2a} = \pm\sqrt{\dfrac{b^2 - 4ac}{4a^2}}$

$$x = -\dfrac{b}{2a} \pm \dfrac{\sqrt{b^2 - 4ac}}{2a}$$

$$\boxed{x = \frac{-b \pm \sqrt{b^2 - 4ac}}{2a}}$$

WORKED EXAMPLE 24

If the sum of the roots of a quadratic equation is -3 and the product of the roots is 2, find the quadratic equation.

SOLUTION 24

$$S = -3 = \alpha + \beta \qquad P = 2 = \alpha\beta.$$

The quadratic equation is given by $x^2 - (\alpha + \beta)x + \alpha\beta = 0$ substituting
$\alpha + \beta = -3$ and $\alpha\beta = 2 \Rightarrow x^2 - (-3)x + 2 = 0 \quad$ or $x^2 + 3x + 2 = 0$.

The Role of the Discriminant $D = b^2 - 4ac$

If $D > 0$, the two roots are real and different. If $D = 0$, the roots are real and both equal to $\alpha = \beta = -\dfrac{b}{2a}$.

If $D < 0$, the roots are complex since the quantity under the square root is negative.

WORKED EXAMPLE 25

Solve the equations by using the formula $x = \dfrac{-b \pm \sqrt{b^2 - 4ac}}{2a}$

(i) $x^2 - 7x + 10 = 0$ (ii) $10x^2 + 7x + 1 = 0$ (iii) $-3x^2 + 4x + 1 = 0$

SOLUTION 25

(i) $x^2 - 7x + 10 = 0$ $x = \dfrac{-(-7) \pm \sqrt{(-7)^2 - 4(1)(10)}}{2}$

$x = \dfrac{7}{2} \pm \dfrac{\sqrt{49 - 40}}{2} = \dfrac{7 \pm 3}{2}.$ $x = 5$ or $x = 2$

(ii) $10x^2 + 7x + 1 = 0$ $x = \dfrac{-7 \pm \sqrt{49 - 4 \times 10}}{20} = \dfrac{-7 \pm 3}{20}$

$x = -\dfrac{1}{2}$ or $x = -\dfrac{1}{5}.$

(iii) $-3x^2 + 4x + 1 = 0$

$x = \dfrac{-4 \pm \sqrt{16 - 4(-3)(1)}}{2 \times (-3)} = \dfrac{-4 \pm \sqrt{28}}{-6}$

$x = -0.215$ or $x = 1.55.$

FACTORISATION

There are five methods by which we can factorise a quadratic equation or function.

WORKED EXAMPLE 26

Factorise the previous quadratic functions:-

(i) $x^2 - 7x + 10$ (ii) $10x^2 + 7x + 1$ (iii) $-3x^2 + 4x + 1$.

SOLUTION 26

(i) $x^2 - 7x + 10$

(a)   Using the formula $x = 5$ or $x = 2$ $x - 5 = 0$ or
$x - 2 = 0$ or $(x - 5)(x - 2) = 0$ or $(x - 5)(x - 2) = 0$
if $x^2 - 7x + 10 = 0$ then $x^2 - 7x + 10 = (x - 5)(x - 2)$.

(b)   Splitting the middle term $x^2 - 7x + 10 = x^2 - 5x - 2x + 10$ observe that
$-5x - 2x = -7x$ also $(-5x) \times (-2x) = 10x^2$ the product of x^2 and 10
is $10x^2$ which agrees with the product of the splitted term, therefore we
conclude that the function is factorisable easily

$$x^2 - 7x + 10 \quad = x^2 - 5x - 2x + 10 = x(x - 5) - 2(x - 5)$$
$$= (x - 5)(x - 2).$$
$$x^2 - 7x + 10 \quad = (x - 5)(x - 2).$$

(c)   Completing the squares

$$x^2 - 7x + 10 = \left(x - \frac{7}{2}\right)^2 - \left(\frac{7}{2}\right)^2 + 10$$

$$= \left(x - \frac{7}{2}\right)^2 - \frac{49}{4} + \frac{40}{4} = \left(x - \frac{7}{2}\right)^2 - \frac{9}{4}$$

$$= \left(x - \frac{7}{2}\right)^2 - \left(\frac{3}{2}\right)^2 = \left[\left(x - \frac{7}{2}\right) - \frac{3}{2}\right]\left[\left(x - \frac{7}{2}\right) + \frac{3}{2}\right]$$

$$= (x - 5)(x - 2)$$

(d) By trial and error $x^2 - 7x + 10 = (x - 2)(x - 5)$.

(e) Graphically $f(x) = x^2 - 7x + 10$

$$f(0) = 10$$

$a > 1$, has a minimum which occurs at $x = = -\dfrac{b}{2a} = \dfrac{-(-7)}{2} = \dfrac{7}{2}$

$$f\left(\frac{7}{2}\right) = \frac{49}{4} - 7\left(\frac{7}{2}\right) + 10 = \frac{49}{4} - \frac{49}{2} + 10 = -\frac{49}{4} + 10 = \frac{-49 + 40}{4} = -\frac{9}{4}.$$

The graph will cut the x-axis at $x = 2$ and $x = 5$.

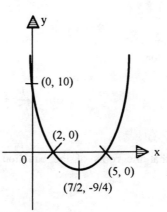

Fig. 1-I/19

EXERCISES 4

1. If α and β are the roots of the quadratic equation $ax^2 + bx + c = 0$ find the values of:-

   (i) $\alpha + \beta$ and $\alpha\beta$ (iv) $\alpha^3 + \beta^3$

   (ii) $\alpha - \beta$ if $\alpha > \beta$ (vii) $\alpha^3 - \beta^3$

   (iii) $(\alpha - \beta)^2$ (viii) $\alpha^2 - \beta^2$

   (iv) $(\alpha + \beta)^2$ (ix) $\alpha^4 + \beta^4$

   (v) $\alpha^2 + \beta^2$ (x) $\dfrac{1}{\alpha^2} + \dfrac{1}{\beta^2}$.

2. If n and m are the roots of the equation $3x^2 - 5x + 7 = 0$.
   Find the imaginary value

   (i) $\dfrac{1}{n} + \dfrac{1}{m}$ (ii) $\dfrac{1}{n^3} - \dfrac{1}{m^3}$.

3. Find the condition that the roots of the equation $ax^2 + bx + c = 0$ are reciprocals.

4. Form the quadratic equation for which the sum of the roots is -7 and the sum of the cubes of the roots is 125.

5. Find the condition between a, b and c such that one root of the equation $ax^2 + bx + c = 0$ is three times the other root.

6. If α and β are the roots of the equation $-7x^2 + 9x - 7 = 0$, find the values of

   (i) $\dfrac{\alpha}{\beta} + \dfrac{\beta}{\alpha}$ (ii) $\dfrac{1}{\alpha^4} + \dfrac{1}{\beta^4}$.

7. If one root of the quadratic equation is twice the other, find the roots

$$kx^2 - (k + 1)x + 9 = 0.$$

8. Find the range of values of k if the equation $kx^2 - (k + 1)x + 9 = 0$ has real roots.

9. Find the roots of the equation $-3x^2 + kx - 4 = 0$ and the values of k if one root is 4 times the other.

10. State the values of the sum and product of the roots for the following quadratic equations:-

(i) $-2x^2 - x - 1 = 0$ (ii) $3x^2 + 5x + 9 = 0$

(iii) $x^2 - 2x + 7 = 0$ (iv) $-x^2 + 4x + 2 = 0$

(v) $5x^2 - 5x - 1 = 0$.

11. The sums and products of quadratic equations are denoted by p and q respectively. Find the quadratic equations for:-

(i) $p = -3, q = 5$ (ii) $p = 25, q = -39$ (iii) $p = 37, q = 2$.

12. If the cubic equation $ax^3 + bx^2 + cx + d = 0$ has roots α, β and γ, find the relationship in terms of a, b, c and d

(i) $\alpha + \beta + \gamma$ (ii) $\alpha\beta\gamma$ (iii) $\alpha\beta + \alpha\gamma + \beta\gamma$.

5. INEQUALITIES

Simple algebraic inequalities, including the use of modulus sign.

Notation of inequality signs

$x > 0$, x is greater than zero, x is positive

$x < 0$, x is less than zero, x is negative

$x = 0$, x is equal to zero.

The inequalities can be represented along the x-axis from the origin to the right, the values of x are positive, from the origin to the left, the values of x are negative.

Other signs are:-

≯ not greater than

≮ not less than

≥ greater than or equal to

≤ less than or equal to

⋡ not greater than or equal to

⋠ not less than or equal to.

Inequalities

$x > y$ ... (1) adding a positive quantity on both sides of the inequality, results $x + k > y + k$ subtracting a positive quantity on both sides of the inequality (1), results $x - k > y - k$.

Multiplying by a positive quantity k both sides of equation (1), results $kx > ky$.

Dividing by a positive quantity k both sides of equation (1), results $\dfrac{x}{k} > \dfrac{y}{k}$.

Multiplying by a negative number k both sides of (1), results in a change of sign of the inequality $-kx < -ky$.

Dividing by a negative number k both sides of (1), results in a change of sign of the inequality $-\dfrac{x}{k} < -\dfrac{y}{k}$

WORKED EXAMPLE 27

Find the set of real values of x for which:-

(i)　$x - 2 > 3(2x - 1)$　　　　　　(ii)　$-5x + 7 < 2x + 2$.

SOLUTION 27

(i)　$x - 2 > 3(2x - 1)$　　$x - 2 > 6x - 3$, $x - 6x > 2 - 3$, $-5x > -1$.

Dividing each side of the inequality by -5　$\dfrac{-5x}{-5} < \dfrac{-1}{-5}$, the inequality sign has changed, therefore

$$\boxed{x < \dfrac{1}{5}}$$

(ii)　$-5x + 7 < 2x + 2$　　$-5x - 2x < -7 + 2$　　$-7x < -5$.

Dividing both sides of the inequality by -7　$\dfrac{-7x}{-7} > \dfrac{-5}{-7}$, the inequality sign has changed, therefore

$$\boxed{x > \dfrac{5}{7}}$$

WORKED EXAMPLE 28

Find the set of real values of x for which:-

(i)　$(x - 1)(x - 6) > 0$　　(ii)　$(x - 1)(x - 6) < 0$.

SOLUTION 28

(i)　$(x - 1)(x - 6) > 0$ or $x^2 - 7x + 6 > 0$.

The quadratic function has a minimum at $x = \dfrac{-b}{2a} = \dfrac{7}{2}$ and it

cuts the x-axis at $x = 1$ and $x = 6$　　$f(x) = (x - 1)(x - 6)$,

$$f\left(\dfrac{7}{2}\right) = \dfrac{5}{2}\left(-\dfrac{5}{2}\right) = -\dfrac{25}{4}$$

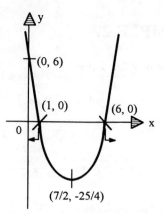

Fig. 1-I/20

The set of values of x for which $(x - 1)(x - 6) > 0$ are $x < 1$ and $x > 6$ as shown.

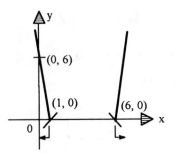

Fig. 1-I/21

(ii)   The set of values of x for which $(x - 1)(x - 6) < 0$
       $x > 1$ and $x < 6$ or $1 < x < 6$

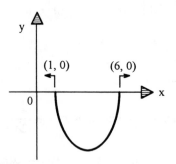

Fig. 1-I/22

1-I/50

Alternatively, we can find the set of real values of x for which

(i) $(x - 1)(x - 6) > 0$

(ii) $(x - 1)(x - 6) < 0$. The table below is constructed.

	$6 > x > 1$	$x < 1$	$x > 6$
$x - 1$	+	-	+
$x - 6$	-	-	+
$(x - 1)(x - 6)$	-	+	+

If $(x - 1)(x - 6) > 0$ $x < 1$ and $x > 6$. If $(x - 1)(x - 6) < 0$ $6 > x > 1$.

WORKED EXAMPLE 29

Find the set of real values of x for which

(i) $x(x - 1)(x + 2) < 0$ (ii) $(x + 1)(x - 1)(x + 2) > 0$

SOLUTION 29

(i)   Construct the table

	$x > 0$	$x < 0$	$x > 1$	$x < 1$	$x > -2$	$x < -2$
x	+	-	+	+	-	-
$x - 1$	-	-	+	-	-	-
$x + 2$	+	+	+	+	+	-
$x(x - 1)(x + 2)$	-	+	+	-	+	-

$x(x - 1)(x + 2) < 0$. The set of real values of x are:-

$$x > 0 \qquad x < 1 \qquad x < -2.$$

Therefore $0 < x < 1$ and $x < -2$.

(ii)   Construct the table

	$x > -1$	$x < -1$	$x > 1$	$x < 1$
$(x + 1)$	+	−	+	+
$(x - 1)$	−	−	+	−
$x + 2$	+	+	+	+
$(x + 1)(x - 1)(x + 2)$	−	+	+	−

	$x > -2$	$x < -2$
$(x + 1)$	−	−
$(x - 1)$	−	−
$x + 2$	+	−
$(x + 1)(x - 1)(x + 2)$	+	−

The set of real values of x are:-

$x < -1$ $x > 1$ and $x > -2$ by reading off the values from the table.

Therefore $-2 < x < -1$ and $x > 1$.

WORKED EXAMPLE 30

Find the set of real values of x for which:-

(i) $\dfrac{1}{x - 3} > \dfrac{1}{x + 1}$.

(ii) $\dfrac{x}{x + 2} < 0$.

SOLUTION 30

(i) $\dfrac{1}{x - 3} > \dfrac{1}{x + 1}$

Multiply both sides of the inequalities by $(x - 3)^2$ and $(x + 1)^2$ hence the sign of the inequality does not change

$$\frac{(x - 3)^2 (x + 1)^2}{(x - 3)} > \frac{(1 + x)^2 (x - 3)^2}{(x + 1)}$$

$(x - 3)(x + 1)^2 - (1 + x)(x - 3)^2 > 0.$

Factorise $(x - 3)(x + 1)[(x + 1) - (x - 3)] > 0$ $(x - 3)(x + 1) 4 > 0.$

The set of real values of x are:- $x < -1, x > 3.$

(ii) $\dfrac{x}{x + 2} < 0.$

Multiplying both sides by $(x + 2)^2$ $\dfrac{x(x + 2)^2}{(x + 2)} < 0(x + 2)^2$ $x(x + 2) < 0.$

Therefore $-2 < x < 0.$

WORKED EXAMPLE 31

Prove that if $x > y$ then $x + k > y + k$ where k is a positive number.

SOLUTION 31

$x > y$ $x - y > 0$ $x + k - k - y > 0$ $\therefore (x + k) > (y + k).$

WORKED EXAMPLE 32

Prove that if $x < y$ then $x - k < y - k.$

SOLUTION 32

$x < y$ $x - y < 0$ $(x - k) < (y - k).$

WORKED EXAMPLE 33

Prove that if $x > y$ and $k > 0$ then $kx > ky.$

SOLUTION 33

$x - y > 0$ $(x - y) k > 0$ $xk - yk > 0$ $kx > ky.$

WORKED EXAMPLE 34

Prove that if $x > y$ and $k < 0$ then $k < ky.$

SOLUTION 34

If $k < 0$ or $0 > k$ or $0 < -k$

Multiplying by $x - y$ the equation $\qquad 0 < -k$ where $x - y > 0$

$0 < -k(x - y)$ $\qquad\qquad 0 < -kx + ky$.

Therefore $kx < ky$.

SET NOTATION

If x lies between -2 and $+3$ this is written as $-2 < x < 3$ which is denoted as:-

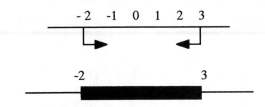

or as

The set notation

$$\{x : -2 < x\} \cap \{x : x < 3\}$$

$\cap$ means intersection or $x : -2 < x < 3$.

If $x > 3$ and $x < -2$, these cannot be combined as before, and can be denoted as

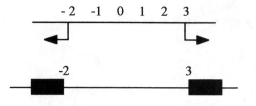

or as

The set notation

$$\{x : 3 < x\} \cup \{x : x < -2\}$$

$\cup$ means union.

To show that $a^2 + b^2 \geq 2ab$, if a and b are real.

If $a \geq b$ then $a - b \geq 0$ and squaring up both sides or multiplying by $a - b$ both sides, we have $(a - b)(a - b) \geq 0$ $\quad (a - b)^2 \geq 0 \quad a^2 - 2ab + b^2 \geq 0$ $a^2 + b^2 \geq 2ab$.

If $a \leq b$ then $a - b \leq 0$ multiplying both sides by $a - b$ which is negative $(a - b)(a - b) \geq 0$ the inequality sign changes $(a - b)^2 = a^2 - 2ab + b^2 \geq 0$

$$\boxed{a^2 + b^2 \geq 2ab}$$

$x - y$ is positive when $x > y$ $\quad x - y$ is negative when $x < y$, $x - y$ is zero when $x = y$

now

$x^2 - y^2 = (x - y)(x + y) > 0$ when $x > y$

$x^2 - y^2 = (x - y)(x + y) < 0$ when $x < y$

$x^2 - y^2 = (x - y)(x + y) = 0$ when $x = y$

If $x > y$

$(x - y)(x^2 - y^2) > 0$ $\qquad\qquad x^3 - xy^2 - yx^2 + y^3 > 0$

$x^3 + y^3 > xy^2 + yx^2$ $\qquad\qquad x^3 + y^3 > xy(y + x)$.

MODULUS SIGN

THE GRAPHICAL SOLUTION

What is the significance of the modulus sign $|x - 1|$?

Let $y = x - 1$, this is a straight line graph

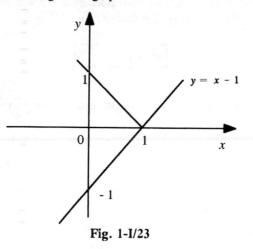

Fig. 1-I/23

$|x - 1|$ the modulus sign of $x - 1$ is the positive value of $x - 1$.

The graph $y = |x - 1|$.

The straight line is now discontinues and is made up of two parts AB and BC, the latter is the reflection in x-axis of BB'.

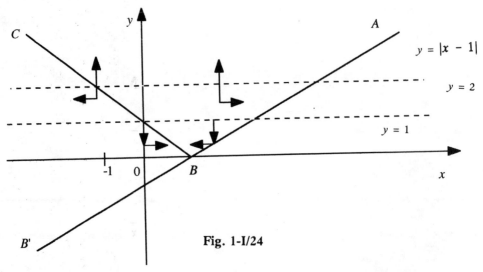

Fig. 1-I/24

WORKED EXAMPLE 35

Find the set of real values of x for which

(i) $|x - 1| > 2$ (ii) $|x - 1| < 1.$

SOLUTION 35

Referring to Fig. 1-I/24.

(i) $|x - 1| > 2.$

   The set of real values of x are: $x > 3$ and $x < -1$

(ii) $|x - 1| < 1.$

   The set of real values of x are: $x < 2$ and $x > 0$ or $0 < x < 2$

Alternatively,

(i) $|x - 1| > 2$ squaring up both sides

   $(x - 1)^2 > 4$ $(x - 1)^2 - 4 > 0$ $[(x - 1) - 2]\,[x - 1 + 2] > 0$

   $(x - 3)(x + 1) > 0$ $x < -1$ $x > 3$

(ii) $|x - 1| < 1$ squaring up both sides $(x - 1)^2 < 1$ $(x - 1)^2 - 1^2 < 0$

   $(x - 1 - 1)(x - 1 + 1) < 0$ $(x - 2)(x) < 0$ $x(x - 2) < 0$ $0 < x < 2.$

WORKED EXAMPLE 36

(i)   Find the set of real values of x for which $|x + 4| > 2|x - 3|.$

(ii)   Find the set of real values of x for which $|x - 2| < |x + 3|.$

SOLUTION 36

(i) $|x + 4| > 2|x - 3|$ squaring up both sides $(x + 4)^2 > 4(x - 3)^2$

   $x^2 + 8x + 16 > 4x^2 - 24x + 36,$ $-3x^2 + 32x - 20 > 0.$

   Multiplying both sides by -1, we have $3x^2 - 32x + 20 < 0$

$$3\left(x^2 - \frac{32}{3}x + \frac{20}{3}\right) < 0 \qquad 3\left[\left(x - \frac{16}{3}\right)^2 - \frac{256}{9} + \frac{20}{3}\right] < 0$$

$$3\left[\left(x - \frac{16}{3}\right)^2 - \frac{196}{9}\right] < 0 \quad \text{or} \quad 3\left[\left(x - \frac{16}{3}\right)^2 - \left(\frac{14}{3}\right)^2\right] < 0$$

$$3\left[\left(x - \frac{16}{3}\right) - \frac{14}{3}\right]\left[\left(x - \frac{16}{3}\right) + \frac{14}{3}\right] < 0 \quad 3(x - 10)\left(x - \frac{2}{3}\right) < 0$$

$$(x - 10)(3x - 2) < 0.$$

The set of real values of x are:- $\dfrac{2}{3} < x < 10$

(ii) $|x - 2| < |x + 3|$ squaring up both sides $(x - 2)^2 < (x + 3)^2$

$[(x - 2) - (x + 3)][(x - 2) + (x + 3)] < 0 \qquad -5(2x + 1) < 0.$

Multiplying both sides by $\left(-\dfrac{1}{5}\right)$ $(2x + 1) > 0$ $\qquad x > -\dfrac{1}{2}.$

WORKED EXAMPLE 37

By sketching the graph of $y = |x - 2| - |x + 1|$ or otherwise find the set of values of x for which $y > 2$.

SOLUTION 37

$|x - 2| - |x + 1| > 2 \qquad |x - 2| > 2 + |x + 1|$ ... (1)

squaring up both sides of (1)

$x^2 - 4x + 4 > x^2 + 2x + 1 + 4|x + 1| + 4$, $-6x - 1 > 4|x + 1|$ squaring up both sides again $36x^2 + 12x + 1 > 16(x^2 + 2x + 1)$, $20x^2 - 20x - 15 > 0$ or $4x^2 - 4x - 3 > 0$ or $4x^2 - 6x + 2x - 3 > 0$ or $2x(2x + 1) - 3(2x + 1) > 0$, $(2x + 1)(2x - 3) > 0$

$x < -\dfrac{1}{2}$ or $x > \dfrac{3}{2}.$

See graphical solution. To obtain the solution $x > \dfrac{3}{2}$ we must take $\|x - 2| - |x + 1\|$. Therefore in the above algebraic method we have, obtained an extra solution. The only

solution is $\boxed{x < -\dfrac{1}{2}}$.

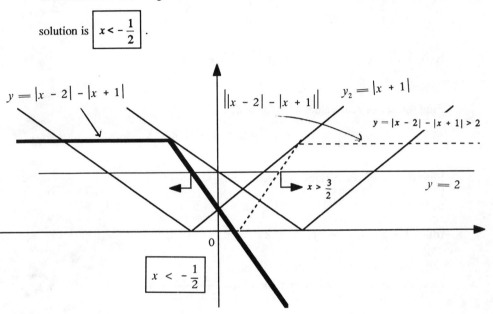

$y = |x - 2| - |x + 1|$

$\|x - 2| - |x + 1\|$

$y_2 = |x + 1|$

$y = |x - 2| - |x + 1| > 2$

$y = 2$

$x > \dfrac{3}{2}$

$\boxed{x < -\dfrac{1}{2}}$

0

Fig. 1-I/25

The <u>following modulus sign inequalities are</u> interesting $|x|$ = the modulus sign of x = the positive values of x

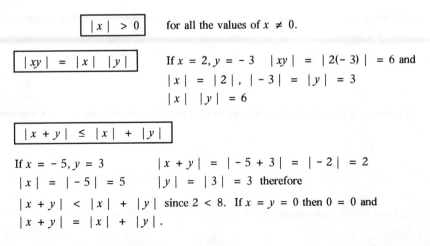

$\boxed{|x| > 0}$ for all the values of $x \neq 0$.

$\boxed{|xy| = |x| \, |y|}$ If $x = 2, y = -3$ $|xy| = |2(-3)| = 6$ and
$|x| = |2|, \; |-3| = |y| = 3$
$|x| \, |y| = 6$

$\boxed{|x + y| \leq |x| + |y|}$

If $x = -5, y = 3$ $|x + y| = |-5 + 3| = |-2| = 2$
$|x| = |-5| = 5$ $|y| = |3| = 3$ therefore
$|x + y| < |x| + |y|$ since $2 < 8$. If $x = y = 0$ then $0 = 0$ and
$|x + y| = |x| + |y|$.

EXERCISES 5

1. Solve the inequalities:-

    (i) $3x + 2 < 5$

    (ii) $-5x - 3 < 5$

    (iii) $\dfrac{3x - 2}{x} \geq 3$

    (iv) $\dfrac{3}{x - 1} > 1$

    (v) $\dfrac{3 + 2x}{3x - 4} < -5$

    (vi) $\dfrac{2x - 5}{x} \geq 1$

    (vii) $\dfrac{1}{x + 1} \leq 1$

    (viii) $\dfrac{5x - 1}{5x} < 1.$

2. Find the set of real values of x for which

    (i) $-x^2 + 2x - 1 < 0$

    (ii) $x^2 - 3x - 4 > 0.$

3. Find the set of real values of x such that:-

    (i) $|\, 2x + 1\, | > 1$

    (ii) $|\, x - 2\, | \leq 1$

    (iii) $|\, -x + 1\, | < |\, -x + 2\, |.$

4. Find the set of real values of x for which $\dfrac{x - 1}{x(x + 1)} < 0.$

5. Solve the inequalities

    (i) $(x - 1)(x + 2)(x - 3) < 0$

    (ii) $x(x + 1)(x - 2) > 0.$

6. Find the set of real values of x in set notation for the following inequalities:-

    (i) $-2x^2 + 11x - 5 > 0$

    (ii) $(2x - 1)(x + 5) < 0$

    (iii) $4x^2 - 5x + 1 < 0.$

7. Express in interval notation the sets of real numbers satisfying

    (i) $|\, x - 2\, | < 3$

    (ii) $|\, 2x + 3\, | \leq 11$

    (iii) $|\, x - 2\, | < 3$ and $|\, 2x + 3\, | \leq 11$ simultaneously.

8. Find the set of real values of x for which $|\, x - 1\, | > 3\, |\, 2x - 3\, |.$

6. FUNCTIONS

RELATIONS OF FUNCTIONS AND THEIR GRAPHS

CARTESIAN AXES

A horizontal line and a vertical line intersect at a point, called <u>the origin</u> and the two lines are called the x-axis and y-axis respectively and the two lines are the cartesian axes.

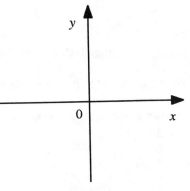

Fig. 1-I/26

DOMAIN, CO-DOMAIN OR RANGE

Let us consider a simple linear relationship connecting x and y the independent and dependent variables respectively, $y = 2x + 1$.

Let us represent this relationship on the cartesian coordinate system, and consider a set of elements for x, 0, 1, 2, 3, 4. This set of elements 0, 1, 2, 3, 4 is called the <u>domain</u> and the corresponding set of elements of y 1, 3, 5, 7, 9 is called the co-domain or <u>range</u>. These two sets of elements of <u>domain</u> and <u>range</u> can be mapped as follows:-

ONE-TO-ONE FUNCTION MAPPING DIAGRAM

A set of elements 0, 1, 2, 3, 4 is called the domain. A set of elements 1, 3, 5, 7, 9 is called the range. This mapping diagram indicates <u>a function.</u>

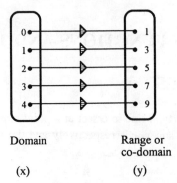

Domain   Range or
                        co-domain

(x)   (y)

Fig. 1-I/27

The values of x are mapped onto $2x + 1$, the set of elements for x are mapped onto the set of elements for y. The values connected by the arrows constitute ordered pairs and the relation may be shown in the form of a diagram.

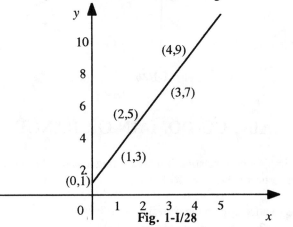

Fig. 1-I/28

FUNCTION NOTATION

f: $x \mapsto 2x + 1$. This reads as follows:-

f is such that x is mapped onto its image, $2x + 1$. Definition of a <u>FUNCTION</u>.

<u>A function</u> is a relation or mapping in which <u>one</u>, and <u>only one</u>, arrowed line leaves each element or member of the domain in the above mapping diagram, which is a one-to-one mapping diagram.

Consider a <u>many-to-one mapping diagram.</u>

MANY-TO-ONE FUNCTION

A function is also indicated for a <u>many-to-one mapping diagram</u>. Two arrowed lines arrive at one of the elements of the range.

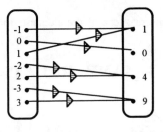

Fig. 1-I/29

Consider the function f: $x \mapsto x^2$ which is graphed below and mapped above. The domain of this function is $\mathbb{R}$, for each $x \in \mathbb{R}$ there exists a unique $y \in \mathbb{R}$.

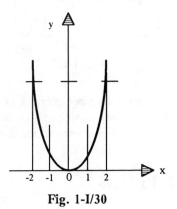

Fig. 1-I/30

<u>Each vertical line cuts the graph in one and only one place, f: $x \mapsto x^2$ or $y = x^2$ is a function.</u> Consider the relation $y^2 = x$, which is graphed below.

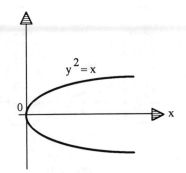

Fig. 1-I/31

For $x = -1$, **i.e.** the vertical line $x = -1$ does not meet the graph at all and the relationship <u>is not a function.</u> This may be mapped as follows:-

For negative elements of the domain, the range is complex, **i.e.** it does not exist. For each positive value of the domain, the range has two elements.

Two arrowed lines leave one or more of the elements in the domain.

ONE-TO-MANY RELATIONSHIP

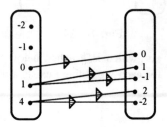

Fig. 1-I/32

Therefore, $y^2 = x$ or f: $x \mapsto \pm \sqrt{x}$ does not define a function. If a relation is not a function, then a vertical line will pass through two ordered pairs when the graph is drawn. Two arrowed lines leave one or more of the elements in the domain.

WORKED EXAMPLE 38

Which of the following mapping diagrams are functions? State in each case the set of elements in the domain, co-domain or range:-

(i)   (ii)   (iii)

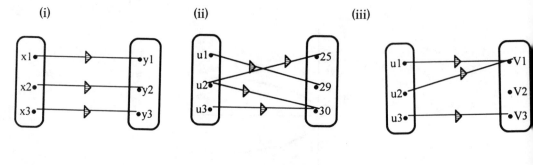

Fig. 1-I/33   **Fig. 1-I/34**   **Fig. 1-I/35**

(iv)　　　　　　　　　　(v)　　　　　　　　　　(vi)

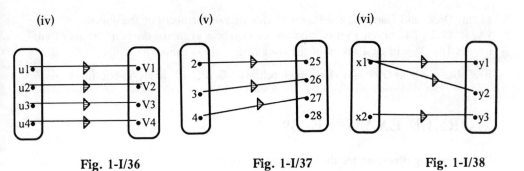

Fig. 1-I/36　　　　　　　Fig. 1-I/37　　　　　　Fig. 1-I/38

SOLUTION 38

(i)　The mapping or arrow diagram is a function and a one-to-one function since one, and <u>only one</u>, arrowed line leaves each element or member of the domain.
The mapping is onto, $\{x_1, x_2, x_3\}$ domain, $\{y_1, y_2, y_3\}$ co-domain or range.

(ii)　The mapping diagram is <u>not</u> a function since two arrowed lines leave one of the elements in the domain. $\{u_1, u_2, u_3\}$ domain, $\{25, 29, 30\}$ co-domain or range.
The mapping is onto.

(iii)　The mapping diagram is a function (one-to-many) since one arrowed line leaves each element of the domain and although two arrowed lines arrive at one of the elements of the range. $\{u_1, u_2, u_3\}$ domain, $\{v_1, v_2, v_3\}$ co-domain.
The mapping is onto.

(iv)　The arrow diagram is a one-to-one function. The mapping is onto, $\{u_1, u_2, u_3, u_4\}$ domain, $\{v_1, v_2, v_3, v_4\}$ co-domain or range.

(v)　The arrow diagram is a one-to-one function $\{2, 3, 4\}$ domain, $\{25, 26, 27, 28\}$ co-domain, $\{25, 26, 27\}$ range. The mapping is into.

(iv)　The arrow diagram is a one-to-many diagram and is not a function.
$\{x_1, x_2\}$ domain, $\{y_1, y_2, y_3\}$ co-domain or range. The mapping is onto.

Tom, Dick and Harry sat for the G.C.E. 'A' examination in Mathematics. Tom achieved a grade 'A'. Dick and Harry achieved grade 'B'.

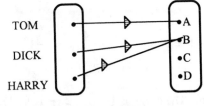

Fig. 1-I/39

{Tom, Dick, and Harry} consist a set of elements or members of the domain, {A, B, C, D, E} consist a set of elements or members of the co-domain, the set of all images {A, B} will be a subset of the co-domain, and is called the range.

It is observed that Dick and Harry both achieved Grade 'B', many-to-one function.

WORKED EXAMPLE 39

Draw mapping diagrams for the following functions:-

(i) $f: x \mapsto -3x - 5$ (ii) $g: x \mapsto x - 1$

(iii) $h: x \mapsto x^2 + 2x + 1$ (iv) $\lambda: x \mapsto -3x^2 - x + 1$

(v) $\mu: x \mapsto 2\sqrt{x}$ (vi) $V: x \mapsto 8x^2$

for the domain {- 2, - 1, 0, 1, 2}. State in each case whether the mapping is onto or into.

SOLUTION 39

(i) $f: x \mapsto -3x - 5$

$x = -2, y = -3(-2) - 5 = 6 - 5 = 1;$ $x = -1, y = -3(-1) - 5 = -2$

$x = 0, \ y = -5$ $x = 1, \ \ y = -3(1) - 5 = -8$

$x = 2, \ y = -3(2) - 5 = -11.$

The mapping is onto. The range is {- 11, - 8, - 5, - 2, 1}

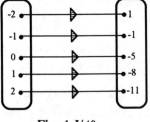

Fig. 1-I/40

(ii) $g: x \mapsto x - 1$

$x = -2, y = -2 - 1 = -3;$ $x = -1, y = -1 - 1 = -2$

$x = 0, y = -1; x = 1, y = 0; \ x = 2, y = 1$

The mapping is onto. The range is {- 3, - 2, - 1, 0, 1}.

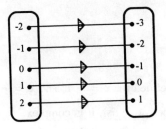

Fig. 1-I/41

(iii) h: $x \mapsto x^2 + 2x + 1$

$x = -2, y = (-2)^2 + 2(-2) + 1 = 1$
$x = -1, y = (-1)^2 + 2(-1) + 1 = 0;$ $x = 0, y = 1$
$x = 1, \quad y = 1^2 + 2(1) + 1 = 4;$ $x = 2, y = 2^2 + 2(2) + 1 = 9$

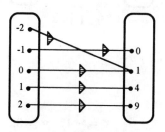

Fig. 1-I/42

The range $\{0, 1, 4, 9\}$. The mapping is onto.

(iv) $\lambda : x \mapsto -3x^2 - x + 1$

$x = -2, y = -12 + 2 + 1 = -9$ $x = -1, y = -3 + 1 + 1 = -1$
$x = 0, \quad y = 1$ $x = 1, \quad y = -3 - 1 + 1 = -3$
$x = 2, \quad y = -12 - 2 + 1 = -13$

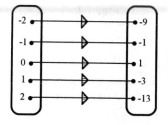

Fig. 1-I/43

The mapping is onto. The range is $\{-13, -9, -3, -1, 1\}$.

(v) $\mu: x \mapsto 2\sqrt{x}$

The function is not defined for $x = -1$, and $x = -2$ $\{x \in \mathbb{R}; x \geq 0\}$.

$x = -2,$ y does not exist, it is complex.

$x = -1,$ y does not exist, it is complex.

$x = 0,$ $y = 0; x = 1, y = 2; x = 2, y = 2\sqrt{2}.$

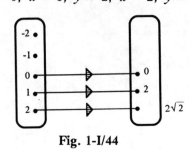

Fig. 1-I/44

The range is $\{0, 2, 2\sqrt{2}\}$

(vi) $V: x \mapsto 8x^2$

$x = -2, \quad y = 32;$ $x = -1, \quad y = 8;$ $x = 0, y = 0;$

$x = 1, \quad y = 8;$ $x = 2, \quad y = 32.$

The range is $\{0, 8, 32\}$.

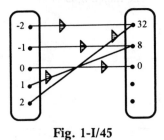

Fig. 1-I/45

WORKED EXAMPLE 40

(a) Sketch the graph of the function $f(x) = -x^2 + 4x - 2$ for $-3 \leq x \leq 3$, $x \in \mathbb{R}$.

(b) Indicate the domain, and range.

(c) Draw a mapping diagram.

(d) Distinguish between range and co-domain.

SOLUTION 40

(a) $f(x)$ is the image of x. For the domain of the function $-3 \leq x \leq 3$, the elements or members of the domain are $-3, -2, -1, 0, 1, 2, 3$ and the image set of the function can be found by substituting the values of x in $f(x) = -x^2 + 4x - 2$.

$f(-3) = -(-3)^2 + 4(-3) - 2 = -23$

$f(-2) = -(-2)^2 + 4(-2) - 2 = -14$

$f(-1) = -(-1)^2 + 4(-1) - 2 = -7; \qquad f(0) = -2$

$f(1) = -(1)^2 + 4(+1) - 2 = 1 \qquad\qquad f(2) = -(2)^2 + 4(2) - 2 = 2$

$f(3) = -(3)^2 + 4(3) - 2 = 1$

(b) **The graph of a function $f(x) = -x^2 - 4x - 2$.**

Range $\{y : -23 \leq y \leq 2\}$ of $f(x)$. $\qquad -3 \leq x \leq 3$.

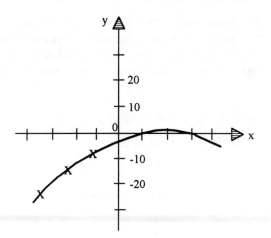

Fig. 1-I/46

(c) **A mapping diagram.**

Many-to-one function. The range (subset of B). The set of B is $-\infty \leq y \leq 2$. The co-domain or image set. The domain of the function.

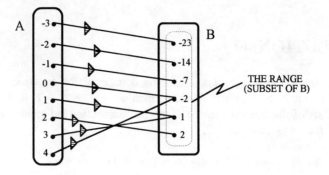

Fig. 1-I/47

(d)   The co-domain or the image set is given as $-\infty < y \le 2(-\infty, 2)$ the range is the subset of the co-domain as illustrated in the mapping diagram.

INVERSE FUNCTIONS

What is an inverse function?

$f(x) = x$ or $y = x$, the inverse function of $f(x)$ is $x = y$ or $f^{-1}(y) = y$.

$f(x) = x^2$ or $y = x^2$, the inverse function of $f(x)$ is $x = y^{1/2}$, or $f^{-1}(y) = y^{1/2}$. $f(x) = \sin x$ or $y = \sin x$, the inverse function of $f(x)$ is $x = \sin^{-1} y$ or $f^{-1}(y) = \sin^{-1} y$. A function maps the domain onto the range. The inverse function maps the range of the function to the domain procedure for finding the inverse function:-

(i)   Write in place of y, x and in place of x, y.

(ii)   Solve, if possible, for y in terms of x.

NOTATION

$$f(x) = \frac{x^2 + 1}{x^2 - 1} \ (x \pm 1) \qquad f: x \mapsto \frac{x^2 + 1}{x^2 - 1}$$

$f^{-1}(x)$ is the inverse function of $f(x)$ $f^{-1}: x \mapsto \pm \sqrt{\dfrac{x + 1}{x - 1}}$ provided $x > 1$

since $\quad x = \dfrac{y^2 + 1}{y^2 - 1}$, $x\,(y^2 - 1) = y^2 + 1$, $y^2\,(x - 1) = x + 1$

$$y^2 = \frac{x + 1}{x - 1} \qquad y = \pm \sqrt{\frac{x + 1}{x - 1}}.$$

WORKED EXAMPLE 41

Determine the inverse function for the following:-

(i) $y = x^2$ (ii) $y = \cos x$ (iii) $f: x \mapsto \dfrac{3x + 1}{2x - 3}$

(iv) $f: x \mapsto \log_e x$ (v) $f: x \mapsto \log_{10} x.$

SOLUTION 41

(i) $y = x^2 \Rightarrow f: x \mapsto x^2$ $x = y^2$ $y = \pm \sqrt{x} \Rightarrow f^{-1}: x \rightarrow \pm \sqrt{x}$
      for this inverse function, we must restrict the new, range to, say, the positive
      square root of x i.e. $\{0, \mathbb{R}^+\}$, $f^{-1}: x \mapsto +\sqrt{x}.$

(ii) $y = \cos x \Rightarrow f: x \mapsto \cos x$ $x = \cos y$ $y = \cos^{-1} x \Rightarrow f^{-1}: x \mapsto \cos^{-1} x.$

(iii) $f: x \rightarrow \dfrac{3x + 1}{2x - 3}$ if $x \neq \dfrac{3}{2}$ $y = \dfrac{3x + 1}{2x - 3}$ $x = \dfrac{3y + 1}{2y - 3}.$

      $(3y + 1) = x(2y - 3)$ $3y + 1 = 2xy - 3x$ $y(3 - 2x) = -1 - 3x$

      $y = \dfrac{1 + 3x}{2x - 3}$ $y = \dfrac{3x + 1}{2x - 3}$ $f^{-1}: x \rightarrow \dfrac{3x + 1}{2x - 3}$ if $x \neq \dfrac{3}{2}$

      an example of a function which is its own inverse.

(iv) $f: x \mapsto \log_e x$ $y = \log_e x$ $x = \log_e y$ $y = e^x$ $f^{-1}: x \mapsto e^x.$

(v) $f: x \mapsto \log_{10} x$ $y = \log_{10} x$ $x = \log_{10} y$ $y = 10^x$ $f^{-1}: x \mapsto 10^x.$

      By definition of the inverse function $ff^{-1}(x) = f^{-1} f(x)$
      $(fg \dots pq)^{-1} = q^{-1} p^{-1} \dots g^{-1} f^{-1}.$

The mapping diagram for a function and its inverse.

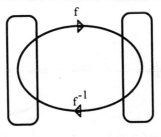

Domain   co-domain

Fig. 1-I/48

The graph of a function and the graph of its inverse function.

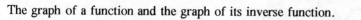

Function $y = \log x$

log x

0

x

Function y = log x

Fig. 1-I/49

The inverse function $y = 10^x$

y 10^x

0

x

Fig. 1-I/50

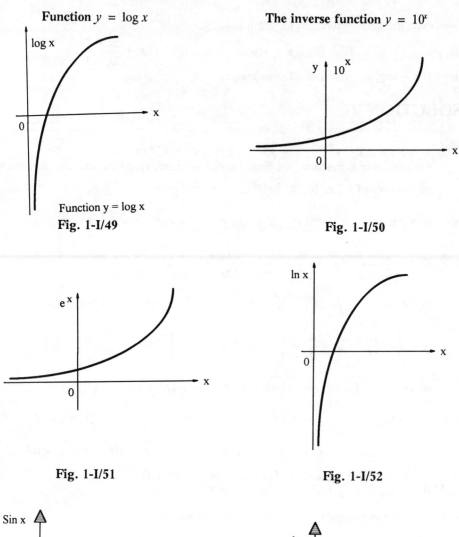

e^x

0

x

Fig. 1-I/51

ln x

0

x

Fig. 1-I/52

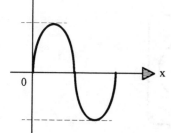

Sin x

0

x

Fig. 1-I/53

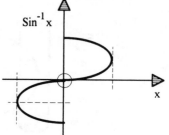

$Sin^{-1} x$

x

Fig. 1-I/54

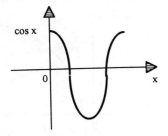

Fig. 1-I/55

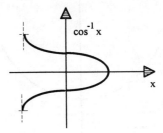

Fig. 1-I/56

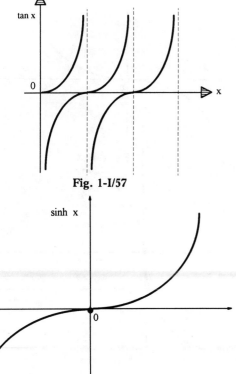

Fig. 1-I/57

Fig. 1-I/58

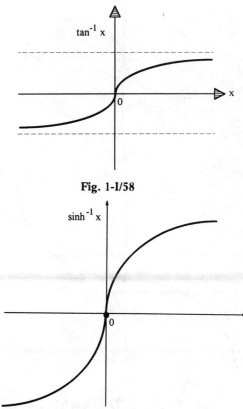

Fig. 1-I/59

Fig. 1-I/60

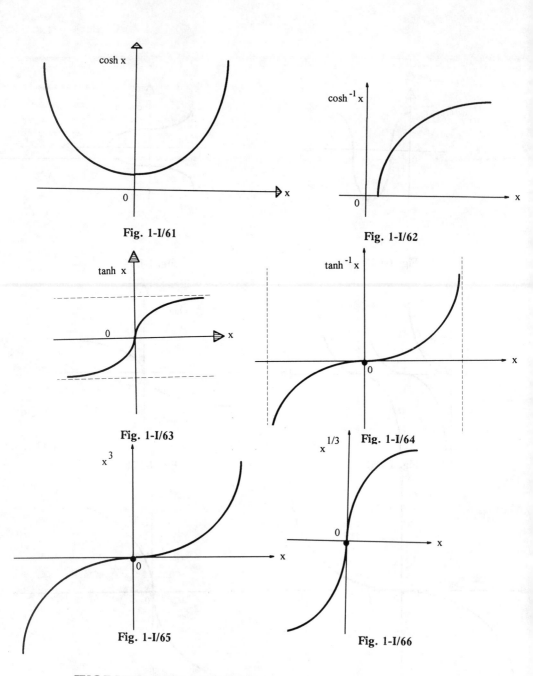

Fig. 1-I/61

Fig. 1-I/62

Fig. 1-I/63

Fig. 1-I/64

Fig. 1-I/65

Fig. 1-I/66

WORKED EXAMPLE 42

Sketch a few logarithmic, exponential, trigonometric, hyperbolic, algebraic functions and their inverses.

SOLUTION 42

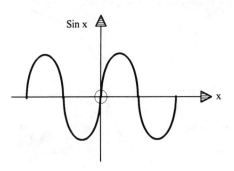

Fig. 1-I/67

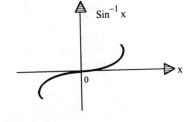

Fig. 1-I/68

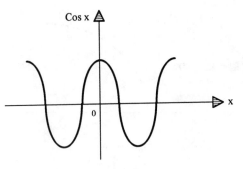

Fig. 1-I/69

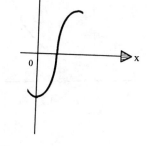

Fig. 1-I/70

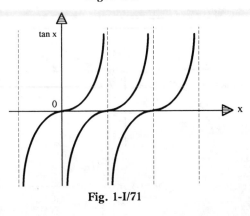

Fig. 1-I/71

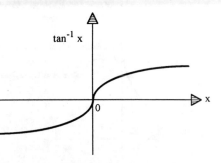

Fig. 1-I/72

1-I/75

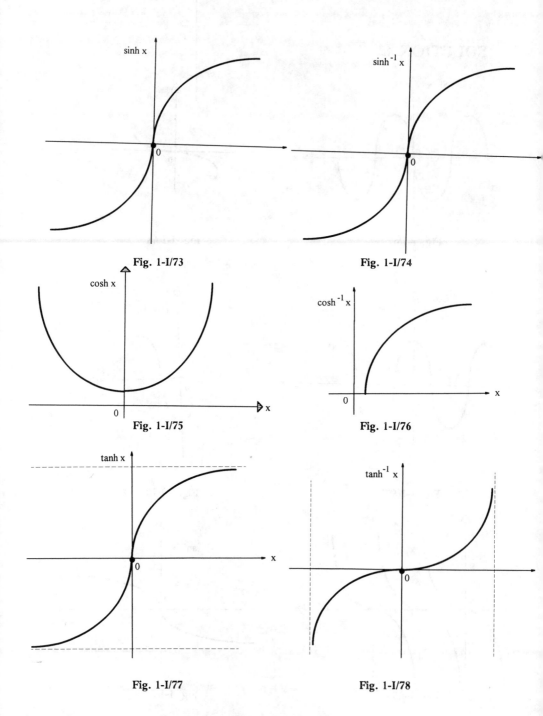

Fig. 1-I/73

Fig. 1-I/74

Fig. 1-I/75

Fig. 1-I/76

Fig. 1-I/77

Fig. 1-I/78

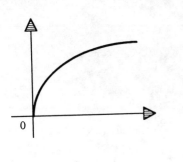

Fig. 1-I/79

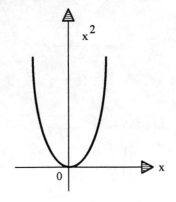

Fig. 1-I/80

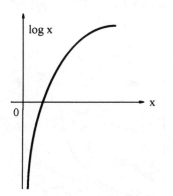

Fig. 1-I/81

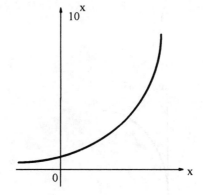

Fig. 1-I/82

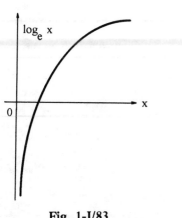

Fig. 1-I/83

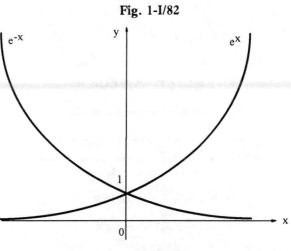

Fig. 1-I/84

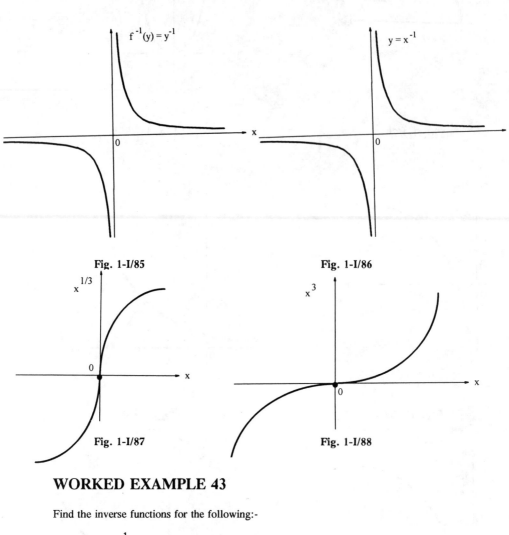

Fig. 1-I/85

Fig. 1-I/86

Fig. 1-I/87

Fig. 1-I/88

WORKED EXAMPLE 43

Find the inverse functions for the following:-

(i) $f: x \mapsto \dfrac{1}{x - 2}$ where $x \in \mathbb{R}$ and $x \neq 2$.

(ii) $g: x \mapsto \ln x$ where $x \in \mathbb{R}^+$

(iii) $h: x \mapsto 3x + 2$ where $x \in \mathbb{R}$

(iv) $k: x \mapsto 5x - 1$ where $x \in \mathbb{R}$

(v) $\varsigma: x \mapsto \dfrac{x - 1}{x + 1}$ where $x \in \mathbb{R}$ and $x \neq -1$.

SOLUTION 43

(i) To find the inverse function, we proceed as follows:-

$$f: x \mapsto \frac{1}{x-2} \quad \text{... (1)}$$

is written as $y = \dfrac{1}{x-2}$, we interchange x and y, and solve for y, this y is the inverse function

$$x = \frac{1}{y-2} \qquad y-2 = \frac{1}{x} \qquad y = \frac{1}{x} + 2 \qquad y = \frac{1+2x}{x}$$

$$\boxed{f^{-1}: x \mapsto \frac{1+2x}{x}}$$

where $x \in \mathbb{R}$ and $x \neq 0$.

(ii) $g: x \mapsto \ln x \qquad y = \ln x \qquad x = \ln y = \log_e y \qquad y = e^x$ or

$$\boxed{g^{-1}: x \mapsto e^x}$$

(iii) $h: x \mapsto 3x + 2$

$$y = 3x + 2 \qquad x = 3y + 2 \qquad 3y = x - 2 \qquad y = \frac{1}{3}x - \frac{2}{3}$$

$$\boxed{h^{-1}: x \mapsto \frac{1}{3}x - \frac{2}{3}}$$

(iv) $k: x \mapsto 5x - 1$

$$y = 5x - 1 \qquad x = 5y - 1 \qquad 5y = x + 1 \qquad y = \frac{1}{5}x + \frac{1}{5}$$

$$\boxed{k^{-1}: x \mapsto \frac{1}{5}x + \frac{1}{5}}$$

(v) $\zeta: x \mapsto \dfrac{x-1}{x+1} \qquad y = \dfrac{x-1}{x+1} \qquad x = \dfrac{y-1}{y+1} \qquad x(y+1) = y - 1$

$$y(x-1) = -x - 1 \qquad\qquad y = \frac{1+x}{1-x}$$

1-I/79

$$\zeta^{-1}: x \mapsto \frac{1 + x}{1 - x}$$

where $x \in \mathbb{R}$ and $x \neq 1$.

Composite function (or function of a function)

$f(x) = x^2 \qquad g(x) = x^{1/2} \qquad gf(x) = g(x^2) = (x^2)^{1/2} = x$

$f(x) = 3x - 1 \quad g(x) = 5x + 2 \quad \text{fog and gof.}$

$\text{fog} = [3(5x + 2) - 1] = 15x + 6 - 1 = 15x + 5$

$\text{gof} = [5(3x - 1) + 2] = 15x - 5 + 2 = 15x - 3 \qquad \text{fog} \neq \text{gof}$

Even and odd functions

An even function f is one for which $f(-a) = f(a)$ for all values of x.

(a) $\cos(-x) = \cos x.$

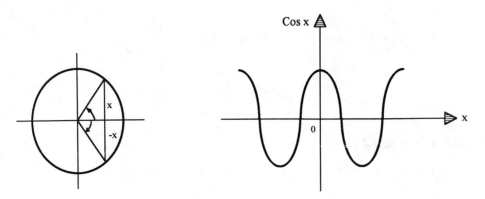

Fig. 1-I/89

(b) $y = x^2 \quad y = (x)^2 \quad y = x^2$ replace x by $(-x)$. $y = x^2$.

The graph of an even function is symmetrical about the y-axis.

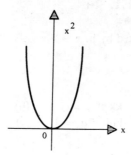

Fig. 1-I/90

(c) $y = \cosh x$ $y = \dfrac{e^x + e^{-x}}{2}$, $x = -x$, $y = \dfrac{e^{-x} + e^{-(-x)}}{2} = \cosh x$

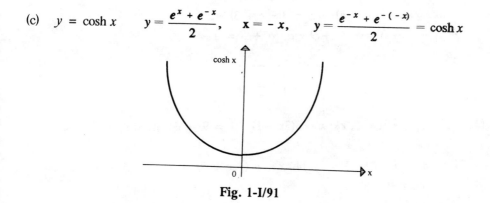

Fig. 1-I/91

An <u>odd function</u> f is one for which $f(-a) = -f(a)$, for all values of x;

e.g. $y = \sin x$, $y = \dfrac{e^x - e^{-x}}{2} = \sinh x$, $y = x^3$.

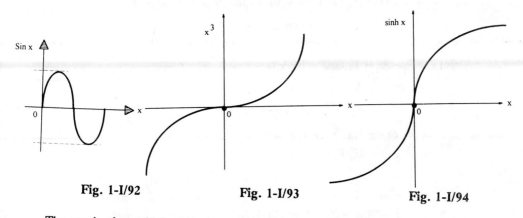

Fig. 1-I/92   **Fig. 1-I/93**   **Fig. 1-I/94**

The graph of an odd function is symmetrical about the origin.

WORKED EXAMPLE 44

The function h and k are defined by h: $x \mapsto -x + 3$, k: $x \mapsto 3x - a$ where $x \in \mathbb{R}$, and a is a constant.

(a) Find a if hk = kh.

(b) Find the values of (i)   kk if $a = 1$ (ii)   hh   (iii) hkh if $a = 3$
                                         (iv) khk if $a = 1$ (v)   kkk if $a = 2$.

SOLUTION 44

(a) hk = $-(3x - a) + 3$; kh = $3(-x + 3) - a$
   if hk = kh $-(3x - a) + 3 = 3(-x + 3) - a$
   $-3x + a + 3 = -3x + 9 - a$, $a + 3 = 9 - a$
   $2a = 6$

$$\boxed{a = 3}$$

(b) (i)   k: $x \mapsto 3x - 1$, kk: $x \mapsto 3(3x - 1) - 1 = 9x - 3 - 1$, kk: $x \mapsto 9x - 4$

   (ii) h: $x \mapsto -x + 3$ hh: $x \mapsto -(-x + 3) + 3 = x - 3 + 3 = x$
         hh: $x \mapsto x$.

   (iii) h: $x \mapsto -x + 3$ k: $\mapsto 3x - 3$
         hk: $x \mapsto (-(3x - 3) + 3] = -3x + 3 + 3 = -3x + 6$
         hk: $x \mapsto -3x + 6$
         hkh: $x \mapsto [-3(-x + 3) + 6] = 3x - 9 + 6 = 3x - 3$
                     hkh: $x \mapsto 3x - 3$

   (iv) k: $x \mapsto 3x - 1$ h : $x \mapsto -x + 3$
         kh: $x \mapsto 3(-x + 3) - 1 = -3x + 9 - 1 = -3x + 8$
                     kh: $x \mapsto -3x + 8$
         khk: $x \mapsto -3(3x - 1) + 8 = -9x + 3 + 8$
         khk: $x \mapsto -9x + 1$

   (v)   k: $x \mapsto 3x - 2$ kk : $x \mapsto 3(3x - 2) - 2 = 9x - 6 - 2 = 9x - 8$
         kkk: $x \mapsto 9(3x - 2) - 8 = 27x - 26$.

WORKED EXAMPLE 45

The function f is defined by f: $x \mapsto -2x^2 + 3x - 1$, where $x \in \mathbb{R}$.

(i)   State whether this function has a minimum or maximum and find this value.

(ii)   The value of x at which this minimum or maximum occurs.

(iii) Sketch the graph of the function for the set of elements of the domain
$\{-3, -2, -1, 0, 1, 2, 3\}$ and state the corresponding range of f.

SOLUTION 45

(i)   f: $x \mapsto -2x^2 + 3x - 1$.

This function has a maximum since the coefficient of x^2 is negative (-2).

The maximum value occurs when $x = -\dfrac{b}{2a} = \dfrac{-(3)}{2(-2)} = \dfrac{3}{4}$ and the maximum

value is $(f:x)_{max} \mapsto -2\left(\dfrac{3}{4}\right)^2 + 3\left(\dfrac{3}{4}\right) - 1 = -\dfrac{18}{16} + \dfrac{9}{4} - 1 = -\dfrac{9}{8} + \dfrac{18}{8} - \dfrac{8}{8} = \dfrac{1}{8}$.

(ii)   The value of x at which this maximum occurs is $x = \dfrac{3}{4}$.

(iii)

x	-3	-2	-1	0	1	2	3
f: x	-28	-15	-6	-1	0	-3	-10

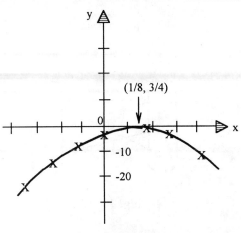

Fig. 1-I/95

1-I/83

EXERCISES 6

1. Explain the terms: (i) DOMAIN
   (ii) CODOMAIN OR RANGE
   (iii) ONE-TO-ONE FUNCTION
   (iv) MAPPING DIAGRAM
   (v) MANY-TO-ONE MAPPING DIAGRAM.

2. Read the following function notations:-

   (i) $f: x \mapsto 5x - 4$

   (ii) $f^{-1} : x \mapsto \dfrac{1}{5}(x + 4)$.

3. What is a function? Illustrate by means of mapping diagrams.

4. Which of the following mapping diagrams are functions? State in each case the set of elements in the domain, co-domain or range.

   (i)

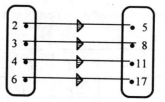

Fig. 1-I/96

   (ii)

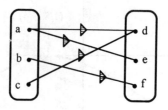

Fig. 1-I/97

(iii)

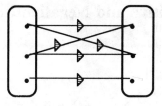

Fig. 1-I/98

5. A function g is defined by g: $x \mapsto 5x + 2$, where x is a real number and $-3 \le x \le 3$.

    (i)   Find the points where the graph of g cuts the x-axis and y-axis.

    (ii) Evaluate $g\left(\dfrac{1}{2}\right)$.

    (iii) Find k such that $g(k) = 0$.

    (iv) Find the set of elements of the range.

6. The domain has a set of elements {1, 2, 3, 4, 5} and the function f is defined by f: $x \mapsto 2x^2 + x - 3$. Find the set of elements or members of the range of f.

7. If f: $x \mapsto + 5\sqrt{x}$, and its range has a set of element {0, 1, 2, 3} state the domain of the function.

8. If h: $x \mapsto 4x^3 + 5x^2 - 3x + 5$, find h(-2) and the values of x for which the function is 5.

9. The function f is defined by f: $x \to \dfrac{1}{x + 1}$ where $x \in \mathbb{R}$ and $x \ne -1$.

    (a) Sketch this function.

    (b) Find the inverse function of f and sketch its graph.

    (c) State the domain and range for f and f^{-1}.

    (d) Evaluate (i) $f^{-1}(1)$ (ii) f(2)   (iii) fff(3)   (iv) $f^{-1}(2)$.

    (e) State whether f and f^{-1} are one-to-one functions or many-to-one functions.

7. INDICES

Positive and Negative Indices

What is the meaning of 2^5?

2 is raised to the power 5.

2 is called the <u>base</u> and $2^5 = 2 \times 2 \times 2 \times 2 \times 2 = 32$.

What about the meaning of 2^{-5}?

2 is raised to the power -5, 2^{-5} is written as $\dfrac{1}{2^5}$ since the index is negative and

$\dfrac{1}{2^5} = \dfrac{1}{2 \times 2 \times 2 \times 2 \times 2} = \dfrac{1}{32}$, therefore $2^{-5} = \dfrac{1}{32}$. 2^{-5} is the reciprocal of 2^5.

WORKED EXAMPLE 46

Simplify $2^5 \times 2^3 \times 2^1$.

SOLUTION 46

$2^5 = 2 \times 2 \times 2 \times 2 \times 2 = 32$, $2^3 = 2 \times 2 \times 2 = 8$, $2^1 = 2$

Therefore $2^5 \times 2^3 \times 2^1 = (2 \times 2 \times 2 \times 2 \times 2) \times (2 \times 2 \times 2) \times 2 = 2^9$
2 is multiplied by itself nine times.

We observe that $2^5 \times 2^3 \times 2^1 = 2^9$, that is the indices are added since they are positive.

The first law of indices may be formulated

$$\boxed{a^m \times a^n = a^{m+n}}$$

Since each base, a, of the numbers a^m and a^n is the same and the indices are m and n, they are added.

This can be extended to many more $a^m \times a^n \times a^p \times a^q = a^{m+n+p+q}$.

ZERO INDEX

We had before the examples 2^5 and 2^{-5}. If we multiply them, we obtain

$2^5 \times 2^{-5} = \dfrac{2^5}{2^5} = 1$ or simply $2^5 \times 2^{-5} = 2^{5-5} = 2^0 = 1$.

Any number raised to the power nought is unity

$$x^0 = 1$$

we can now write the second law of indices $a^m \div a^n$

$$\frac{a^m}{a^n} = a^{m-n}$$

so, when we divide two numbers with indices m and n, having the same base, a, then we subtract the indices.

Let us now extend all the above ideas.

If $2^5 \times 2^5 \times 2^5 = (2^5)^3 = 2^{15}$.

Therefore, the superpowers

$$(a^m)^n = a^{mn}$$

If a^m is raised to the power n, a^m is multiplied by itself n times. Further this law can be extended

$$\left(\left(\left(a^m\right)^n\right)^p\right)^q = a^{mnpq}.$$

Summarising, all the above, we have three simple rules:-

(i) $a^m \times a^n = a^{m+n}$ (ii) $\dfrac{a^m}{a^n} = a^{m-n}$ (iii) $(a^m)^n = a^{mn}$

A Surd number

It is also necessary to point out the meaning of roots.

What is the square root of 2, or $\sqrt{2}$, is a number approximately equal to 1.4142136 multiplied by itself it gives what is under the square root.

If we multiply $1.4142136 \times 1.4142136$ using a calculator, we shall obtain the number 2.0000001, it is observed that the result is not exactly 2 but 2.0000001 which is also an approximate number. Really there is not a number which when multiplied by itself gives exactly the number 2.

Therefore $\sqrt{2}$ is called a surd number other examples are $\sqrt{3}, \sqrt{5}, \sqrt{7}$.

Rational and irrational numbers

The well known letter π which is approximately 3.1415927 to seven decimal places is never ending.

In earlier work, π was given approximately as a rational number $\pi = \dfrac{22}{7}$

which is approximately equal 3.14 to two decimal places, or three significant figures.

A better approximation for π as a rational number is $\dfrac{355}{113}$ which may be remembered

from 113355, by writing the last three digits and dividing by the first three digits,

$\dfrac{355}{113} = 3.1415929$ or 3.141592 to six decimal places.

The number π is an <u>irrational number</u>, it cannot be expressed exactly as a <u>rational</u>

<u>number</u> as $\dfrac{355}{113}$.

What is the meaning of $2^{3/2}$?

A positive number such as 2, raised to rational number such as $\dfrac{3}{2}$.

The number $2^{3/2} = \sqrt[2]{2^3}$.

The numerator of the rational number is the power or index of 2 and the denominator

of the rational number $\dfrac{3}{2}$ is the root of the number 2.

In general

$$\boxed{N^{m/n} = \sqrt[n]{N^m}}$$

so N raised to the power m/n, means the nth root of, N raised to m as shown. It is

convenient some times to write a number as $N^{m/n}$, or as $\sqrt[n]{N^m}$, $N^{1/2} = \sqrt[2]{N^1} = \sqrt{N}$.

SUMMARY

1. $a^m \times a^n = a^{m+n}$ 5. $a^0 = 1$

2. $a^m/a^n = a^{m-n}$ 6. $a^{-n} = \dfrac{1}{a^n}$

3. $(a^m)^n = a^{mn}$ 7. $a^{-b} \to 0$ when $b \to \infty$.

4. $N^{m/n} = \sqrt[n]{N^m}$

WORKED EXAMPLE 46

Simplify the following:-

(i) $32^{-4/3} \times 128^{3/7} \times 16^{5/3}$ (ii) $81^{1/2} \times 3^5 \times 729^{-1/2}$

(iii) $(125)^{-1} \times 25^{4/3} \times 5^{1/3}$.

SOLUTION 46

(i) $32^{-4/3} \times 128^{3/7} \times 16^{5/3}$ $= (2^5)^{-4/3} \times (2^7)^{3/7} \times (2^4)^{5/3}$

$$= 2^{-20/3} \times 2^3 \times 2^{20/3} = 8$$

(ii) $81^{1/2} \times 3^5 \times 729^{-1/2} = (3^4)^{1/2} \times 3^5 \times (3^6)^{-1/2} = 3^2 \times 3^5 \times 3^{-3} = 3^4 = 81$

(iii) $125^{-1} \times 25^{4/3} \times 5^{1/3} = (5^3)^{-1} \times (5^2)^{4/3} \times 5^{1/3} = 5^{-3} \times 5^{8/3} \times 5^{1/3} = 5^0 = 1$.

WORKED EXAMPLE 47

Determine the values of x:

(i) $32^x = 4$ (ii) $625^{1/x} = 5$ (iii) $729^{-1/x} = 3 \times 3$

SOLUTION 47

(i) $32^x = 4$, $(2^5)^x = 2^2$, $2^{5x} = 2^2$, $5x = 2$, $x = 0.4$

(ii) $625^{1/x} = 5$, $(5^4)^{1/x} = 5^1$, $5^{4/x} = 5^1$, $\dfrac{4}{x} = 1$, $x = 4$

(iii) $729^{-1/x} = 3 \times 3$, $(3^6)^{-1/x} = 3^2$, $3^{-6/x} = 3^2$, $\dfrac{-6}{x} = 2$, $x = -3$.

WORKED EXAMPLE 48

Simplify the following:-

(i) $z^7 \dfrac{z^5}{z^{-3}}$　　(ii) $y^{-4}y^3(y^2)^5$　　(iii) $w^5 \dfrac{(w^{-3})^{-2}}{w^7}$

SOLUTION 48

(i) $z^7 \dfrac{z^5}{z^{-3}} = z^7 \, z^5 \, z^3 = z^{15}$　(ii) $y^{-4}y^3(y^2)^5 = y^{-4} \, y^3 \, y^{10} = y^9$

(iii) $w^5 \dfrac{(w^{-3})^{-2}}{w^7} = w^5 \, w^6 \, w^{-7} = w^4$.

WORKED EXAMPLE 49

Simplify the following by using the rules of indices:-

(i) $\left(5\dfrac{1}{5}\right)^2$

(ii) $(5 + 3)^{-3}$

(iii) $\left(27\dfrac{1}{3}\right)^{-1/3}$

(iv) $32^{5/2}$

(v) $\left(\dfrac{169}{144}\right)^{-1/2}$

(vi) $(128)^{-2/3}$

(vii) $\left(\dfrac{3}{5} \times \dfrac{5}{3} \times \dfrac{1}{2} \times \dfrac{3}{8}\right)^0$

(viii) $\left(5\dfrac{3}{4}\right)^{-1/2} \times \left(3\dfrac{3}{8}\right)^{5/2}$

(ix) $(-16)^{2/3}$

(x) $\left(2\dfrac{16}{27}\right)^{1/2}$.

SOLUTION 49

(i) $\left(5\dfrac{1}{5}\right)^2 = \left(\dfrac{26}{5}\right)^2 = \dfrac{676}{25}$

(ii) $(5+3)^{-3} = 8^{-3} = (2^3)^{-3} = 2^{-9} = \dfrac{1}{2^9} = \dfrac{1}{512}$

(iii) $\left(27\dfrac{1}{3}\right)^{-1/3} = \left(\dfrac{82}{3}\right)^{-1/3} = \dfrac{3^{1/3}}{82^{1/3}}$

(iv) $32^{5/2} = (2^5)^{5/2} = 2^{12.5} = 2^{12}\,2^{0.5} = 4096\sqrt{2}$

(v) $\left(\dfrac{169}{144}\right)^{-1/2} = \left(\dfrac{13^2}{12^2}\right)^{-1/2} = \left(\dfrac{13}{12}\right)^{-1} = \dfrac{12}{13}$

(vi) $(128)^{-2/3} = (2^7)^{-2/3} = 2^{-14/3} = 1/2^{14/3}$

(vii) $\left(\dfrac{3}{5} \times \dfrac{5}{3} \times \dfrac{1}{2} \times \dfrac{3}{8}\right)^0 = 1$

(viii) $\left(5\dfrac{3}{4}\right)^{-1/2} \times \left(3\dfrac{3}{8}\right)^{5/2} = \left(\dfrac{23}{4}\right)^{-1/2} \times \left(\dfrac{27}{8}\right)^{5/2} = \dfrac{2}{\sqrt{23}} \times \dfrac{3^{15/2}}{2^{15/2}} = \dfrac{3^{7.5}}{23^{1/2} \times 2^{13/2}}$

(ix) $(-16)^{2/3} = (-2^4)^{2/3} = \sqrt[3]{(-2)^8} = \sqrt[3]{2^8} = 2^{8/3}$

(x) $\left(2\dfrac{16}{27}\right)^{1/2} = \left(\dfrac{70}{27}\right)^{1/2} = \dfrac{\sqrt{70}}{\sqrt{27}}.$

EXERCISES 7

1. Simplify the following indicial numbers:

   (i) 2^{-6} (ii) $81^{1/2}$ (iii) 2^{-3}

   (iv) $64^{-1/2}$ (v) 125^{-3} (vi) $125^{3/2}$

   (vii) $16^{3/4}$ (viii) $16^{5/3} \times 2^3 \times 32^{-4/3}$ (ix) $81^{1/4} \times 3^5 \times 9^{-3/5}$

   (x) $128^{3/7}$.

2. Solve the following indicial equations:-

   (i) $64^{-1/x} = 2$ (ii) $125^x = 5$ (iii) $\left(\dfrac{49}{81}\right)^{-x} = 9/7$.

3. (i) $\left(\dfrac{625}{144}\right)^{-3/2} \times \left(\dfrac{12}{25}\right)^{-4/3}$ (ii) $\left(\dfrac{729}{169}\right)^{-1/2}$ (iii) $\left(\dfrac{125}{49}\right)^{-1}$

   (iv) $1000^{-1/3}$ (v) $\left(\dfrac{81}{125}\right)^{-1/3} \times 3^{4/3}$.

4. Solve the following indicial equations:-

   (i) $(e^2)^x - e^x - 2 = 0$ (ii) $6\,e^{2x} + e^x - 1 = 0$

   (iii) $1 - e^{-2x} = 0$

5. Simplify $45 \times 5^{6x+7} - 25 \times 125^{2x+2}$.

6. Solve the equation $25^x - 5^{x+1} - 6 = 0$.

7. Solve the following equations involving exponents.

   (i) $3^{x+5} = 1$ (ii) $27^x = \dfrac{1}{\sqrt[3]{3}}$

   (iii) $8^{6x+7} = 16^{-x-5}$ (iv) $x^{-7/5} = 81 \times 125^{3/4}$

   (v) $4^{2x+2} = 2^{x-1}$

8. Simplify the following:-

(i) $\dfrac{3^x 9^{x+1}}{8^{x+2}}$

(ii) $\dfrac{4^{-x} 16^{2x}}{4^{-1+x} \times 2^{3x-2}}$

(iii) $\dfrac{36^{2x+1} \times 6^3}{216^2 \times 6^0}$.

9. Simplify

(i) $\dfrac{x^{-1} + y^{-1}}{x^{-2} + y^{-2}}$

(ii) $\left(\dfrac{1}{\sqrt{x}} + \sqrt{x}\right)^2$

(iii) $\dfrac{x\, y^{-1} + y\, x^{-1}}{x^3 - y^3}$.

10. Solve the following simultaneous equations:-

(i) $3^{x-y} = 27,\ 5^{y+x} = 1$

(ii) $5^x\, 25^y = 1,\ 6^x = 36^y\, 216$.

8. LOGARITHMS

Definition of a Logarithm

The logarithm of a number is denoted as 'log'

$$\boxed{\log_b N = R}. \quad \text{The Logarithmic form}$$

N = the positive number whose logarithm is required
b = the base of the logarithm
R = the result

What is the meaning of $\log_b N = R$, $b^R = N$, the base b is raised to the result R and

gives the positive number N, $\boxed{b^R = N}$. The indicial form.

Let us suppose that we required to find the logarithm of 1000 to the base 10, $\log_{10} 1000$.

Let x be the result $\log_{10} 1000 = x$ by the above definition, the base 10 is raised to the power x and the result is equal to 1000, $10^x = 1000$, $10^x = 10^3$, therefore, $x = 3$ since the bases are the same.

$$\log_{10} 1000 = 3.$$

WORKED EXAMPLE 50

Find the following results using the definition of a logarithm.

(i) $\log_2 8$ (ii) $\log_{1/2} 64$ (iii) $\log_3 243$ (iv) $\log_b b$

(v) $\log_e e$ (vi) $\log_5 25$ (vii) $\log_{10} 10^b$

(viii) $\log_{1/x} x$ (ix) $\log_{1/3} 81$ (x) $\log_{10} 0.0001$.

SOLUTION 50

(i) $\log_2 8 = x \Rightarrow 2^x = 8 \Rightarrow 2^x = 2^3 \Rightarrow x = 3$

$$\boxed{\log_2 8 = 3}$$

(ii) $\log_{1/2} 64 = x \Rightarrow (1/2)^x = 64 \Rightarrow (2^{-1})^x = 2^6 \Rightarrow 2^{-x} = 2^6 \ x = -6$ and

$$\boxed{\log_{1/2} 64 = -6}$$

(iii) $\log_3 243 = x \Rightarrow 3^x = 3^5 \Rightarrow x = 5$ and

$$\boxed{\log_3 243 = 5}$$

(iv) $\log_b b = x \Rightarrow b^x = b^1 \Rightarrow x = 1$ and

$$\boxed{\log_b b = 1}$$

If the base of the logarithm and the number are equal positive number the result is unity $\log_x x = 1$ where x is a positive number.

(v)
$$\boxed{\log_e e = 1}$$

which follows from the previous example.

(vi) $\log_5 25 = x \Rightarrow 5^x = 5^2 \Rightarrow x = 2$ and

$$\boxed{\log_5 25 = 2}$$

(vii) $\log_{10} 10^b = x \Rightarrow 10^x = 10^b \Rightarrow x = b$

$$\boxed{\log_{10} 10^b = b}$$

(viii) $\log_{1/x} x = y \Rightarrow (1/x)^y = x \Rightarrow x^{-y} = x^1 \Rightarrow y = -1$

$$\boxed{\log_{1/x} x = -1}$$

(ix) $\log_{1/3} 81 = x \Rightarrow (1/3)^x = 81 \Rightarrow 3^{-x} = 3^4 \Rightarrow x = -4$

$$\boxed{\log_{1/3} 81 = -4}$$

(x) $\log_{10} 0.0001 = x \Rightarrow 10^x = 0.0001 = 10^{-4} \Rightarrow x = -4$

$$\boxed{\log_{10} 0.0001 = -4}$$

RULES OF LOGARITHMS

Logarithms to the base 10.

To show $\log_{10} AB = \log_{10} A + \log_{10} B$

$A = 10^{\log A}$ and $B = 10^{\log B}$.

MULTIPLICATION

Multiplication of A and B gives $AB = 10^{\log A} \cdot 10^{\log B}$

$AB = 10^{(\log A + \log B)}$

$$\boxed{\log_{10} AB = \log_{10} A + \log_{10} B}$$

This is of course true to any base b $\log_b AB = \log_b A + \log_b B$ and it can be extended to many more factors $\log_b ABCD = \log_b A + \log_b B + \log_b C + \log_b D$ $\log_b$ A.A.A.A. ... to n factors $\log_b A^n = \log_b A + \log_b A + ...$ therefore

$$\boxed{\log_b A^n = n \log_b A}$$

Division

To show that $\log_b \dfrac{A}{B} = \log_b A - \log_b B$

$A = b^{\log_b A}$ and $B = b^{\log_b B}$

$$\boxed{\log_b \dfrac{A}{B} = \log_b A - \log_b B}$$

CHANGE OF BASE

To show that $\log_b N = \dfrac{\log_a N}{\log_a b}$.

Let $y = \log_b N$ by definition $b^y = N$.

Taking logarithms on both sides to the base $'a'$, $\log_a b^y = \log_a N$

$$y \log_a b = \log_a N \qquad y = \frac{\log_a N}{\log_a b}.$$

Therefore,

$$\boxed{\log_b N = \frac{\log_a N}{\log_a b}}$$

WORKED EXAMPLE 51

To show that $\log_x y = \dfrac{1}{\log_y x}$.

SOLUTION 51

Applying the formula of change of base above $\log_x y = \dfrac{\log_y y}{\log_y x} = \dfrac{1}{\log_y x}$ therefore

$$\boxed{\log_x y = \frac{1}{\log_y x}}$$

WORKED EXAMPLE 52

Prove that $\log_B A \, \log_C B \, \log_A C = 1$.

SOLUTION 52

Expressing $\log_B A$, $\log_C B$, $\log_A C$ in terms of logs to the base 10 we have

$$\log_B A = \frac{\log A}{\log B} \qquad \log_C B = \frac{\log B}{\log C} \qquad \log_A C = \frac{\log C}{\log A}$$

$$\log_B A \, \log_C B \, \log_A C = \frac{\log A}{\log B} \times \frac{\log B}{\log C} \times \frac{\log C}{\log A} = 1.$$

WORKED EXAMPLE 53

Solve the simultaneous equations $\log_2 (3x - y - 1) = 0$, $\log_2 (x + y - 4) = 1$.

SOLUTION 53

$\log_2 (3x - y - 1) = 0 \qquad 3x - y - 1 = 2^0$. By definition

$$\boxed{3x - y = 2} \quad \dots (1)$$

$\log_2 (x + y - 4) = 1 \qquad x + y - 4 = 2$

$$\boxed{x + y = 6} \quad \dots (2)$$

Adding equation (1) and (2) $4x = 8 \Rightarrow \boxed{x = 2}$

substituting $x = 2$ in equation (2),

$$\boxed{y = 4}.$$

SUMMARY

1. $\log ABC = \log A + \log B + \log C$

2. $\log \dfrac{A}{B} = \log A - \log B$

3. $\log A^n = n \log A$

4. $\log_a N = \dfrac{\log_b N}{\log_b a}$

5. $\log_b y = x, \qquad b^x = y$ by the definition.

EXERCISES 8

1. Express the following logarithmic forms into the indicial forms:-

   (i) $\log_5 625 = 4$ (ii) $\log_{12} 144 = 2$ (iii) $\log_2 128 = 7$

   (iv) $\log_{13} 169 = 2$ (v) $\log_{1/5} 25 = -2$ (vi) $\log_{1/7} 49 = -2$

   (vii) $\log_{1/11} 121 = -2$ (viii) $\log_M N = P$ (ix) $\log_y x^2 = 2$

   (x) $\log_B A = C$ (xi) $z \log_y x = w$ (xii) $\log_e 625 = 4 \log_e 5$.

2. Express the following indicial forms into their logarithmic counterparts, to the base indicated.

   (i) $2^{10} = 1024$ (To the base 2)   (ii) $3^5 = 243$ (To the base 3)

   (iii) $2^{10} = 1024$ (to the base 1024)   (iv) $3^5 = 243$ (To the base 243)

   (v) $i = Ie^{-t/T}$ (To the base e)   (vi) $v = Ve^{-t/T}$ (to the base e)

   (vii) $q = Q e^{-1/T}$ (to the base e)   (viii) $24^2 = 576$ (to the base 24)

   (ix) $143^2 = 20449$ (to the base 143)   (x) $8^4 = 4096$ (to the base 8).

3. Repeat all the examples of question 2 to the base 10.

4. Simplify the following:-

   (i) $e^{\ln x}$ (ii) $e^{\ln 1/3}$ (iii) $e^{\ln y}$

   (iv) $e^{\ln 1/e}$ (v) $e^{\ln x^2}$ (vi) $\log_a a$

   (vii) $\log_{1/a} \dfrac{1}{a}$ (viii) $\log_x x$ (ix) $\log_a a^2$

   (x) $\log_{1/3} \dfrac{1}{27}$ (xi) $\log_{25} \dfrac{1}{625^2}$ (xii) $\log_4 \dfrac{1}{64}$

   (xiii) $e^{e^{\ln x}}$ (xiv) $a^{\log_a 7}$ (xv) $10^{\log 25}$

   (xvi) $5^{\log_5 5^2}$ (xvii) $75^{\log_{75} 3}$ (xviii) $10^{\ln x}$

   (xix) $y^{\log_y b}$ (xxi) $\left(\dfrac{1}{2}\right)^{\frac{1}{2} \log_{1/2} 2}$.

5. Simplify $5 \log 64 - \log 36 - 3 \log \left(\dfrac{1}{8}\right) + 3 \log 100$ by using the rules and then evaluate.

6. Simplify $\dfrac{\log 8 - \log 4}{3 \log 2 + \log 32}$ without using a calculator.

7. Simplify (i) $e^{\log y}$ (ii) $10^{\ln x}$ (iii) $z^{\log_z 10}$

   (iv) $5^{\log_5 5}$ (v) $7^{2 \log_7 3}$.

8. Simplify $3 \log_2 (1/8) - 3 \log_{1/2} (1/8)$.

9. Solve the simultaneous equations $x^3 = y$, $x \log 8 = (x + y) \log 2$.

10. Solve the following indicial equations:-

   (i) $5^x = 7$ (ii) $3^x = 8^2$ (iii) $2^{x-1} = 8^{2+x}$

   (iv) $3^{x-2} = 3^{2x}$ (v) $4^{1/x} = 7$ (vi) $5^{\frac{1}{x} - 1} = 25$

   (vii) $3^x \times 5^{x+1} = 9^2$ (viii) $3.76^x = 7.95$ (ix) $11^x = 4$

   (x) $3.6^{-x} = 25$ (xi) $\left(\dfrac{1}{3.9}\right)^{x-1} = 37.37$ (xii) $7.3^x = 9.9$

   (xiii) $\left(\dfrac{1}{5.9}\right)^x = \dfrac{1}{25.25}$ (xiv) $(4.7)^x = \dfrac{1}{3.9}$ (xv) $(3900)^x = 47$

   (xvi) $(81000)^x = 39000$ (xvii) $680^x = 3.9$.

11. Solve the equation $5^{x+3} + 5^{x+1} = 100$.

12. Find the values of x which satisfy the equation $2^{3x} - 6 \times 2^{2x+1} + 41 \times 2^x = 30$.

13. Find the values of y in terms of x in the following equations:-

   (i) $e^y - e^{-y} - 2x = 0$ (ii) $e^y + e^{-y} - 2x = 0$

14. Express the following relations in a form not involving logarithms:-

   (i) $5 \log x = \log 10$
   (ii) $4 \log x^{1/2} - 3 \log x^2 + 2 \log x^3 - \log x^4 + \log 10 = 0$
   (iii) $3 \log x + 4 \log y + 5 \log z + 7 \log w = 3$
   (iv) $\log y + 1 = 3 \log x$
   (v) $\log y + 2 = \log x$.

9. EXPONENTIAL AND LOGARITHMIC FUNCTIONS
(EXPONENTIAL FUNCTIONS)

$$y = a^x$$

a is the base and the exponent, x, is the variable quantity, the function is termed as the exponential function.

$y = 2^x$ and $y = 3^x$ are exponential functions, or, more generally, $y = a^x$. e is a number between 2 and 3 and it is given by the power series

$$e^1 = 1 + \frac{1}{1!} + \frac{1}{2!} + \frac{1}{3!} + \ldots$$

which is an infinite power series, that is, it possesses infinite terms.
$3! = $ three factorial $= 1 \times 2 \times 3$

$$y = e^x = 1 + \frac{x}{1!} + \frac{x^2}{2!} + \frac{x^3}{3!} + \ldots$$

The special property of this function is that the derivative, $\frac{dy}{dx}$ is the same as the function.   The only function in Mathematics that possesses this special feature.

The graphs of $y = e^x$ and $y = e^{-x}$.

x	-2.5	-2.0	-1.5	-1.0	-0.5	0
e^x	0.082	0.135	0.223	0.368	0.607	1
e^{-x}	12.18	7.39	4.48	2.718	1.649	1

x	0.5	1.0	1.5	2.0	2.5
e^x	1.649	2.718	4.482	7.39	12.18
e^{-x}	0.607	0.369	0.223	0.135	0.082

The graphs of $y = e^{x/2}$ and $y = e^{-x/2}$.

x	-2.0	-1.5	-1.0	-0.5	0	0.5	1.0
$e^{x/2}$	0.368	0.472	0.607	0.779	1	1.284	1.649
$e^{-x/2}$	2.718	2.117	1.649	1.284	1	0.779	0.607

x	1.5	2.0
$e^{x/2}$	2.117	2.718
$e^{-x/2}$	0.472	0.368

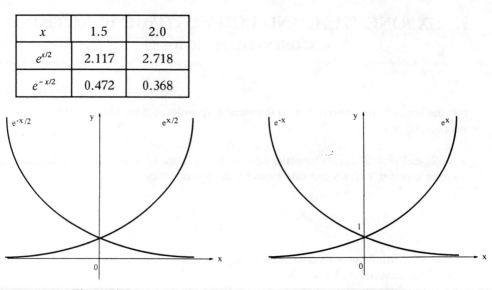

Fig. 1-I/99   Fig. 1-I/100

$$y = e^{kx}$$

if k is an positive integer and increasing the curves still pass through (0, 1) and are increasing more rapidly.

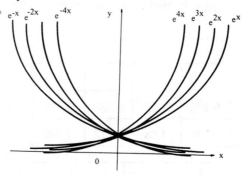

Fig. 1-I/101

The curves $y = e^{kx}$ and $y = e^{-kx}$ are always positive, that is, are above the x-axis. The x-axis is an asymptote to the curves, as $x \to \infty$ for $y = e^{-kx}$, $y \to 0$ and as $x \to -\infty$ for $y = e^{kx}$, $y \to 0$.

LOGARITHMIC FUNCTIONS
NATURAL (NAPERIAN) LOGARITHMS

The logarithm of a number N to the base e is equal to x, that is $\log_e N = x$ by the definition of a logarithm, the base e when it is raised to the power x gives the number N, that is $e^x = N$. $\log_e N$ is abbreviated to $\ln N$ as $\log_e N = \ln N$.

1-I/102

THE RELATIONSHIP BETWEEN COMMON AND NATURAL (NAPERIAN) LOGARITHMS

The logarithm of a number to the base 10 is called a common logarithm and it is denoted as $\log_{10} N$ or simply $\log N$. In this case, the base 10 is implied, it is the only base that can be omitted.

$$\log_{10} N = \log N = \lg N \text{ (sometimes denoted)}$$

$y = \log_e N$, $e^y = N$ by definition and taking logarithms on both sides to the base 10, we have $\log e^y = \log N$ $y \log e = \log N$

$$y = \frac{\log N}{\log e} \qquad \log_e N = \frac{\log N}{\log e} \qquad \log_e N = \frac{1}{\log e} \log N \qquad \log_e N = \frac{1}{0.4343} \log N$$

$$\boxed{\log_e N = 2.303 \log N}$$

or $\log N = \log e \, \log_e N$

$$\boxed{\log N = 0.4343 \log_e N}$$

GRAPHS

The Graphs of $\log |x|$ and $\log_e |x|$.

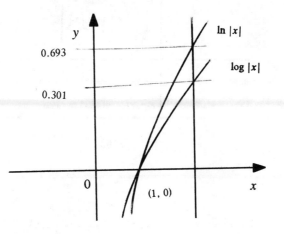

Fig. 1-I/102

x is always positive, that is, $|x|$.

WORKED EXAMPLE 54

(a) Sketch the graphs (i) $y = \ln x, x > 0$

　　　　　　　　　　　(ii) $y = \log x, x > 0.$

(b) Sketch the graphs (i) $y = |\ln x|, x > 0$

　　　　　　　　　　　(ii) $y = |\log x|, x > 0.$

(c) Calculate, correct to three decimal places, the values of x for which $|\ln x| = 3$. State the number of real roots of the equation $|\ln x| = 3 + x$.

SOLUTION 54

(a) See graphs in Fig. 1-I/102

(b)

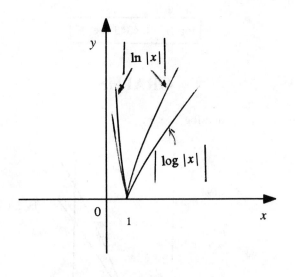

Fig. 1-I/103

(c)

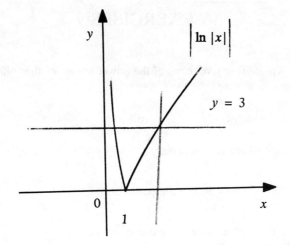

Fig. 1-I/104

The line $y = 3 + x$ cuts the graph $|\ln x|$ at one point when
$x = 0.049787068 \approx 0.05$ when $x = 0.05$, $\ln 0.05 \approx -3$, when $|\ln 0.05| \approx 3$.

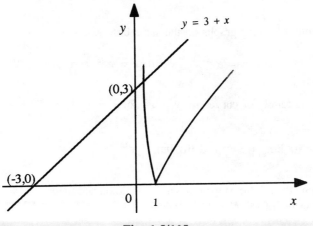

Fig. 1-I/105

EXERCISES 9

1. Write down the first five terms of the power series for the following exponential functions:-

   (i) $e^{1/2}$ (ii) e^{-1} (iii) e^{-y} (iv) e^2 (v) $e^{x/2}$

   and evaluate where it is necessary.

2. Express $f(x) = e^{2x}$ as an infinite power series.

3. Express $f(x) = e^{3x}$ as an infinite power series.

4. Find the power series for the following

   (i) $\dfrac{e^x + e^{-x}}{2}$ and   (ii) $\dfrac{e^x - e^{-x}}{2}$.

5. Sketch the following graphs on the same base axis:-

   (i) $y = e^x$ and $y = e^{-x}$ (ii) $y = e^{x/2}$ and $y = e^{-x/2}$.

6. Sketch the family of curves for $y = e^{kx}$ for $k = \pm 1, \pm 2, \pm 3, \pm 4$.

7. Find the (i) $\lim_{x \to \infty} e^{-kx}$ and (ii) $\lim_{x \to \infty} e^{kx}$.

8. Determine the relationship between the common and natural logarithms. Express $\ln N$ in terms of $\log N$ and vice versa.

9. Sketch a family of curves for $y = \ln kx$ when $k = 1, 2, 3$.

10. Sketch the graphs:-

    (i) $|\ln x|$ (ii) $|\log_{10} 5x|$.

10. ARITHMETIC PROGRESSION

WHAT IS AN ARITHMETIC PROGRESSION?

An Arithmetic Progression (A.P.) is a sequence of numbers or terms such as 1, 2, 3, 4, 5, ... The first term is 1, the second term is obtained by adding 1 to the first term, thus obtaining 2, the third term is obtained by adding 1 to the number of 2, thus obtaining 3, and so on. The number that we add every time to the previous number in order to obtain the next number is called the <u>common difference</u>. If a is the first term, then the second term is $a + d$ where d = the common difference, the third term is found by adding d to the second term $a + d + d = a + 2d$, the fourth term is obtained by adding again d to the third term, $a + 2d + d = a + 3d$ and so on.

The fourth term is $a + 3d$, we observe that there are 3d, for the ninth term, $a + 8d$, is 8d and so on.

$$a, a + d, a + 2d, a + 3d, a + 4d, a + 5d, \ldots \boxed{a + (n - 1)\, d}$$

terms first, second, third, fourth, fifth, sixth $\cdots$ n^{th} term.

The following are examples of arithmetic progressions:-

(i)   1, 2, 3, 4, 5, 6, 7, ...   (ii)   1, 0, $-$ 1, $-$ 2, $-$ 3, $-$ 4, $-$ 5, ...

(iii)   1, $\dfrac{3}{2}$, 2, $\dfrac{5}{2}$, 3, $\dfrac{7}{2}$, 4, ...   (iv)   2, 0, $-$ 2, $-$ 4, $-$ 6, $-$ 8, ...

(v) $a, a + 1, a + 2, a + 3, a + 4,$...   (vi) $b, b + a, b + 2a, b + 3a, b + 4a,$ ...

(vii) $\dfrac{1}{2}$, 1, $\dfrac{3}{2}$, 2, $\dfrac{5}{2}$, 3, $\dfrac{7}{2}$ (viii) $-$ 3, $-$ 2, $-$ 1, 0, 1, 2, 3

(ix) $\dfrac{1}{4}$, $\dfrac{1}{2}$, $\dfrac{3}{4}$, 1, $\dfrac{5}{4}$, $\dfrac{3}{2}$, $\dfrac{7}{4}$, ...   (x) $x + y, x + 2y, x + 3y, x + 4y,$ ...

What is the first term in each case for the above A.P.s?

(i) 1   (ii) 1   (iii) 1   (iv) 2   (v) a (vi) b (vii) $\dfrac{1}{2}$ (viii) $-$ 3   (ix) $\dfrac{1}{4}$ (x) $x + y$.

To find the common difference of an A.P. you write down the second term minus the first term or the next term minus the previous term. If an A.P. has terms a, b, c the common difference = d = second term $-$ first term $d = b - a$ or $d = c - b$ = third term $-$ second term.

WORKED EXAMPLE 55

Find the 25th term of the A.P. 7, 5, 3, 1, – 1, ...

SOLUTION 55

The A.P. is 7, 5, 3, 1, – 1, ...

The first term is 7, the common difference is $3 - 5 = -2$, therefore $a = 7$, $d = -2$.

The nth term of an A.P. is given by the formula

$$\boxed{a + (n - 1)\, d}$$

or if this is the last term, then we denote $l = a + (n - 1)\, d$. The required term is $l = 7 + (25 - 1)(-2) = 7 - 48 = -41$ and therefore the 25th term of the A.P. is – 41.

WORKED EXAMPLE 56

Write down the first term, the common difference and the nth term of the following series:-

(i) 13, – 2, – 17, – 32, ...   (ii) 1, 3, 5, 7, 9, ...   (iii) 25, 30, 35, 40, 45, ...

SOLUTION 56

(i) $a = 13$, $d = -2 - 13 = -15$, $l = a + (n - 1)\, d = 13 + (n - 1)(-15)$

$l = 13 - 15n + 15 = 28 - 15n$.

Therefore $\boxed{a = 13}$ $\boxed{d = -15}$ $\boxed{l = 28 - 15n}$

(ii) $a = 1$, $d = 3 - 1 = 2$, $l = a + (n + 1)\, d = 1 + (n - 1)\, 2 = 1 + 2n - 2$

$l = 2n - 1$.

Therefore $\boxed{a = 1}$ $\boxed{d = 2}$ $\boxed{l = 2n - 1}$

(iii) $a = 25$, $d = 30 - 25 = 5$,

$l = a + (n - 1)\, d = 25 + (n - 1)\, 5 = 25 + 5n - 5$, $l = 20 + 5n$.

Therefore $\boxed{a = 25}$ $\boxed{d = 5}$ $\boxed{l = 20 + 5n}$

WORKED EXAMPLE 57

(a)   Find an expression for n^{th} even number.

(b)   Find an expression for n^{th} odd number.

SOLUTION 57

(a)   The following sequence gives the even numbers 2, 4, 6, 8, ...

$$a = 2, d = 4 - 2 = 2, l = a + (n - 1) \ d = 2 + (n - 1) \ 2 = 2 + 2n - 2$$

$$\boxed{l = 2n}$$

Therefore the A.P. is 2, 4, 6, 8, ... $2n$.

(b)   The following sequence gives the odd numbers 1, 3, 5, 7, ...

$$a = 1, d = 2, l = a + (n - 1) \ d = 1 + (n - 1) \ 2 = 1 + 2n - 2 = 2n - 1$$

$$\boxed{l = 2n - 1}$$

Therefore the A.P. is 1, 3, 5, 7, ... $(2n - 1)$.

SUMMARY

$l = a + (n - 1) \ d$.

The nth or last term is l, a is the first term, d is the common difference and the arithmetic progression has n terms.

THE SUM OF A FINITE
ARITHMETIC PROGRESSION

A finite arithmetic series is one A.P. series which is not infinite.

Let S_n denote the sum of n terms,

$$S_n = a + (a + d) + (a + 2d) + (a + 3d) + (a + 4d) + \ldots + [a + (n - 1) \ d] \ldots (1).$$

This sum can be written as back to front

$$S_n = [a + (n - 1) \ d] + [a + (n - 2) \ d] + [a + (n - 3) \ d] + \ldots + (a + 2d) + (a + d) + a \quad \ldots (2).$$

Adding the equations (1) and (2)

$$2S_n = \{a + (n - 1)\, d]\} + \{(a + d) + [a + (n - 2)\, d]\} + \{(a + 3d) +$$
$$[a + (n - 3)\, d] + \ldots + \{[a + (n - 1)\, d] + a\}$$

$$2S_n = [2a + (n - 1)\, d] + [2a + (n - 1)\, d] + [2a + (n - 1)\, d] + \ldots +$$
$$[2a + (n - 1)\, d].$$

There are n terms, therefore, $2S_n = n\,[2a + (n - 1)\, d]$ dividing each term by 2

$$\boxed{S_n = \frac{n}{2}\,[2a + (n - 1)\, d]}$$

If the first term is p and the common difference is q and the number of terms are 15 what is the sum?

$$S_{15} = \frac{15}{2}\,[2p + (15 - 1)q] \qquad S_{15} = 15p + 105q.$$

WORKED EXAMPLE 58

(a) Find the sum of the first 25 terms of the A.P. $\dfrac{1}{3}, \dfrac{4}{3}, \dfrac{7}{3}, \ldots$

(b) Write down the 27th term and the nth term.

SOLUTION 58

(a) $S_n = \dfrac{n}{2}\,[2a + (n - 1)\, d] \qquad n = 25, \ a = \dfrac{1}{3}, \ d = \dfrac{4}{3} - \dfrac{1}{3} = 1$

$$S_{25} = \frac{25}{2}\left[2\left(\frac{1}{3}\right) + 24 \times 1\right] = \frac{25}{3} + 25 \times 12 = 308\,\frac{1}{3}$$

$S_{25} = 308\,\dfrac{1}{3}$, the sum of the first 25 terms.

(b) $l = a + (n - 1)\, d \qquad l = \dfrac{1}{3} + 26 \times 1 = 26\,\dfrac{1}{3}$ the 27th term

$$l = \frac{1}{3} + (n - 1)\,1 = n - \frac{2}{3} \text{ the } n\text{the term.}$$

WORKED EXAMPLE 59

Find the sum of 39 terms of the A.P. 6, 11, 16, 21, ...

SOLUTION 59

$$S_n = \frac{n}{2}\left[2a + (n - 1)\,d\right] \text{ where } n = 39, a = 6, d = 5$$

$$S_{39} = \frac{39}{2}\left[2 \times 6 + 38 \times 5\right] = 39 \times 101 = 3939.$$

WORKED EXAMPLE 60

The nth term of an A.P. is $7n - 5$. Find the sum to 15 terms.

SOLUTION 60

The nth term or last term of an A.P. is $7n - 5$, the first term of this A.P. is found by substituting $n = 1$, $7 \times 1 - 5 = 2$, the second term of this A.P. is found when $n = 2$, $7 \times 2 - 5 = 9$, the third term of this A.P. is found when $n = 3$, $7 \times 3 - 5 = 16$. Therefore, the sequence is 2, 9, 16, 23, 30, ... The sum of 15 terms is found by applying the formula

$$S_n = \frac{n}{2}\left[2a + (n - 1)\,d\right] \qquad S_{15} = \frac{15}{2}\left[2 \times 2 + 14 \times 7\right] = 15 \times 51 = 765.$$

WORKED EXAMPLE 61

The sum to n terms of a sequence is $\frac{1}{2}n\,(n + 1)$. Find the first five terms.

SOLUTION 61

If $n = 1$, the first term is found $a = \frac{1}{2} \times 1 \times 2 = 1$ if $n = 2$, the sum of the first two terms is

$$a + (a + d) = \frac{1}{2}\,2\,(3) = 3 \text{ since } a = 1, 2a + d = 3 \text{ or } 2 + d = 3, \text{ or } d = 1,$$

therefore, $a = 1$, $d = 1$ and the sequence is 1, 2, 3, 4, 5.

WORKED EXAMPLE 62

The sum to n terms of an A.P. is $\dfrac{n}{6}(5 - n)$. Find the nth term.

SOLUTION 62

$S_n = \dfrac{n}{6}(5 - n)$ the sum of n terms for $n = 1$,

$S_1 = \dfrac{1}{6}(5 - 1) = \dfrac{2}{3}$ for $n = 2$, $S_2 = \dfrac{2}{6}(5 - 2) = \dfrac{2}{6} \times 3 = 1$

the sum of the first two terms is 1, $\dfrac{2}{3} + \dfrac{2}{3} + d = 1$ or $d = -\dfrac{1}{3}$.   Therefore the A.P. is as follows:-

$$\dfrac{2}{3}, \dfrac{1}{3}, 0, -\dfrac{1}{3}, ...$$

The nth term is given by $l = a + (n - 1)d$

$$l = \dfrac{2}{3} + (n - 1)\left(-\dfrac{1}{3}\right) = \dfrac{2}{3} - \dfrac{1}{3}n + \dfrac{1}{3} = 1 - \dfrac{1}{3}n, \quad l = \dfrac{3 - n}{3}.$$

WORKED EXAMPLE 63

How many terms are there in the A.P.

$$\dfrac{3}{4}, \dfrac{1}{2}, \dfrac{1}{4}, 0, -\dfrac{1}{4}, -\dfrac{1}{2}, ... \left(1 - \dfrac{n}{2}\right)$$

SOLUTION 63

Let x be the number of terms $a = \dfrac{3}{4}$ $d = \dfrac{1}{2} - \dfrac{3}{4} = -\dfrac{1}{4}$

$$l = \dfrac{3}{4} + (x - 1)\left(-\dfrac{1}{4}\right) = \dfrac{3}{4} - \dfrac{1}{4}x + \dfrac{1}{4} = 1 - \dfrac{1}{4}x = 1 - \dfrac{n}{2}, \quad -\dfrac{1}{4}x = -\dfrac{n}{2}$$

therefore $\boxed{x = 2n}$.

SUMMARY

$$S_n = \frac{n}{2}\left[2a + (n-1)a\right] = \frac{n}{2}\left[a + l\right].$$

Determines one or more arithmetic means

ARITHMETIC MEAN

What is an arithmetic mean $>$?

An arithmetic mean of three consecutive terms of an A.P. such as a, b, c, is

$b = \dfrac{a+c}{2}$. An arithmetic mean of five consecutive terms of an A.P. such as a, b, c,

d, e is $c = \dfrac{a+e}{2}$.

WORKED EXAMPLE 64

Find the arithmetic means of the following A.P.s:-

(i)   4, x, 12   (ii) 1, x, y, z, 5   (iii) 5, x, y, 29.

SOLUTION 64

(i)   4, x, 12, is an A.P. therefore $x = \dfrac{4+12}{2} = 8$ the arithmetic mean of

4 and 12 is 8.

(ii) 1, x, y, z, 5 is an A.P., the arithmetic means of 1 and 5 is $y = \dfrac{1+5}{2} = 3$,

therefore 1, x, 3, z, 5 the arithmetic mean of 1 and 3 is $x = \dfrac{1+3}{2} = 2$ and the

arithmetic mean of 3 and 5 is $z = \dfrac{3+5}{2} = 4$.

Therefore the A.P. is 1, 2, 3, 4, 5.

(iii) 5, x, y, 29 is an A.P. $x = \dfrac{5 + y}{2} \Rightarrow 2x - y = 5$ and

$y = \dfrac{x + 29}{2} \Rightarrow 2y - x = 29$ solving the simultaneous equations

$$2x - y = 5$$
$$\underline{-2x + 4y = 58}$$
$$3y = 63$$
$$y = 21$$

and $x = \dfrac{5 + 21}{2} = 13$.

The A.P. is 5, 13, 21, 29, therefore $x = 13$, $y = 21$.

WORKED EXAMPLE 65

The 25th term of an A.P. is 25 and 33rd term is 33. Find the first term and the common difference.

SOLUTION 65

$l = a + (n - 1) d$ $\qquad$ $25 = a + 24d$ ... (1) $\qquad$ $33 = a + 32d$ ... (2)

subtracting (1) from (2) $\qquad$ $33 - 25 = a - a + 32d - 24d$ $\quad$ $8 = 8d$

$$\boxed{d = 1}$$

$25 = a + 24$ $\qquad\qquad\qquad\qquad$ $\boxed{a = 1}$

SUMMARY

The arithmetic mean of two numbers is $\dfrac{a + c}{2}$.

EXERCISES 10

1. Calculate the sum of the odd numbers from 1 to 199.

2. Calculate the sum of the first 17 terms of an A.P. whose 5th term is 16, and whose 19th term 47.

3. Given the A.P. 3, 6, 9, 12, ...

   Find (a) the value of the 28th term.

         (b) the sum of the first 20 terms.

4. The sum of an A.P. is 180, whose first term is 4 and whose common difference is 2. Calculate the number of terms in the series.

5. Find the least number of terms of the A.P. $199 + 194 + 189 + ...$ needed to give a negative sum.

6. Deduce the formula $l = a + (n - 1)d$ for n terms of an A.P. whose first term is a and common difference is d.

7. Derive the sum of n term whose first term is N and M is the common difference.

8. If 100, x, y, 82 are in A.P. find x and y.

9. Find the sum of all even numbers less than 2000.

10. Find the nth term of the series $\log 3 + \log 12 + \log 48 + ...$ and hence calculate the sum of the n terms.

11. Show that the sum of n terms of the A.P. $a, a + d, a + 2d, ... a + (n - 1)d$ is given by the formula $S_n = \dfrac{n}{2} [a + l]$ where $l = a + (n - 1)d$, the nth or last term.

12. The nth term of an A.P. is N and the sum of the first n terms is S_n. Find an expression for the first term in terms of N and S_n.

13. Find the 27th term of the arithmetic progression 1, 2, 3, 4, ...

14. Find the 35th term of the a.p. – 3, – 1, 1, ...

15. Find the 5th term of the a.p. $\frac{1}{4}, \frac{5}{8}, 1, ...$

16. Find the 12th term of the a.p. – 7, – 12, – 17, ...

17. Find the 50th term of the a.p. $-\frac{1}{2}, -1, -3/2, ...$

18. Find the nth terms of the following A.P. series.

    (i)   1, 6, 11, 16, ...   (ii) 1, – 3, – 7, – 11, ...

    (iii) $\frac{3}{8}, \frac{1}{2}, \frac{5}{8}, \frac{3}{4}, ...$

19. The last term of an A.P. is 27 and its first term is 5, calculate the common difference, if $n = 5$.

20. Find the 37th term of the A.P. 3, 8, 13, ...

21. The nth term of an A.P. is $(2n - 1)$ where n is a positive integer, write out the series.

22. The nth term of an A.P. is $2n$ where n is a positive integer, write out the series.

23. Find the 45th term of the A.P. $\frac{1}{2}, \frac{1}{4}, 0, -\frac{1}{4}, ...$

24. Find the nth term of the A.P. 0.1, 0.3, 0.5, ...

25. Find the sum of 25 terms of the A.P. $-\frac{1}{4}, -\frac{1}{2}, -\frac{3}{4}, ...$

26. Find the sum of 33 terms of the A.P. 0.125, 0.25, 0.375, 0.5, ...

27. The first term of an A.P. is 1, and the common difference is 6, find n if the last term is 247.

28. Write down the nth term of an A.P. given that x is the first term and y is the common difference of the series.

29. Write down the formula for the nth term of an A.P. given that N is the first term and D is the common difference.

30. Show that the sum of P terms of an A.P. with common difference Q and the first term A is given $S_p = \dfrac{P}{2} [A + (P - 1) Q]$.

31. The sum to n terms of a sequence is $\dfrac{n (n + 1)}{2}$. Find the first five terms.

32. The sum to n terms of a sequence is $n^2 - 7n$. Find the first three terms.

33. a, b, c are three terms of an A.P., show that $b = \dfrac{a + c}{2}$.

34. If $1, x, 51, y$ are in A.P., find the values of x and y.

35. The nth term of a sequence is $5 (n + 1)$. Find the sum of 25 terms.

11. GEOMETRIC PROGRESSIONS (G.P.)
COMMON RATIO

If a, b, c, is a G.P. then the common ratio is the next term over the previous term,

$$r = \text{common ratio} = \frac{b}{a} = \frac{c}{b}.$$

What is a Geometric Progression? A geometric progression is a sequence of numbers whose the following term over the previous term is always the same.

Is the following sequence a G.P.?   1, 3, 9, 27, ...

Yes

Since $\dfrac{3}{1} = r = 3$, $\dfrac{9}{3} = r = 3$, $\dfrac{27}{9} = r = 3$

the next term should be 81 and the one after that 243 and so on.

If a is the first term and r is the common ratio then the G.P. is as follows:-

a, ar, ar^2, ar^3, ar^4, ... , ar^{n-1}.

The first, second, third, fourth, fifth, ... n^{th} terms so the last or n^{th} term is $a\,r^{n-1}$.

$$\boxed{l = ar^{n-1}}$$

The following series are G.P.s.

(i)   1, 2, 4, 8, 16, 32, ...

(ii) a, a^2, a^3, a^4, a^5, ...

(iii) r, r^2, r^3, r^4, r^5, ...

(iv) $\dfrac{1}{2}$, $\dfrac{1}{4}$, $\dfrac{1}{8}$, $\dfrac{1}{16}$, ...

(v) -3, 1, $-\dfrac{1}{3}$, $\dfrac{1}{9}$, $-\dfrac{1}{27}$, ...

(vi)   1, 6, 36, 216, ...

(vii) 1, -5, 25, -125, 625, ...

(viii) 15, 3, $\dfrac{3}{5}$, $\dfrac{3}{25}$ ...

(ix)   1, 0.01, 0.01^2, 0.01^3 ...

(x) n^2, n^4, n^6, n^8, ...

What is the first term and the common ratio for the above examples? The first terms are:

(i)   1   (ii) a (iii) r (iv) $\dfrac{1}{2}$ (v) -3

(vi)   1   (vii)   1   (viii) 15   (ix)   1   (x) n^2.

The common ratios are:-

(i)   2   (ii) a (iii) r (iv) $\dfrac{1}{2}$ (v) $-\dfrac{1}{3}$

(vi)   6   (vii) -5 (viii) $\dfrac{1}{5}$ (ix) 0.01   (x) n^2.

WORKED EXAMPLE 66

What is the 22nd term of the G.P. 1, 3, 3^2, 3^3, ... ?

SOLUTION 66

$l = ar^{n-1}$ $a = 1, r = \dot{3}\, l = 1 \times r^{22-1} = 3^{21}$ the 22nd term is 3^{21}.

WORKED EXAMPLE 67

Write down the fifth term of the G.P. $-\dfrac{1}{3}$, $+1$, -3,...

SOLUTION 67

$$a = -\frac{1}{3},\ r = \frac{1}{\left(-\dfrac{1}{3}\right)} = -3 \qquad l = ar^{n-1} = \left(-\frac{1}{3}\right)(-3)^{5-1} = \frac{1}{3}(-3)^4 = -27.$$

WORKED EXAMPLE 68

Find the nth terms of the following G.P. series:-

(i) $\dfrac{1}{3^0}, \dfrac{1}{3^1}, \dfrac{1}{3^2}, \dfrac{1}{3^3}$, ...   (ii) $r,\ -r^2, r^3,\ -r^4, r^5,$ ...

(iii)   243, 81, 27, ...

SOLUTION 68

(i) $\dfrac{1}{3^0}, \dfrac{1}{3^1}, \dfrac{1}{3^2}, \dfrac{1}{3^3},$ $\qquad l = ar^{n-1} = 1\left(\dfrac{1}{3}\right)^{n-1} = \dfrac{1}{3^{n-1}}$

(ii) $l = ar^{n-1} = r(-r)^{n-1}$ where common ratio $= \dfrac{-r^2}{r} = -r$

(iii) $l = a\,r^{n-1} = 243\left(\dfrac{81}{243}\right)^{n-1} = 243\,\dfrac{1}{3^{n-1}} = 3^5\,\dfrac{1}{3^{n-1}} = \dfrac{1}{3^{n-6}}.$

SUMMARY

$$\boxed{l = ar^{n-1}}$$

Forms the sum of a finite geometric series

THE SUM OF A FINITE GEOMETRIC PROGRESSION

To find the sum of $a, ar, ar^2, ar^3, \ldots ar^{n-1}$.

Let S_n be the sum of n terms of a G.P.

$$S_n = a + ar + ar^2 + ar^3 + \ldots + ar^{n-1} \qquad \ldots (1)$$

multiplying each term of equation (1) by r

$$rS = ar + ar^2 + ar^3 + ar^4 + \ldots + ar^n \qquad \ldots (2)$$

(2) – (1) $rS_n - S_n = ar + ar^2 + ar^3 + ar^4 + \ldots + ar^n - a - ar - ar^2 - ar^3 - ar^4 - \ldots - ar^{n-1}$

$$(r-1)S_n = ar^n - a = a(r^n - 1)$$

$$S_n = \dfrac{a(r^n-1)}{(r-1)} = \dfrac{ar^n - a}{r-1} = \dfrac{-(a - ar^n)}{-(1-r)} = \dfrac{a(1-r^n)}{(1-r)}$$

If $r > 1$ it is convenient to use

$$\boxed{S_n = \dfrac{a(r^n-1)}{(r-1)}}$$

1-I/120

WORKED EXAMPLE 69

Given the G.P. $1, \dfrac{1}{2}, \dfrac{1}{4}, \dfrac{1}{8}, \ldots$

Find (a) the sum of 10 terms correct to 3 decimal places   (b) the sum of 500 terms.

SOLUTION 69

(a)   The G.P. $1, \dfrac{1}{2}, \dfrac{1}{4}, \dfrac{1}{8}, \ldots$

$$\boxed{a = 1} \qquad\qquad r = \frac{1/2}{1} = \frac{1/4}{1/2} = \frac{1}{2} \qquad\qquad \boxed{r = \frac{1}{2}}$$

Using the formula $S_n = \dfrac{a\,(1 - r^n)}{(1 - r)}$

$$S_{10} = \frac{1.\left(1 - \left(\dfrac{1}{2}\right)^{10}\right)}{1 - \dfrac{1}{2}} = \frac{1 - \left(\dfrac{1}{2}\right)^{10}}{\dfrac{1}{2}} = 2\,(1 - 0.5^{10}) = 1.998$$

$$= 2\left[1 - \left(\frac{1}{2}\right)^{500}\right] = 2\,(1 - 0.5^{500}) = 2.$$

(b) $0.5^{500} = 0.5 \times 0.5 \times 0.5 \times \ldots \text{ (500 times)} \approx 0.$

Therefore, the sum of an infinite geometric series is

$$\boxed{S_\infty = \frac{a}{1 - r}}$$

It looks like that the formula for a very large number of terms when the common ratio $(r < 1)$ is $r = \dfrac{1}{2}$, is $S_{500} = \dfrac{a}{1 - r}$.

The sum of infinite number of terms is therefore

$$\boxed{S_\infty = \frac{a}{1 - r}}$$

<u>Forms the sum of an infinite geometric series with $\mid r \mid < 1$.</u>

If $r < 1$ it is convenient to use

$$S_n = \frac{a\,(1 - r^n)}{1 - r}$$

What is the usefulness of this formula?
The following worked example will illustrate.

WORKED EXAMPLE 70

Express the decimal number 0.36969696969 ..... as a fractional number.

SOLUTION 70

0.36969 ... = 0.36̇9̇ the dots on top of 6 and 9 indicate that the numbers 6 and 9 are recurring indefinitely

$0.36̇9̇ \quad = 0.3696966969 \ .....$

$\qquad = 0.3 + 0.069 + 0.00069 + 0.0000069 + ...$

$\qquad = \dfrac{3}{10} + 0.069 \left(1 + \dfrac{0.00069}{0.069} + \dfrac{0.0000069}{0.069} + ...\right)$

$\qquad = \dfrac{3}{10} + \dfrac{69}{1000}\,(1 + 0.01 + 0.01^2 + 0.01^3 + ...)$

investigate the infinite geometric series $1 + 0.01 + 0.01^2 + 0.01^3 + ...$

$a = 1,\ r = \dfrac{0.01}{1} = \dfrac{0.01^2}{0.01} = 0.01$ and since it is an infinite geometric series with r

being much less than 1 $(r = 0.01)$ then $S_\infty = \dfrac{a}{1 - r} = \dfrac{1}{1 - 0.01} = \dfrac{1}{0.99} = \dfrac{100}{99}$.

Therefore, $0.36̇9̇ \quad = \dfrac{3}{10} + \dfrac{69}{1000} \times \dfrac{100}{99} = \dfrac{3}{10} + \dfrac{69}{990} = \dfrac{3 \times 99 + 69}{990} = \dfrac{366}{990}$

$\qquad\qquad = \text{this cancels down to a simpler fraction} = \dfrac{183}{495} = \dfrac{61}{165}.$

THE SUM OF AN INFINITE GEOMETRIC SERIES

We have seen from the previous worked example that if $|r| < 1$, **i.e.** the magnitude of r or the absolute value of r is less than 1, then from the equation $S_n = \dfrac{a(1 - r^n)}{1 - r}$.

If $n \to \infty$ then $r^\infty \to 0$ if $|r| < 1$, remember. Therefore $0.3696969 \ldots = \dfrac{61}{165}$.

Divide 61 by 165 and check that the answer is $0.3696969 \ldots$

Determines one or more geometric means.

GEOMETRIC MEAN

If a, b, c are three terms of a G.P. the geometric mean is $b = \sqrt{ac}$ this is derived as follows:-

$$r = \frac{b}{a} = \frac{c}{b} \text{ therefore } \frac{b}{a} = \frac{c}{b} \text{ or } b^2 = ac \text{ and } \boxed{b = \sqrt{ac}}$$

If a, b, c, d, e are five terms of a G.P. the geometric means of a and c is $b = \sqrt{ac}$, the geometric mean of a and e is $c = \sqrt{ae}$, the geometric mean of b and d is $c = \sqrt{bd}$.

WORKED EXAMPLE 71

Find three geometric means between 1 and 6561.

SOLUTION 71

Let x, y, z be the geometric means $1, x, y, z, 6561$ $y = \sqrt{1 \times 6561} = 81$

$1, x, 81, z, 6561$ $x = \sqrt{1 \times 81} = 9$ $z = \sqrt{81 \times 6561} = 729$.

Therefore the G.P. is 1, 9, 81, 729, 6561 and $x = 9, y = 81$ and $z = 729$.

WORKED EXAMPLE 72

Find two geometric means between 2 and 1024.

SOLUTION 72

2, x, y, 1024 $\dfrac{x}{2} = \dfrac{1024}{y} = \dfrac{y}{x}$ $\dfrac{x}{2} = \dfrac{y}{x}$ or $x^2 = 2y$

$\dfrac{1024}{y} = \dfrac{y}{x}$ or $y^2 = 1024x$ $x = \dfrac{y^2}{1024}$ substituting in $x^2 = 2y$

$\left(\dfrac{y^2}{1024}\right)^2 = 2y$ $\dfrac{y^4}{1024^2} = 2y$ $y^4 = 2y\,1024^2$ $y(y^3 - 2 \times 1024^2) = 0$

$y = 0$ or $y^3 = 2 \times 1024^2$ $y = 128$ and $x = \dfrac{128^2}{1024} = 16$.

Therefore $x = 16$, $y = 128$.

The G.P. is 2, 16, 128, 1024.

Alternatively and easier the last term $l = ar^{n-1} = 2r^3 = 1024$.
$r = 8$, therefore the terms are 2, 16, 128 and 1024.

WORKED EXAMPLE 73

The 7th term of a G.P. is 35 and the 10th term 595. Find the sum of the first three terms of the series to three decimal places.

SOLUTION 73

$l_7 = ar^6 = 35$ $\dfrac{a\,r^9}{a\,r^6} = \dfrac{595}{35} = 17$ $r^3 = 17$

$l_{10} = ar^9 = 595$ $r = 17^{1/3} = 2.571$

$a = \dfrac{35}{r^6} = \dfrac{35}{(17^{1/3})^6} = \dfrac{35}{17^2} = \dfrac{35}{289}$ $\dfrac{35}{289}, \dfrac{35}{289}17^{1/3}, \dfrac{35}{289}17^{2/3}$

or 0.121, 0.311, 0.7996

$S_3 = \dfrac{a(1 - r^3)}{1 - r} = \dfrac{a(1 - r)(1 + r + r^2)}{1 - r} = 0.121\,(1 + 2.571 + 2.571^2)$

$= 0.121 \times 10.181041 = 1.231$ or $S_3 = 0.121 + 0.311 + 0.800 = 1.232$.

COMPOUND INTEREST

Let C be the capital or principal borrowed, r be the percentage interest rate per annum t be the number of years the principal is borrowed or invested.

The sum of money owed including the principal will be $C + \dfrac{r}{100} C$ at the end of the first year or $C\left(1 + \dfrac{r}{100}\right)$.

At the end of the second year this sum will be $\left[C\left(1 + \dfrac{r}{100}\right)\right] \times \left(1 + \dfrac{r}{100}\right)$.

At the end of t years, this sum will be

$$S = C\left(1 + \frac{r}{100}\right)^t$$

Note that the interest is compounded annually if it is compounded m times a year, the sum is

$$S = C\left(1 + \frac{r}{100m}\right)^{mt}$$

MORTGAGE REPAYMENTS

A man borrows £c on 1st January 1988 at an interest rate of $\dfrac{r}{12}\%$ per calendar month where r is the annual interest rate, the interest being added on the last day of each month. The man repaid the loan in n equal monthly instalments each of £x, made on the first day of each succeeding month, the first repayment being made on 1st February 1988. Find a formula for the monthly repayments.

At the end of January 1988, the amount owed is £$\left(C + \dfrac{r}{1200} C\right)$.

At 1st of February 1988, the man repaid £x and hence the amount owed is

$$£\left[C\left(1 + \frac{r}{1200}\right) - x\right].$$

At the end of February 1988, the man owed $£\left[C\left(1+\dfrac{r}{1200}\right)-x\right]\times\left(1+\dfrac{r}{1200}\right)$

at the 1st of March 1988, the man owed $£\left[C\left(1+\dfrac{r}{1200}\right)-x\right]\times\left(1+\dfrac{r}{1200}\right)-x$

at the end of March 1988, the man owed

$$£\left\{\left[C\left(1+\dfrac{r}{1200}\right)-x\right]\times\left(1+\dfrac{r}{1200}\right)-x\right\}\times\left(1+\dfrac{r}{1200}\right)$$

at 1st of April 1988, the man owed

$$£\left\{\left[C\left(1+\dfrac{r}{1200}\right)-x\right]\times\left(1+\dfrac{r}{1200}\right)-x\right\}\times\left(1+\dfrac{r}{1200}\right)-x.$$

At the first of May 1988, the man owed

$$\left\{C\left(1+\dfrac{r}{1200}\right)^2-x\left(1+\dfrac{r}{1200}\right)-x\right\}\times\left\{\left(1+\dfrac{r}{1200}\right)-x\right\}\times\left(1+\dfrac{r}{1200}\right)-x \text{ or}$$

$$C\left(1+\dfrac{r}{1200}\right)^4-x\left(1+\dfrac{r}{1200}\right)^3-x\left(1+\dfrac{r}{1200}\right)^2-x\left(1-\dfrac{r}{1200}\right)-x,$$

that is, after four months.

After n months the man paid off the loan, plus the interest.

$$C\left(1+\dfrac{r}{1200}\right)^n-x\left(1+\dfrac{r}{1200}\right)^{n-1}-x\left(1+\dfrac{r}{1200}\right)^{n-2}-x\left(1+\dfrac{r}{1200}\right)^{n-3}-\ldots-x=0$$

$$C\left(1+\dfrac{r}{1200}\right)^n=x\left[1+\left(1+\dfrac{r}{1200}\right)^1+\ldots+\left(1+\dfrac{r}{1200}\right)^{n-1}\right]$$

$$1+\left(1+\dfrac{r}{1200}\right)^1+\left(1+\dfrac{r}{1200}\right)^2+\ldots+\left(1+\dfrac{r}{1200}\right)^{n-1} \text{ is a G.P. with}$$

common ratio $1+\dfrac{r}{1200}$, $a=1=$ first term and n^{th} term $\left(1+\dfrac{r}{1200}\right)^{n-1}$, the sum of

this progression

$$S_n = \frac{1 - \left(1 + \dfrac{r}{1200}\right)^n}{1 - \left(1 + \dfrac{r}{1200}\right)} = \frac{\left(1 + \dfrac{r}{1200}\right)^n - 1}{1 + \dfrac{r}{1200} - 1}$$

$$C\left(1 + \frac{r}{1200}\right)^n = x \; \frac{\left(1 + \dfrac{r}{1200}\right)^n - 1}{\dfrac{r}{1200}}$$

$$\boxed{x = \frac{\pounds\, C\left(1 + \dfrac{r}{1200}\right)^n \dfrac{r}{1200}}{\left(1 + \dfrac{r}{1200}\right)^n - 1}}$$

WORKED EXAMPLE 74

If $n = 300$ months $= 25$ years, $r = 9.8\%$ interest rate per annum $C = \pounds 50,000$. Determine the monthly instalment. Repeat the calculation if $n = 180$.

SOLUTION 74

$$x = \pounds\; \frac{50,000\left(1 + \dfrac{9.8}{1200}\right)^{300} \dfrac{9.8}{1200}}{\left(1 + \dfrac{9.8}{1200}\right)^{300} - 1}$$

$$x = \pounds\, 50,000 \times \frac{11.473614}{10.473614} \times 8.1666666 \times 10^{-3} = \underline{\pounds\, 447.32}$$

$$x = \frac{\pounds\, 50,000\left(1 + \dfrac{9.8}{1200}\right)^{180} \dfrac{9.8}{1200}}{\left(1 + \dfrac{9.8}{1200}\right)^{300} - 1} = \frac{\pounds\, 50,000 \times 4.3233474}{3.3233474} \times \frac{8.1666667}{1000} = \underline{\pounds\, 531.}$$

WORKED EXAMPLE 75

A loan of £60,000 is borrowed from a Building Society for 25 years at a percentage annual rate of (i) 9%, (ii) 10%, (iii) 11% and (iv) 15.4%. Calculate the monthly instalment to be paid in each case.

SOLUTION 75

$$\frac{£\,C\left(1 + \dfrac{r}{1200}\right)^n \dfrac{r}{1200}}{\left(1 + \dfrac{r}{1200}\right)^n}.$$

(i)
$$\frac{£60{,}000\left(1 + \dfrac{9}{1200}\right)^{300} \dfrac{9}{1200}}{\left(1 + \dfrac{9}{1200}\right)^{300} - 1} = \frac{60{,}000 \times 9.4084145 \times 7.5 \times 10^{-3}}{8.4084145}$$

$$= £503.52$$

(ii)
$$\frac{£60{,}000\left(1 + \dfrac{10}{1200}\right)^{300} \dfrac{10}{1200}}{\left(1 + \dfrac{10}{1200}\right)^{300} - 1} = £60{,}000 \;\; \frac{\times 12.056945}{11.056945} \times 8.33333 \times 10^{-3}$$

$$= £545.22.$$

(iii)
$$\frac{£60{,}000 \times \left(1 + \dfrac{11}{1200}\right)^{300}}{\left(1 + \dfrac{11}{1200}\right)^{300} - 1} \dfrac{11}{1200} = £60{,}000 \times \frac{15.447888}{14.447888} \times 9.1666667 \times 10^{-3}$$

$$= £588.07.$$

(iv)
$$\frac{£60{,}000 \times \left(1 + \dfrac{15.4}{1200}\right)^{300} \times \dfrac{15.4}{1200}}{\left(1 + \dfrac{15.4}{1200}\right)^{300} - 1} = \frac{£60{,}000 \times 45.85595987 \times 12.833 \times 10^{-3}}{44.85595987}$$

$$= £787.17.$$

Compound Interest

A Building Society offers 8.5% per annum for investments of any amount.. What does this mean?

A capital of £100 is deposited with the building society the 1st February, at the end of January, twelve months later the investment of £100 becomes, £100 plus £8.50, the total amount is £108.50 at the end of January, the interest is compounded once. Assuming once the interest remains the same, 8.5%, what is the total amount after ten years?

At the end of the first year $C + \dfrac{8.5}{100} C$ where C is the capital and 8.5% or $\dfrac{8.5}{100}$ of C

is paid. The new capital is $C (1 + 0.085)$, at the end of the second year the amount

will be $C (1 + 0.085) + 0.085 C (1 + 0.085) = (1 + 0.085) C (1 + 0.085)$
$$= C (1 + 0.085)^2.$$

At the end of the third year the amount will be $C (1 + 0.085)^2 + 0.085 C (1 + 0.085)^2 = C (1 + 0.085)^2 (1 + 0.085)$ or $C (1 + 0.085)^3$.

Therefore, at the end of the ten years the total amount will be $C (1 + 0.085)^{10}$ and at the end of n years, the total amount will be

$$\boxed{S = C (1 + 0.085)^n}$$

This is the formula for a capital C, earning 8.5% per annum at the end of n years.

If the capital to be invested is C and the per annum interest is r and n is the number of years then we have a more generalised formula.

$$\boxed{S = C \left(1 + \frac{r}{100}\right)^n} = \text{total sum}$$

WORKED EXAMPLE 76

Calculate the number of years required to treble your capital if the interest is 7%.

SOLUTION 76

If C is the capital, then $3C$ is required, $3C = C\left(1 + \dfrac{7}{100}\right)^n$ $\quad 3 = (1 + 0.0.07)^n$

$3 = 1.07^n$.

Taking logarithms on both sides of the equation $\log 3 = n \log 1.07$

$n = \dfrac{\log 3}{\log 1.07} = 16.237574 \quad n = 16$ years 87 days approximately

$n = 16$ years 2 months and 27 days.

WORKED EXAMPLE 77

£1,750 is invested for 7 years at 11% per annum compound interest.

Calculate the total amount to be received at the end of that period and the net interest.

SOLUTION 77

Total amount $= C\left(1 + \dfrac{r}{100}\right)^n = 1750\left(1 + \dfrac{11}{100}\right)^7$

$$= 1750 \times 2.0761602 = £3633.28$$

Net interest $= £3633.28 - £1750 = £1883.28$.

EXERCISES 11

1. Find the next four terms and the nth term of the following G.P.s:-

    (i)   2, 4, 8, ...   (vi) 729, 243, 81, ...

    (ii) $1, \dfrac{1}{2}, \dfrac{1}{4}, ...$ (vii) $-2, 4, -8, ...$

    (iii) $x, -x, x ...$ (viii) 1, 7, 49, ...

    (iv) 1, 3, 9, ...   (ix) 3, 6, 12, ...

    (v) $a, ar, ar^2, ...$ (x)   1, 5, 25, ...

2. Write down the 15th term of the G.P.s above.

3. How many terms of the G.P. 2, 4, 8, ... are needed to give a sum greater than 500.

4. How many terms of the G.P. 729, 243, 81, ... are needed to give a sum greater than 1093.

5. How many terms of the G.P. 1, 3, 9, ... are needed to give a sum greater than 10,000.

6. Insert three geometric means between 3 and 2187.

7. The nth term of a G.P. is $7 \times 3^{n-3}$, find the first three terms and the sum of 25 terms.

8. The nth term of a G.P. is $\dfrac{1}{3} 5^{2n-2}$, find the first three terms and the sum of 35 terms.

9. Find the sums of 30 terms of the series in question 1.

10. Find by the sum to infinity method the rational number of the following decimal numbers:-

    (i) 0.33   (ii) 3.767676 ...   (iii) 2.169169169 ...

11. The 7th term of a G.P. is 250, the 17th term is 1525. Find the first three terms of the series.

12. The first term of a G.P. is P and the common ratio R, show that the sum of x terms is given $S_x = P\,\dfrac{(1 - R^x)}{1 - R}$. If $|R| < 1$, hence, show that $S_\infty = \dfrac{P}{1 - R}$.

13. If $l_n = ar^{n-1}$, and $S_n = l_1 + l_2 + l_3 + \ldots + l_n$, find, in terms of a, r and n,
    (i) S_n (ii) $l_1 l_2 l_3 \ldots l_n$.

14. The first, second and third terms of a G.P. are a, b, c respectively. Find an expression for the sum of n terms in terms of a and c.

15. a, b, c are the first, third and fifth terms of a G.P. insert the second and fourth terms as the geometric means, in terms of a and c.

16. Find the sum of 30 terms of the G.P. $1 + 1.01 + 1.01^2 + \ldots$

17. Find the nth term and sum of n terms of the G.P. $\dfrac{a + 1}{b^0}, \dfrac{(a + 1)^2}{b^1}, \dfrac{(a + 1)^3}{b^2}, \ldots$

18. Use an infinite geometric progression to find the following decimal number
    (i) $0.46\dot{5}$ (ii) $1.\dot{2}\dot{3}\dot{5}$ (ii) $2.35656 \ldots$ in the form $\dfrac{N}{D}$
    where N and D are positive integers.

19. Find the sum of n terms of the series $1, x^2, x^4, \ldots$ and hence find the sum to infinity of the series $1 + 2x^2 + 3x^4 + \ldots$ for $|x| < 1$.

20. The sum to infinity of the G.P. $1, x, x^2, x^3, \ldots$ is 5 and the sum to infinity of 1^2, $x^2, x^4, x^6, \ldots$ is 4. Find the series.

21. Express the recurring decimal $0.7\dot{2}\dot{5}$ in the form $\dfrac{N}{D}$ where N and D are integers.

22. a, b, c is an A.P. and $2a$, $2b$, $2c$ is a G.P., and given that $b = \dfrac{a^2}{a - 1}$, and $c = \dfrac{b^2}{b - 1}$. Find the nth term of each series and the sum of n terms of the G.P.

23. If $S_n = a + ar + ar^2 + \ldots + ar^{n-1}$ and $P_n = a\,(ar)\,(ar^2)\,(ar^3) \ldots (ar^{n-1})$.

    Determine $\dfrac{1}{a} + \dfrac{1}{ar} + \dfrac{1}{a\,r^2} + \ldots + \dfrac{1}{a\,r^{n-1}}$ and $\dfrac{1}{a\,(ar)\,(ar^2) \ldots (ar^{n-1})}$.

24. A G.P. is $\dfrac{1}{2}, \dfrac{1}{6}, \dfrac{1}{18}, \ldots$ Find S_n and S_∞. Hence find the value of n such that
    $S_\infty - S_n > 0.0001$.

12. THE BINOMIAL THEOREM

(Sir Isaac Newton (1642 - 1727))

Binomial is an expression containing two terms

From basic algebra, we have learnt that the expansion

$(a + b)^2 \equiv a^2 + 2ab + b^2$ and $(a + b)^3 \equiv a^3 + 3a^2b + 3ab^2 + b^3$.

What happens now if we want to expand $(a + b)$ to a power greater than three?

$(a + b)^2 = (a + b)(a + b) = a^2 + ab + ab + b^2 = a^2 + 2ab + b^2$

$(a + b)^3 = (a + b)(a + b)(a + b) = (a^2 + 2ab + b^2)(a + b)$

$= a^3 + 2a^2 b + ab^2 + a^2 b + 2a b^2 + b^3 = a^3 + 3 a^2 b + 3 ab^2 + b^3$.

Expand $(a + b)^n$ where n is a positive integer.

$$(a + b)^n = \frac{a^n}{0!} b^0 + \frac{n}{1!} a^{n-1} b^1 + \frac{n(n-1)}{2!} a^{n-2} b^2 + \frac{n(n-1)(n-2)}{3!} a^{n-3} b^3 +$$

$$\frac{n(n-1)(n-2)(n-3)}{4!} a^{n-4} b^4 + ... + \frac{n!}{n!} a^0 b^n$$

$$\boxed{(a + b)^n = a^n + na^{n-1} b^1 + \frac{n(n-1)}{1 \times 2} a^{n-2} b^2 + \frac{n(n-1)(n-2)}{1 \times 2 \times 3} a^{n-3} b^3 + ...}$$

There are $(n + 1)$ terms if n is a positive integer.

Expand $(a + b)^5$.

$$(a + b)^5 = a^5 + 5 a^4 b + \frac{5 \times 4}{1 \times 2} a^3 b^2 + \frac{5 \times 4 \times 3}{1 \times 2 \times 3} a^2 b^3 + \frac{5 \times 4 \times 3 \times 2}{1 \times 2 \times 3 \times 4} ab^4 +$$

$$\frac{5 \times 4 \times 3 \times 2 \times 1}{1 \times 2 \times 3 \times 4 \times 5} b^5 \text{ simplifying}$$

$$(a + b)^5 = a^5 + 5a^4 b + 10a^3 b^2 + 10a^2 b^3 + 5ab^4 + b^5.$$

WORKED EXAMPLE 78

Expand the following Binomial Expressions:-

(i) $(x + 2y)^4$ (ii) $(3x - 2y)^5$.

SOLUTION 78

(i) $(x + 2y)^4 = x^4 + 4x^3(2y) + \dfrac{4 \times 3\, x^2}{1 \times 2}(2y)^2 + \dfrac{4 \times 3 \times 2}{1 \times 2 \times 3} x (2y)^3 + (2y)^4$

$= x^4 + 8x^3y + 24x^2y^2 + 32xy^3 + 16y^4$

(ii) $(3x - 2y)^5 = (3x)^5 + 5(3x)^4(-2y) + \dfrac{5 \times 4}{1 \times 2}(3x)^3(-2y)^2 + \dfrac{5 \times 4 \times 3}{1 \times 2 \times 3}(3x)^2(-2y)^3 +$

$\dfrac{5 \times 4 \times 3 \times 2}{1 \times 2 \times 3 \times 4}(3x)(-2y)^4 + (-2y)^5$

$= 243\,x^5 - 810\,x^4 y + 1080\,x^3 y^2 - 720\,x^2 y^3 + 240\,x\,y^4 - 32\,y^5$

$(a + b)^n$ may be written as $\left[a \left(1 + \dfrac{b}{a} \right) \right]^n = a^n \left(1 + \dfrac{b}{a} \right)^n$

$x = \dfrac{b}{a}$, then $(a + b)^n = a^n (1 + x)^n$.

The expansion $(1 + x)^n$

$(1 + x)^n = 1 + nx + \dfrac{n(n-1)}{1 \times 2} x^2 + \dfrac{n(n-1)(n-2)}{1 \times 2 \times 3} x^3 + \dots + x^n$

If n is a positive integer then there is no constraint on x, **i.e.** x can be any value.

If n is not a positive integer then

$$\boxed{(1 + x)^n = 1 + nx + \dfrac{n(n-1)}{2!} x^2 + \dfrac{n(n-1)(n-2)}{3!} x^3 + \dots}$$

and $-1 < x < 1$.

$$^nC_r = \frac{n!}{r!\,(n-r)!} \quad \text{or} \quad \binom{n}{r}$$

$$(1+x)^n = 1 + \binom{n}{1}x = \binom{n}{2}x^2 + \binom{n}{3}x^3 + \dots + \binom{n}{r}x^r + \dots \quad \text{or}$$

$$\boxed{(1+x)^n = 1 + {}^nC_1\,x + {}^nC_2\,x^2 + {}^nC_3\,x^3 + \dots + {}^nC_r\,x^r + \dots} \quad \text{and} \quad -1 < x < 1.$$

WORKED EXAMPLE 79

Write down the first five terms in the expansion of (i) $\sqrt{1-2x}$ and (ii) $\sqrt{1+2x}$.

SOLUTION 79

(i) $\quad \sqrt{1-2x} \quad = (1-2x)^{1/2} = 1 + \dfrac{1}{2}(-2x) + \dfrac{1}{2}\left(-\dfrac{1}{2}\right)(-2x)^2\,\dfrac{1}{2!} +$

$$\left(\dfrac{1}{2}\right)\left(-\dfrac{1}{2}\right)\left(-\dfrac{3}{2}\right)(-2x)^3\,\dfrac{1}{3!} + \dfrac{1}{2}\left(-\dfrac{1}{2}\right)\left(-\dfrac{3}{2}\right)\left(-\dfrac{5}{2}\right)(-2x)^4\,\dfrac{1}{4!}$$

$$= 1 - x - \dfrac{1}{2}x^2 - \dfrac{1}{2}x^3 - \dfrac{5}{8}x^4.$$

(ii) $\quad \sqrt{1+2x} \quad = (1+2x)^{1/2} = 1 + \dfrac{1}{2}(2x) + \dfrac{1}{2}\left(-\dfrac{1}{2}\right)(2x)^2\,\dfrac{1}{2!} +$

$$\dfrac{1}{2}\left(-\dfrac{1}{2}\right)\left(-\dfrac{3}{2}\right)(2x)^3\,\dfrac{1}{3!} + \dfrac{1}{2}\left(-\dfrac{1}{2}\right)\left(-\dfrac{3}{2}\right)\left(-\dfrac{5}{2}\right)(2x)^4\,\dfrac{1}{4!}$$

$$= 1 + x - \dfrac{1}{2}x^2 + \dfrac{1}{2}x^3 - \dfrac{5}{8}x^4.$$

WORKED EXAMPLE 80

If $(1-2x)^{1/2} \approx 1 - x - \dfrac{1}{2}x^2$ and $(1+2x)^{1/2} \approx 1 + x - \dfrac{1}{2}x^2$ by substituting $x = \dfrac{1}{100}$

and $x = \dfrac{1}{20}$, estimate $\sqrt{102}$ and $\sqrt{10}$ respectively to three significant figures.

SOLUTION 80

$(1 - 2x)^{1/2} \approx 1 - x - \dfrac{1}{2} x^2.$ If $x = \dfrac{1}{20}$

$$\boxed{\left(1 - \dfrac{2}{20}\right)^{1/2} = \left(1 - \dfrac{1}{10}\right)^{1/2} = \left(\dfrac{10 - 1}{10}\right)^{1/2} = \dfrac{9\frac{1}{2}}{10\frac{1}{2}} = \dfrac{3}{\sqrt{10}}}$$

$\dfrac{3}{\sqrt{10}} = 1 - \dfrac{1}{20} - \dfrac{1}{2}\dfrac{1}{20^2} = 1 - 0.05 - 0.00125 = 0.94875$

$\dfrac{3\sqrt{10}}{10} = 0.94875$ $\sqrt{10} = \dfrac{9.4875}{3} = 3.1625 \approx 3.163$

$(1 + 2x)^{1/2} = 1 + x - \dfrac{1}{2} x^2$ if $= \dfrac{1}{100}$

$\left(1 + \dfrac{2}{100}\right)^{1/2} = \left(\dfrac{102}{100}\right)^{1/2} = \dfrac{\sqrt{102}}{10} = 1 + \dfrac{1}{100} - \dfrac{1}{2}(10^{-2})^2 = 1 + 0.01 - 0.00005$

$\sqrt{102} = 10\,(1.00995) = 10.0995 \approx 10.1.$

Pascal's Triangle

Blaise Pascal (1623 – 1662). The following expansions are written by referring to the following

$$(a + b)^0 = 1 \qquad (a + b)^1 = a + b \qquad (a + b)^2 = a^2 + 2ab + b^2$$

$$(a + b)^3 = a^3 + 3a^2b + 3ab^2 + b^3 \text{ and so on.}$$

```
                               1
                          1         1
                     1         2         1
                1         3         3         1
           1         4         6         4         1
      1         5        10        10         5         1
 1         6        15        20        15         6         1
    1         7        21        35        35        21         7         1
 1         8        28        56        70        56        28         8         1
1         9        36        84       126       126        84        36         9        1
1    10        45       120       210       252       210       120        45        10        1
```

The following can be observed from the above triangle.

1. We write 1 s along the sides of the triangle.

2. The first 1 is the answer to the expansion $(a + b)^0 = 1$.

3. The second row of 1s are the coefficients of $(a + b)^1 = 1a + 1b$.

4. The third row shows the coefficients of 1, 2, 1 of the expansion

   $(a + b)^2 = a^2 + 2ab + b^2$, the 2 is derived by adding the 1s of the second row.

5. The fourth row has coefficients 1, 3, 3, 1, the 3 is derived by adding 1 and 2 from the third row and so on.

   Pascal's Triangle enables us to write down the following expansions without very much trouble.

   Pascal's Triangle method is rather efficient for values of n less than 10. For values of n greater than 10 Newton's method of writing the coefficients is much easier.

$(1 + x)^0 = 1$

$(1 + x)^1 = 1 + x$

$(1 + x)^2 = 1 + 2x + x^2$

$(1 + x)^3 = 1 + 3x + 3x^2 + x^3$

$(1 + x)^4 = 1 + 4x + 6x^2 + 4x^3 + x^4$

$(1 + x)^5 = 1 + 5x + 10x^2 + 10x^3 + 5x^4 + x^5$

$(1 + x)^6 = 1 + 6x + 15x^2 + 20x^3 + 15x^4 + 6x^5 + x^6$

$(1 + x)^7 = 1 + 7x + 21x^2 + 35x^3 + 35x^4 + 21x^5 + 7x^6 + x^7$

$(1 + x)^8 = 1 + 8x + 28x^2 + 56x^3 + 70x^4 + 56x^5 + 28x^6 + 8x^7 + x^8$

WORKED EXAMPLE 81

Using the Pascal triangle binomial coefficients, give the expansion of the following:-

(i) $(1 - x)^5$ (ii) $(1 + x)^9$ (iii) $(a + b)^6$

(iv) $\left(1 + \dfrac{1}{2}x\right)^4$ (v) $\left(1 - 3\dfrac{x}{y}\right)^3$.

SOLUTION 81

(i) $(1 - x)^5 = 1 - 5x + 10x^2 - 10x^3 + 5x^4 - x^5$.

(ii) $(1 + x)^9 = 1 + 9x + 36x^2 + 84x^3 + 126x^4 + 126x^5 + 84x^6 + 36x^7 + 9x^8 + x^9$

(iii) $(a + b)^6 = a^6 + 6\,a^5\,b + 15\,a^4\,b^2 + 20\,a^3\,b^3 + 15\,a^2\,b^4 + 6\,a\,b^5 + b^6$

(iv) $\left(1 + \dfrac{1}{2}x\right)^4 = 1 + 4\left(\dfrac{1}{2}x\right) + 6\left(\dfrac{1}{2}x\right)^2 + 4\left(\dfrac{1}{2}x\right)^3 + \left(\dfrac{1}{2}x\right)^4$

$$= 1 + 2x + \frac{3}{2}x^2 + \frac{1}{2}x^3 + \frac{1}{16}x^4.$$

(v) $\left(1 - 3\dfrac{x}{y}\right)^3 = 1 - 3\left(3\dfrac{x}{y}\right) + 3\left(3\dfrac{x}{y}\right)^2 - \left(3\dfrac{x}{y}\right)^3$

$$= 1 - 9\frac{x}{y} + 27\frac{x^2}{y^2} - 27\frac{x^3}{y^3}.$$

WORKED EXAMPLE 82

Find the values of the following by using Newton's binomial expansion.

(i) $(2 + \sqrt{3})^4 + (2 - \sqrt{3})^4$ (ii) $(\sqrt{2} + \sqrt{3})^5 + (\sqrt{2} - \sqrt{3})^5$

(iii) $(\sqrt{6} + \sqrt{2})^6 - (\sqrt{6} - \sqrt{2})^6$

SOLUTION 82

(i) $(2 + \sqrt{3})^4 + (2 - \sqrt{3})^4 = 2^4 + 4 \times 2^3 \times \sqrt{3} + \dfrac{4 \times 3}{1 \times 2} \times 2^2 (\sqrt{3})^2 +$

$$\dfrac{4 \times 3 \times 2}{1 \times 2 \times 3} \times 2 (\sqrt{3})^3 + (\sqrt{3})^4 + 2^4 - 4 \times 2^3 \sqrt{3} +$$

$$\dfrac{4 \times 3}{1 \times 2} \times 2^2 (\sqrt{3})^2 - \dfrac{4 \times 3 \times 2}{1 \times 2 \times 3} 2 (\sqrt{3})^3 + (\sqrt{3})^4$$

$(2 + \sqrt{3})^4 + (2 - \sqrt{3})^4 = 32 + 144 + 18 = 194$

$$\boxed{(2 + \sqrt{3})^4 + (2 - \sqrt{3})^4 = 194.}$$

(ii) $(\sqrt{2} + \sqrt{3})^5 + (\sqrt{2} - \sqrt{3})^5$

$= (\sqrt{2})^5 + 5 (\sqrt{2})^4 \sqrt{3} + \dfrac{5 \times 4}{1 \times 2} (\sqrt{2})^3 (\sqrt{3})^2 + \dfrac{5 \times 4 \times 3}{1 \times 2 \times 3} (\sqrt{2})^2 (\sqrt{3})^3 +$

$\dfrac{5 \times 4 \times 3 \times 2}{1 \times 2 \times 3 \times 4} (\sqrt{2})(\sqrt{3})^4 + (\sqrt{3})^5 + (\sqrt{2})^5 - 5 (\sqrt{2})^4 \sqrt{3} + \dfrac{5 \times 4}{1 \times 2} (\sqrt{2})^3 (\sqrt{3})^2 -$

$\dfrac{5 \times 4 \times 3}{1 \times 2 \times 3} (\sqrt{2})^2 (\sqrt{3})^3 + \dfrac{5 \times 4 \times 3 \times 2}{1 \times 2 \times 3 \times 4} (\sqrt{2})^4 - (\sqrt{3})^5$

$= 2 (\sqrt{2})^5 + 20 (\sqrt{2})^3 (\sqrt{3})^2 + 10 \sqrt{2} (\sqrt{3})^4 = 8 \sqrt{2} + 120 \sqrt{2} + 90 \sqrt{2}$

$= 218 \sqrt{2}.$

(iii) $(\sqrt{6} + \sqrt{2})^6 - (\sqrt{6} - \sqrt{2})^6 = [(\sqrt{6} + \sqrt{2})^3 - (\sqrt{6} - \sqrt{2})^3] [(\sqrt{6} + \sqrt{2})^3 + (\sqrt{6} - \sqrt{2})^3]$

$= [(6\sqrt{6} + 3 \times 6\sqrt{2} + 3\sqrt{6} \times 2 + 2\sqrt{2}) - (6\sqrt{6} - 3 \times 6\sqrt{2} + 3\sqrt{6} (2) 2 - 2\sqrt{2})] \times$

$[(6\sqrt{6} + 3 \times 6\sqrt{2} + 3\sqrt{6} \times 2 + 2\sqrt{2}) + (6\sqrt{6} - 3 \times 6\sqrt{2} + 3\sqrt{6} \times 2 - 2\sqrt{2})]$

$= (36\sqrt{2} + 4\sqrt{2})(12\sqrt{6} + 12\sqrt{6}) = 48 (10\sqrt{2})(2\sqrt{6}) = 960 \times 2\sqrt{3} = 1920\sqrt{3}$

THE ^nC_r OR $\binom{n}{r}$ NOTATION

$$(1 + x)^n = {}^nC_o\, x^0 + {}^nC_1\, x^1 + {}^nC_2\, x^2 + {}^nC_3\, x^3 + {}^nC_4\, x^4 + \dots + {}^nC_n\, x^n \dots \text{(1)}$$

If $x = 0$, $1^n = {}^nC_o = 1$

$$\boxed{{}^nC_o = 1}$$

Differentiating equation (1) w.r.t. x

$$n\,(1 + x)^{n-1} = {}^nC_1 + 2\,{}^nC_2\, x + 3\,{}^nC_3\, x^2 + 4\,{}^nC_4\, x^3 + \dots + n\,{}^nC_n\, x^{n-1} \quad \dots \text{(2)}$$

If $x = 0$ $\qquad n\,(1 + 0)^{n-1} = {}^nC_1$

$$\boxed{{}^nC_1 = n}$$

Differentiating equation (2) w.r.t. x

$$n\,(n-1)\,(1+x)^{n-2} = 2\,{}^nC_2 + 3\times 2\,{}^nC_3\, x + \dots + n\,(n-1)\,{}^nC_n\, x^{n-2} \quad \dots \text{(3)}$$

If $x = 0$ $\qquad\qquad n(n-1) = 2\,{}^nC_2$

$$\boxed{{}^nC_2 = \frac{n\,(n-1)}{2}}$$

Differentiating equation (3) w.r.t. x.

$$n\,(n-1)\,(n-2)\,(1+x)^{n-3} = 3\times 2\times 1\,{}^nC_3 + \dots + n\,(n-1)\,(n-2)\,{}^nC_n\, x^{n-3}.$$

If $x = 0$

$$\boxed{\frac{n\,(n-1)\,(n-2)}{1\times 2\times 3} = {}^nC_3}$$

Therefore ${}^nC_o = 1$, ${}^nC_1 = n$, ${}^nC_2 = \dfrac{n\,(n-1)}{2}$, ${}^nC_3 = \dfrac{n\,(n-1)\,(n-2)}{1\times 2\times 3}$

and hence in general ${}^nC_r = \dfrac{n\,(n-1)\,(n-2)\,(n-3)\dots[n-(r-1)]}{r\,(r-1)\,(r-2)\,(r-3)\dots 3.2.1}$ where $1 \leq r \leq n$.

THE FACTORIAL NOTATION $x!$

$x! = 1.2.3.4.... x$ $x!$ is read as x factorial

$5! = $ five factorial $= 1.2.3.4.5 = 120$

$5! = 120$

$x! = (x - 1)! \, x.$

If $x = 1$,
$$\boxed{1! = 0!}$$

one factorial is equal to zero factorial.

If $x = 2$, $2! = 1! \, 2$.

If $x = 3$, $3! = 2! \, 3$ and so on $^nC_o = 1 = \dfrac{n!}{(n - 0)! \, 0!} = \dfrac{n!}{n! \, 0!} = \dfrac{1}{0!} = \dfrac{1}{1} = 1$

$$^nC_1 = n = \frac{n!}{(n - 1)! \, 1!} = \frac{(n - 1)! \, n}{(n - 1)! \, 1!} = \frac{n}{1} = n$$

$$^nC_2 = \frac{n \, (n - 1)}{2} = \frac{n!}{(n - 2)! \, 2!} = \frac{(n - 2! \, (n - 1) \, n}{(n - 2)! \, 2!} = \frac{n \, (n - 1)}{2!}$$

$$^nC_3 = \frac{n \, (n - 1) \, (n - 2)}{3 \times 2 \times 1} = \frac{n!}{(n - 3)! \, 3!} = \frac{(n - 3! \, (n - 2) \, (n - 1) \, n}{(n - 3)! \, 3!}$$

$$= \frac{n \, (n - 1) \, (n - 2)}{3!}$$

and in general, where $1 \leq r \leq n$

$$^nC_r = \frac{n!}{(n - r)! \, r!} = \frac{1.2.3.4.5.6.. \, (n - 3) \, (n - 2) \, (n - 1) \, n}{1.2.3... \, (n - r) \, 1.2.3... \, (r - 1) \, r}$$

$$= \frac{n \, (n - 1) \, (n - 2) \, (n - 3) \, ... \, [n - (r - 1)]}{1.2.3... \, (r - 2) \, (r - 1) \, r}$$

$$\boxed{^nC_r = \frac{n!}{(n - r)! \, r!}}$$

The Pascal Triangle Result $^nC_{r-1} + {}^nC_r = {}^{n+1}C_r$

$$(1 + x)^{n+1} = (1 + x)(1 + x)^n$$

$$= (1 + x)\left({}^nC_o x^0 + {}^nC_1 x^1 + {}^nC_2 x^2 + ... + {}^nC_{r-1} x^{r-1} + {}^nC_r x^r + ... + {}^nC_n x^n \right)$$

The coefficient of x^r in the above expansion is $\quad {}^nC_{r-1} + {}^nC_r \; ... \; (1)$

$$(1 + x)^{n+1} = {}^{n+1}C_0 x^0 + {}^{n+1}C_1 x^1 + {}^{n+1}C_2 x^2 + ... + {}^{n+1}C_r x^r + ... + {}^{n+1}C_{n+1} x^{n+1}.$$

The coefficient of x^r in this expansion is $\quad {}^{n+1}C_r \; ... \; (2)$

Therefore the coefficients of (1) and (2) are equal

$$\boxed{{}^nC_{r-1} + {}^nC_r = {}^{n+1}C_r} \quad ... \; (3)$$

$1 \le r \le n$ the Pascal triangle result.

WORKED EXAMPLE 83

Verify the following equations:-

(i) $\quad {}^8C_5 + {}^8C_6 = {}^9C_6$

(ii) $\quad {}^{12}C_7 + {}^{12}C_8 = {}^{13}C_8$

(iii) $\quad {}^kC_4 + {}^kC_5 \; {}^{k+1}C_5$

SOLUTION 83

(i) $\quad {}^8C_5 = \dfrac{8!}{5!\,(8-5)!} = \dfrac{8!}{5!\,3!} = \dfrac{6 \times 7 \times 8}{1 \times 2 \times 3} = 56$

$\quad {}^8C_6 = \dfrac{8!}{6!\,2!} = \dfrac{7 \times 8}{1 \times 2} = 28 \qquad {}^9C_6 = \dfrac{9!}{6!\,3!} = \dfrac{7 \times 8 \times 9}{1 \times 2 \times 3} = 84$

$\quad {}^8C_5 + {}^8C_6 = {}^9C_6 \qquad$ L.H.S. $= 56 + 28 = 84 \qquad$ R.H.S. $= 84$

(ii) $\quad {}^{12}C_7 + {}^{12}C_8 = {}^{13}C_8 \qquad\qquad {}^{12}C_7 = \dfrac{12!}{5!\,7!} = \dfrac{8 \times 9 \times 10 \times 11 \times 12}{1 \times 2 \times 3 \times 4 \times 5} = 792$

$\quad {}^{12}C_8 = \dfrac{12!}{4!\,8!} = \dfrac{9 \times 10 \times 11 \times 12}{1 \times 2 \times 3 \times 4} = 495$

$$^{13}C_8 = \frac{13!}{8!5!} = \frac{9 \times 10 \times 11 \times 12 \times 13}{1 \times 2 \times 3 \times 4 \times 5} = 1287$$

$^{12}C_7 + {}^{12}C_8 = 792 + 495 = 1287.$ Therefore $^{12}C_7 + {}^{12}C_8 = {}^{13}C_8.$

(iv) $^kC_4 + {}^kC_5 = {}^{k+1}C_5$ $^kC_4 = \dfrac{k!}{(k-4)!\,4!} = \dfrac{k\,(k-1)\,(k-2)\,(k-3)}{1 \times 2 \times 3 \times 4}$

$$^kC_5 = \frac{k!}{(k-5)!\,5!} = \frac{k\,(k-1)\,(k-2)\,(k-3)\,(k-4)}{1 \times 2 \times 3 \times 4 \times 5}$$

$$^kC_4 + {}^kC_5 = \frac{k\,(k-1)\,(k-2)\,(k-3)}{1 \times 2 \times 3 \times 4} + \frac{k\,(k-1)\,(k-2)\,(k-3)\,(k-4)}{1 \times 2 \times 3 \times 4 \times 5}$$

$$= \frac{(k+1)\,k\,(k-1)\,(k-2)\,(k-3)}{1 \times 2 \times 3 \times 4 \times 5}$$

Therefore $^kC_4 + {}^kC_5 = {}^{k+1}C_5.$

To prove by mathematical induction that $^nC_r = \dfrac{n\,(n-1)\,(n-2)\,...\,[n-(r-1)]}{r\,(r-1\,(r-2)\,...\,3.2.1}$

$$^nC_k = \frac{n\,(n-1)\,(n-2)\,....\,[n-(k-1)]}{k\,(k-1)\,(k-2)\,...\,3.2.1} \qquad 1 \le k \le n$$

$$^nC_{k-1} = \frac{n\,(n-1)\,(n-2\,...\,\{n-[k-1)-1]\}}{(k-1)\,(k-2)\,(k-3)\,...\,3.2.1}.$$

Using the Pascal Triangle relation $^{n+1}C_k = {}^nC_{k-1} + {}^nC_k$

$$^{n+1}C_k = \frac{n\,(n-1)\,(n-2)\,....\,(n-k+2)}{(k-1)\,(k-2)\,(k-3)\,...\,3.2.1} + \frac{n\,(n-1)\,(n-2)\,....\,(n-(k-1)}{k\,(k-1)\,(k-2)\,...\,3.2.1}$$

$$= \frac{n\,(n-1)\,(n-2)\,....\,(n-k+2)\,k + n\,(n-1)\,(n-2)\,...\,(n-k+2)\,(n-k+1)}{k\,(k-1)\,(k-2)\,...\,3.2.1}$$

$$= \frac{[n\,(n-1)\,(n-2)\,....\,(n-k+2)]\,[k+n-k+1]}{k\,(k-1)\,(k-2)\,...\,3.2.1}$$

$$^{n+1}C_k = \frac{n\,(n-1)\,(n-2)\,...\,(n-k+2)\,(n+1)}{k\,(k-1\,(k-2)\,...\,3.2.1}$$

If $n + 1$ is replaced by n and k by r

$$\,^nC_r = \frac{n\,(n-1)\,(n-2)\,...\,(n-r+1)}{r\,(r-1)\,(r-2)\,...\,3.2.1}$$

In the above C stands for coefficients, but C has another meaning, C stands for combinations. Use of binomial expansion for approximate calculations.

$$(1+x)^n = 1 + nx + \frac{n\,(1-1)}{1 \times 2}\,x^2 + \frac{n\,(n-1)\,(n-2)}{1 \times 2 \times 3}\,x^3 + ...$$

If $x << 1$, then $(1+x)^n \approx 1 + nx + \dfrac{n\,(n-1)}{1 \times 2}\,x^2$.

If $x = 0.01$ and $n = 9$ then $(1.01)^9 \approx 1 + 9\,(0.01) + \dfrac{9 \times 8}{1 \times 2}\,0.01^2$

$$= 1 + 0.09 + 36 \times 0.001 = 1 + 0.09 + 0.0036 = 1.0936$$

correct to four decimal places. If we use one more term

$$(1.01)^9 \approx 1 + 9\,(0.01) + \frac{9 \times 8}{1 \times 2}\,0.01^2 + \frac{9 \times 8 \times 7}{1 \times 2 \times 3}\,0.01^3$$

$= 1 + 0.09 + 0.0036 + 0.000084 = 1.093684$ correct to four decimal places.

If the answer is required correct to three decimal places, it would be 1.09, therefore $(1+x)^n \approx 1 + nx = 1 + 0.09 = 1.09$, therefore, for approximate

calculations and correct to three significant figures $\boxed{(1+x)^n \approx 1 + nx}$ If $x << 1$.

WORKED EXAMPLE 84

Use the Binomial theorem to evaluate approximately to three decimal places the following numbers:-

(i) 1.005^{-3} (ii) 1.005^5 (iii) $1.005^{-7/3}$.

SOLUTION 84

(i) $1.005^{-3} = (1 + 0.005)^{-3} \approx 1 + (-3)\,(0.005) = 1 - 0.015 = 0.985$

$1.005^{-3} = 0.985$.

(ii) $1.005^5 = (1 + 0.005)^5 = (1 + 0.005)^5 \approx 1 + 5 \times 0.005 = 1 + 0.025 = 1.025$

$1.005^5 \approx 1.025.$

(iii) $1.005^{-7/3} = (1 + 0.005)^{-7/3} \approx 1 + \left(-\dfrac{7}{3}\right)0.005 = 1 - \dfrac{0.035}{3} = 1 - 0.001167$

$1.005^{-7/3} \approx 0.98833 \approx 0.988.$

WORKED EXAMPLE 85

Use the binomial theorem to find the value of 1.01^{13} correct to 6 significant figures.

SOLUTION 85

$$1.01^{13} = (1 + 0.01)^{13} \approx 1 + 13 \times 0.01 + \frac{13 \times 12}{1 \times 2}0.01^2 + \frac{13 \times 12 \times 11}{1 \times 2 \times 3}0.01^3$$

$$= 1 + 0.13 + 0.0078 + 0.000286 = 1.138086 \approx 1.13809.$$

WORKED EXAMPLE 86

Write down approximations for:-

(i) 1.08^5 (ii) 1.001^{-3} (iii) $\dfrac{1}{99^{25}}$ (iv) 0.99^{-5} (v) 99^7

SOLUTION 86

(i) $1.08^5 = (1 + 0.08)^5 \approx 1 + 5 \times 0.08 + \dfrac{5 \times 4}{1 \times 2}0.08^2$

$= 1 + 0.4 + 0.064 = 1.464 \approx 1.46$

(ii) $1.001^{-3} = (1 + 0.001)^{-3} \approx 1 - 3(0.001) = 0.997$

(iii) $\dfrac{1}{99^{25}} = 99^{-25} = (100 - 1)^{-25} = 100^{-25}\left(1 - \dfrac{1}{100}\right)^{-25}$

$\dfrac{1}{10^{50}}(1 - 0.01)^{-25} \approx (1 + 25 \times 01)\,10^{-50} = 1.25 \times 10^{-50}$

(iv) $0.99^{-5} = (1 - 0.01)^{-5} \approx 1 + 0.05 = 1.05$

(v) $99^7 = (100 - 1)^7 = 100^7 \left(1 - \dfrac{1}{100}\right)^7 = 10^{14} (1 - 0.01)^7 \approx 10^{14} (1 - 7 \times 0.01)$

$= 10^{14} (1 - 0.07) = 9.3 \times 10^{13}.$

WORKED EXAMPLE 87

The series expansion of $\sin x$ in ascending power of x is given as $\sin x \approx x - \dfrac{x^3}{3!}$

where x is small and expressed in radians. Find the first five terms of the series

expansion $\dfrac{1}{\sqrt{(1 + \sin x)}}$ in ascending powers of x.

SOLUTION 87

$\sin x = x - \dfrac{x^3}{6}$

$\dfrac{1}{\sqrt{1 + \sin x}} = (1 + \sin x)^{-1/2} = 1 - \dfrac{1}{2} \sin x + \left(-\dfrac{1}{2}\right)\left(-\dfrac{3}{2}\right) \dfrac{\sin^2 x}{2!}$

$= 1 - \dfrac{1}{2} \sin x + \dfrac{3}{8} \sin^2 x = 1 - \dfrac{1}{2}\left(x - \dfrac{x^3}{6}\right) + \dfrac{3}{8}\left(x - \dfrac{x^3}{6}\right)^2$

$= 1 - \dfrac{1}{2} x + \dfrac{1}{12} x^3 + \dfrac{3}{8} x^2 - \dfrac{1}{8} x^4 + \dfrac{1}{96} x^6$

$= 1 - \dfrac{1}{2}x + \dfrac{3}{8} x^2 + \dfrac{1}{12} x^3 - \dfrac{1}{8} x^4 + \dfrac{1}{96} x^6.$

WORKED EXAMPLE 88

If y is small compared with x, find the expansion of $\sqrt{x + y}$, and hence show

that $\sqrt{x + y} - \sqrt{x} \approx \dfrac{1}{2} x^{-1/2} y.$

SOLUTION 88

$$\sqrt{x + y} = \sqrt{x\left(1 + \frac{y}{x}\right)} = \sqrt{x}\left(1 + \frac{y}{x}\right)^{1/2} \approx \sqrt{x}\left(1 + \frac{1}{2}\frac{y}{x}\right)$$

and since y is small compared with x, then $y/x << 1$

$$\sqrt{x}\left(1 + \frac{1}{2}\,y/x\right) = \sqrt{x} + \frac{1}{2}\frac{y\sqrt{x}}{x} = \sqrt{x} + \frac{1}{2}\frac{y\,x^{1/2}}{x}.$$

Therefore $\sqrt{x + y} - \sqrt{x} = \sqrt{x} + \frac{1}{2}\,yx^{-1/2} - \sqrt{x} = \frac{1}{2}\,x^{-1/2}\,y.$

EXPANSION OF LOGARITHMIC FUNCTIONS

The expansion for $\ln(1 + x)$ in ascending powers of x

$$\log_e(1 + x) = \frac{x}{1} - \frac{x^2}{2} + \frac{x^3}{3} - \frac{x^4}{4} + \frac{x^5}{5} - \frac{x^6}{6} + \ldots + (-1)^{r+1}\frac{x^r}{r} + \ldots$$

if $-1 < x \leq 1$ $\log_e(1 - x) = -\frac{x}{1} - \frac{x^2}{2} - \frac{x^3}{3} - \frac{x^4}{4} - \frac{x^5}{5} - \frac{x^6}{6} - \ldots - \frac{x^r}{r} \ldots$

If $-1 \leq x < 1$

$$\ln\frac{1 + x}{1 - x} = \ln(1 + x) - \ln(1 - x) = \frac{x}{1} - \frac{x^2}{2} + \frac{x^3}{3} - \ldots + \frac{x}{1} + \frac{x^2}{2} + \frac{x^3}{3} + \ldots$$

$$= 2\left(\frac{x}{1} + \frac{x^3}{3} + \frac{x^5}{5} + \ldots 1\right) \text{ and } -1 < x < 1.$$

If $x = \frac{1}{y}$ where $|y| > 1$

$$\ln\frac{1 + 1/y}{1 - 1/y} = \ln\frac{y + 1}{y - 1} = 2\left(\frac{1}{y} + \frac{1}{3y^3} + \frac{1}{5y^5} + \ldots\right)$$

$$\ln\left(1 + \frac{1}{n}\right) = \frac{1}{n} - \frac{1}{2n^2} + \frac{1}{2n^2} + \frac{1}{3n^3} - \frac{1}{4n^4} + \ldots$$

where n is a positive integer.

If $x = 1$ $\quad\ln(1 + 1) = \ln 2 = \dfrac{1}{1} - \dfrac{1}{2} + \dfrac{1}{3} - \dfrac{1}{4} + \dfrac{1}{5} - \dfrac{1}{6} + \ldots$

If $x = \dfrac{1}{2}$ $\quad\ln\left(1 + \dfrac{1}{2}\right) = \ln\dfrac{3}{2} = \dfrac{1}{2} - \dfrac{1}{2.2^2} + \dfrac{1}{3.2^3} - \dfrac{1}{4.2^4} + \dfrac{1}{5.2^5} - \dfrac{1}{6.2^6} + \ldots$

If $x = -\dfrac{1}{2}$ $\quad\ln\left(1 - \dfrac{1}{2}\right) = \ln\dfrac{1}{2} = 1\left(\dfrac{1}{2} + \dfrac{1}{2^2.2} + \dfrac{1}{2^3.3} + \dfrac{1}{2^4.4} + \dfrac{1}{2^5.5} + \ldots\right)$

$$\ln 2 = \dfrac{1}{2} + \dfrac{1}{2^2.2} + \dfrac{1}{2^3.3} + \dfrac{1}{2^4.4} + \dfrac{1}{2^5.5} + \ldots$$

To show that the infinite series

$$x - \dfrac{x^2}{2} + \dfrac{x^3}{3} - \dfrac{x^4}{4} + \ldots + (-1)^{r+1}\dfrac{x^r}{r} + \ldots \text{ is equal to } \log_e(1 + x) \text{ if } |x| < 1.$$

Let $y = x - \dfrac{x^2}{2} + \dfrac{x^3}{3} - \dfrac{x^4}{4} + \ldots + (-1)^{r+1}\dfrac{x^r}{r} + \ldots$ differentiating with respect to x

$$\dfrac{dy}{dx} = 1 - x + x^2 - x^3 + \ldots (-1)^{r+1} x^{r-1} + \ldots$$

The righthand expression is a geometric series with a common ratio $r = -x$, this series has a sum to infinity when $|x| < 1$.

$$S_\infty = \dfrac{1}{1 - r} = \dfrac{1}{1 - (-x)} = \dfrac{1}{1 + x}$$

$$\dfrac{dy}{dx} = \dfrac{1}{1 + x} = 1 - x + x^2 - x^3 + \ldots + (-1)^{r+1} x^{r-1} + \ldots$$

Integrating with respect to x

$$\int \dfrac{1}{1 + x}\, dx = \int \left(1 - x + x^2 - x^3 + \ldots + (-1)^{r+1} x^{r-1} + \ldots\right) dx$$

$$\boxed{\ln(1 + x) = x - \dfrac{x^2}{2} + \dfrac{x^3}{3} - \dfrac{x^4}{4} + \ldots + (-1)^{r+1}\dfrac{x^r}{r} + \ldots}$$

provided $-1 < x \leq 1$.

If $x = 1$
$$\ln 2 = 1 - \frac{1}{2} + \frac{1}{3} - \frac{1}{4} + \frac{1}{5} - \ldots$$

but if $x = -1$, $\ln (1 + x)$ does not exist since $\ln 0$ is not defined.

If x is replaced by $-x$ in the above series

$$\ln (1 - x) = -x - \frac{x^2}{2} - \frac{x^3}{3} - \frac{x^4}{4} - \ldots - (-1)^{r+1} \frac{x^r}{r} - \ldots$$

$$\ln (1 - x) = -\left(x + \frac{x^2}{2} + \frac{x^3}{3} + \frac{x^4}{4} + \ldots + (-1)^{r+1} \frac{x^r}{r} + \ldots \right) \quad \text{or}$$

$$-\ln (1 - x) = \left(x + \frac{x^2}{2} + \frac{x^3}{3} + \frac{x^4}{4} + \ldots + (-1)^{r+1} \frac{x^r}{r} + \ldots \right)$$

$$\ln (1 - x)^{-1} = \ln \frac{1}{1 - x} = x + \frac{x^2}{2} + \frac{x^3}{3} + \ldots + (-1)^{r+1} \frac{x^r}{r} + \ldots$$

If $x = \dfrac{1}{2}$

$$\ln \frac{1}{1 - 1/2} = \ln \frac{1}{1/2} = \ln 2 = \frac{1}{2} + \frac{1}{2^2 \, 2} + \frac{1}{2^3 . 3} + \ldots + (-1)^{r+1} \frac{1}{2^r \, r} + \ldots$$

Expansion of trigonometric functions $\sin x = x - x^3/3! + x^5/5! - x^7/7! + \ldots$

$$\cos x = 1 - x^2/2! + x^4/4! - x^6/6! + \ldots$$

where x is expressed in radians.

Expansion of exponential functions

$$e^x = 1 + \frac{x}{1!} + \frac{x^2}{2!} + \frac{x^3}{3!} + \frac{x^4}{4!} + \ldots$$

$$e^{-x} = 1 - \frac{x}{1!} + \frac{x^2}{2!} - \frac{x^3}{3!} + \frac{x^4}{4!} - \ldots$$

If $x = \dfrac{1}{2}$ $e^{1/2} = 1 + \dfrac{1}{2.1!} + \dfrac{1}{2^2 . 2!} + \dfrac{1}{2^3 . 3!} + \dfrac{1}{2^4 \, 4!} + \ldots$

If $x = \dfrac{3}{4}$ $e^{3/4} = 1 + \dfrac{3/4}{1!} + \dfrac{(3/4)^2}{2!} + \dfrac{(3/4)^3}{3!} + \ldots$

EXERCISES 12

1. Write down the first three terms in the expansion, in ascending powers of x for the following binomial expressions:-

   (i) $(1 - 5x)^{-3}$ (ii) $(1 + 3x)^{3/4}$ (iii) $(1 - 4x)^{-1/3}$

   (iv) $(1 - x)^{1/2}$ (v) $(1 + x)^{-1/2}$.

2. Find the first three non-zero terms in the expansions, in ascending powers of x:

   (i) $(1 + px)^n$ (ii) $(1 - px)^{-n}$ (iii) $(1 + 3\,ax)^{-n}$

   (iv) $(1 - 2bx)^n$ (v) $(1 - bx)^n$.

3. Find the first three non-zero terms in the following expansions, in ascending powers of y:

   (i) $\sqrt{\dfrac{1 - y}{1 + y}}$ (ii) $\dfrac{1}{\sqrt{1 - y^2}}$

   (iii) $\sqrt{9 + ax}$ (iv) $\dfrac{1}{\sqrt{16 - bx}}$.

4. Expand $(25 + x)^{1/2}$ in ascending powers of x up to and including the term in x^2.

5. Expand in ascending powers of x up to and including the term in x^3.

   (i) $(1 + 2x)^{1/3}$ (ii) $(1 - 3x)^{-1/5}$.

   Given that $(1 + 2x)^{1/3} + 25 (1 - 3x)^{-1/5} = a + bx + c\,x^2 + d\,x^3 + \ldots$ find the numerical values of a, b, c and d.

6. Find the coefficients of x^3 in the expansions:-

   $(1 + 2x)^{1/2} (1 - 3x)^{-1/2}$.

7. Expand $(1 - 7x)^{-1/3}$ in ascending powers of x up to and including the term in x^3.

8. Write down the term containing b^r in the binomial expansion of $(a + b)^n$ where n is a positive integer.

9. Write down the coefficient of x^{25} in the binomial expansion of $(1 - 3x)^{37}$.

10. The period T of a simple pendulum is given by the formula $T = 2\pi \sqrt{\dfrac{l}{g}}$

where l is the length of the pendulum and g is the acceleration due to gravity. It is required to calculate g from the formula above. If errors of $+ 1\%$ in T and $- 0.5\%$ in l are made, use the binomial expansion to determine the percentage error in the calculated value of g, giving your answer correct to three decimal places.

11. It is required to determine f from the formula $f = k \dfrac{\sqrt{W}}{l}$

If errors of $- 2\%$ in l and $+ 1\%$ in W are made, use the binomial expansion, to find the percentage error in the calculated value of f. (Hint expand

$(1 + x)^{1/2}$ and $(1 - 2x)^{-1}$ in ascending powers of x up to and including the term in x^2).

12. Write down and simplify the first four terms in the expansion of $(1 + x)^n$ in ascending powers of x when $n = 3$, $n = - 3$ and when $n = -\dfrac{1}{3}$.

13. Find correct to 4 decimal places the values of:-

(i) $\dfrac{1}{(1.005)^3}$

(ii) $\sqrt[3]{27.003}$

(iii) $(1.005)^{1/5}$

(iv) $0.995^{- 1/3}$

14. Express (i) $(1 + x)^{1/2}$ and (ii) $(1 - x)^{-3}$ as series of ascending powers of x in each case up to and including the term in x^2.

Hence show that, if x is small $\dfrac{(1 + x)^{1/2}}{(1 - x)^3} = 1 + \dfrac{7}{x} + \dfrac{59}{8} x^2$.

Calculate the percentage change which occurs in the value of $\dfrac{W^{1/2}}{Z^3}$.

If W is increased by 1% and Z is decreased by 1%.

13. THE SIGMA NOTATION AND SERIES

Consider the series $u_1, u_2, u_3, u_4, \ldots, u_r, \ldots u_n$. The sum of this series is written as $u_1 + u_2 + u_3 + \ldots u_r + u_n$ and in an abbreviated form, this sum is denoted as

$$\sum_{r=1}^{r=n} u_r \text{ where } r \text{ is a general term.}$$

WORKED EXAMPLE 89

(i) $\displaystyle\sum_{r=0}^{r=\infty} \frac{x^r}{r!}$ (ii) $\displaystyle\sum_{r=1}^{r=\infty} \frac{1}{3^r + r}$ (iii) $\displaystyle\sum_{r=1}^{r=n} \frac{1+r}{r^2}$

SOLUTION 89

(i) $\displaystyle\sum_{r=0}^{r=\infty} \frac{x^r}{r!}$ $= \dfrac{x^0}{0!} + \dfrac{x^1}{1!} + \dfrac{x^2}{2!} + \dfrac{x^3}{3!} + \ldots + \dfrac{x^r}{r!} + \dfrac{x^n}{n!} + \ldots$

$= 1 + \dfrac{x}{1!} + \dfrac{x^2}{21} + \dfrac{x^3}{3!} + \ldots + \dfrac{x^r}{r!} + \ldots + \dfrac{x^n}{n!} \ldots$

(ii) $\displaystyle\sum_{r=1}^{r=\infty} \frac{1}{3^r + r}$ $= \dfrac{1}{3^1 + 1} + \dfrac{1}{3^2 + 2} + \dfrac{1}{3^3 + 3} + \dfrac{1}{3^4 + 4} + \ldots + \dfrac{1}{3^n + n} + \ldots$

(iii) $\displaystyle\sum_{r=1}^{r=\infty} \frac{1+r}{r^2}$ $= \dfrac{1+1}{1^2} + \dfrac{1+2}{2^2} + \dfrac{1+3}{3^2} + \ldots + \dfrac{1+r}{r^2} + \ldots + \dfrac{1+n}{n^2} + \ldots$

WORKED EXAMPLE 90

Write in sigma notation the summation of the following series:-

(i) $1 + \dfrac{1}{2} + \dfrac{1}{3} + \dfrac{1}{4} + \ldots + \dfrac{1}{r} + \ldots \dfrac{1}{n} + \ldots$

(ii) $1 + \dfrac{1}{\sqrt{2}} + \dfrac{1}{\sqrt{3}} + \dfrac{1}{\sqrt{4}} + \ldots + \dfrac{1}{\sqrt{r}} \ldots + \dfrac{1}{\sqrt{n}} + \ldots$

(iii) $\dfrac{x}{1!} - \dfrac{x^3}{3!} + \dfrac{x^5}{5!} - \dfrac{x^7}{7!} + \ldots + (-1)^{r+1} \dfrac{x^{2r-1}}{(2r-1)!} + \ldots$

(iv) $1 - \dfrac{x^2}{2!} + \dfrac{x^4}{4!} - \dfrac{x^6}{6!} + \ldots + (-1)^r \dfrac{x^{2r}}{(2r)!} + \ldots$

(v) $x + \dfrac{x^3}{3!} + \dfrac{x^5}{5!} + \dfrac{x^7}{7!} + \ldots + \dfrac{x^{2r-1}}{(2r-1)!} + \ldots$

(vi) $1 + \dfrac{x^2}{2!} + \dfrac{x^4}{4!} + \dfrac{x^6}{6!} + \ldots + \dfrac{x^{2r}}{(2r)!} + \ldots$

(vii) $1 + nx + \dfrac{n(n-1)}{2!} x^2 + \dfrac{n(n-1)(n-2)}{3!} x^3 + \ldots + n(n-1) \ldots (n-r+1) \dfrac{x^r}{r!} + \ldots$

$\quad = 1 + {}^nC_1 x + {}^nC_2 x^2 + {}^nC_3 x^3 + \ldots + {}^nC_r x^r + \ldots$

(viii) $x - \dfrac{x^2}{2} + \dfrac{x^3}{3} - \dfrac{x^4}{4} + \ldots + (-1)^{r+1} \dfrac{x^r}{r} + \ldots$

(ix) $f(0) + x\, f'(0) + \dfrac{x^2}{2!} f''(0) + \ldots + \dfrac{x^r}{r!} f^r(0) + \ldots + \dfrac{x^n}{n!} f^n(0) \ldots$

(x) $\quad - x - \dfrac{x^2}{2} - \dfrac{x^3}{3} - \dfrac{x^4}{4} - \ldots - \dfrac{x^r}{r} - \ldots \dfrac{x^n}{r} - \ldots$

SOLUTION 90

(i) $\quad 1 + \dfrac{1}{2} + \dfrac{1}{3} + \dfrac{1}{4} + \ldots + \dfrac{1}{r} + \ldots + \dfrac{1}{n} + \ldots \qquad = \displaystyle\sum_{r=1}^{r=\infty} \dfrac{1}{r}.$

(ii) $\quad 1 + \dfrac{1}{\sqrt{2}} + \dfrac{1}{\sqrt{3}} + \ldots + \dfrac{1}{\sqrt{r}} + \ldots + \dfrac{1}{\sqrt{n}} + \ldots \qquad = \displaystyle\sum_{r=1}^{r=\infty} \dfrac{1}{\sqrt{r}}.$

(iii) $\dfrac{x}{1!} - \dfrac{x^3}{3!} + \dfrac{x^5}{5!} - \dfrac{x^7}{7!} + \ldots + (-1)^{r+1} \dfrac{x^{2r-1}}{(2r-1)!} + \ldots \quad = \displaystyle\sum_{r=1}^{r=\infty} (-1)^{r+1} \dfrac{x^{2r-1}}{(2r-1)!}$

(iv) $1 - \dfrac{x^2}{2!} + \dfrac{x^4}{4!} - \dfrac{x^6}{6!} + \ldots + (-1)^r \dfrac{x^{2r}}{(2r)!} + \ldots \quad = \displaystyle\sum_{r=0}^{r=\infty} \dfrac{x^{2r}}{(2r)!}.$

(v) $\quad x + \dfrac{x^3}{3!} + \dfrac{x^5}{5!} + \dfrac{x^7}{7!} + \dots + \dfrac{x^{2r-1}}{(2r-1)!} + \dots \qquad = \sum\limits_{r=1}^{r=\infty} \dfrac{x^{2r-1}}{(2r-1)!}$

(vi) $\quad 1 + \dfrac{x^2}{2!} + \dfrac{x^4}{4!} + \dots + \dfrac{x^{2r}}{(2r)!} + \dots \qquad = \sum\limits_{r=0}^{r=\infty} \dfrac{x^{2r}}{(2r)!}$

(vii) $\quad 1 + {}^nC_1\, x + {}^nC_2\, x^2 + \dots + {}^nC_r\, x^r + \dots \qquad = \sum\limits_{r=1}^{r=n} {}^nC_r$

(viii) $\quad x - \dfrac{x^2}{2} + \dfrac{x^3}{3} - \dfrac{x^4}{4} + \dots + (-1)^{r+1}\dfrac{x^r}{r} + \dots \qquad = \sum\limits_{r=1}^{r=n} (-1)^{r+1}\dfrac{x^r}{r}$

(ix) $\quad f(0) + \dfrac{x}{1!}\, f'(0) + \dfrac{x^2}{2!}\, f''(0) + \dots + \dfrac{x^r}{r!}\, f^r(0) + \dots \qquad = \sum\limits_{r=0}^{r=\infty} \dfrac{x^r}{r!}\, f^r(0).$

(x) $\quad -x - \dfrac{x^2}{2} - \dfrac{x^3}{3} - \dots - \dfrac{x^r}{r} - \dots - \dfrac{x^n}{n} - \dots \qquad = \sum\limits_{r=1}^{r=\infty} \dfrac{x^r}{r}.$

CONVERGENCY

$$\log_e (1 + x) = x - \dfrac{x^2}{2} + \dfrac{x^3}{3} - \dfrac{x^4}{4} + \dots + (-1)^{r+1}\dfrac{x^r}{r} + \dots \text{ for } -1 < x \le 1.$$

If $x = 1$, $\ln 2 = 1 - \dfrac{1}{2} + \dfrac{1}{3} - \dfrac{1}{4} + \dots + (-1)^{r+1}\ \dfrac{1}{r} + \dots$

therefore, the series $1 - \dfrac{1}{2} + \dfrac{1}{3} - \dfrac{1}{4} + \dots$ is convergent since it is summed to infinity and is equal to $\ln 2$.

DIVERGENCY

COMPARISON TEST

Consider the series $\sum\limits_{r=1}^{r=\infty} \dfrac{1}{r} = \dfrac{1}{1} + \dfrac{1}{2} + \dfrac{1}{3} + \dfrac{1}{4} + \dfrac{1}{5} + \dots$

$$= 1 + \frac{1}{2} + \left(\frac{1}{3} + \frac{1}{4}\right) + \left(\frac{1}{5} + \frac{1}{6} + \frac{1}{7} + \frac{1}{8}\right) +$$

$$\left(\frac{1}{9} + \frac{1}{10} + \frac{1}{11} + \frac{1}{12} + \frac{1}{13} + \frac{1}{14} + \frac{1}{15} + \frac{1}{16}\right) + \ldots$$

From this formation of the series, it can be deduced that the series

$$1 + \frac{1}{2} + \left(\frac{1}{4} + \frac{1}{4}\right) + \left(\frac{1}{8} + \frac{1}{8} + \frac{1}{8} + \frac{1}{8}\right) + \left(\frac{1}{16} + \frac{1}{16} + \ldots + \frac{1}{16}\right) + \ldots$$

$$= 1 + \left(\frac{1}{2}\right) + \left(\frac{1}{2}\right) + \left(\frac{1}{2}\right) + \left(\frac{1}{2}\right) + \ldots \text{ infinite values of}$$

$$\left(\frac{1}{2}\right) = \text{divergent series which is less than } \sum_{r=1}^{r=\infty} \frac{1}{r}.$$

TO FIND THE SUMMATION OF SERIES

$$\sum_{r=1}^{r=n} r = 1 + 2 + 3 + \ldots + r + \ldots + n.$$

This series is an arithmetic series where the first term, $a = 1$, the common difference, $d = 1$. Using the formula for an arithmetic mean, we have

$$S_n = \frac{n}{2}[2a + (n - 1)d]$$

$$= \frac{n}{2}[2(1) + (n - 1)(1)] = \frac{n}{2}(2 + n - 1) = \frac{n}{2}(n + 1).$$

This sum can be found alternatively.

$$n^2 - (n - 1)^2 = n^2 - n^2 + 2n - 1 \qquad\qquad = 2n - 1$$

$$(n - 1)^2 - (n - 2)^2 = n^2 - 2n + 1 - n^2 + 4n - 4 \qquad = 2(n - 1) - 1$$

$$(n - 2)^2 - (n - 3)^2 = n^2 - 4n + 4 - n^2 + 6n - 9 \qquad = 2(n - 2) - 1$$

$$(n - 3)^2 - (n - 4)^2 = n^2 - 6n + 9 - n^2 + 8n - 16 \qquad = 2(n - 3) - 1$$

$$\vdots \qquad\qquad\qquad \vdots$$

$$2^2 - 1^2 \ = 4 - 1 \qquad\qquad = 2 \times 2 - 1$$
$$1^2 - 0^2 \ = 1 \qquad\qquad\quad = 2 \times 1 - 1$$

$$\overline{}\qquad\qquad\overline{}$$

$$n^2 \ = \qquad\qquad\qquad = 2\sum_{r=1}^{n} r - n$$

$$2\sum_{r=1}^{n} r - n = n^2 \qquad\qquad 2\sum_{r=1}^{n} r = n^2 + n = n(n+1)$$

Therefore

$$\boxed{\sum_{r=1}^{n} r = \frac{n(n+1)}{2}}$$

Although the alternative method is more difficult and longer for the summation

$\displaystyle\sum_{r=1}^{n} r$, it is very useful for $\displaystyle\sum_{r=1}^{n} r^2, \ \sum_{r=1}^{n} r^3, \ \sum_{r=1}^{n} r^4$ and so on.

To find the summation $\displaystyle\sum_{r=1}^{n} r^2$.

$$n^3 - (n-1)^3 \ = (n^3 - n^3 - 3n^2 + 3n - 1) \qquad = 3n^2 - 3n +$$
$$(n-1)^3 - (n-2)^3 \ = \qquad\qquad\qquad\qquad = 3(n-1)^2 - 3(n-1) + 1$$

$$\vdots \qquad \vdots \qquad\qquad\qquad \vdots \qquad\qquad\qquad \vdots$$

$$1^3 - 0^3 \ = \qquad\qquad\qquad\qquad\qquad = 3 \times 1^2 - 3 \times 1 + 1$$

$$\overline{}\qquad\qquad\overline{}$$

$$n^3 \ = \qquad\qquad\qquad = 3\sum_{r=1}^{n} r^2 - 3\sum_{r=1}^{n} r + n$$

$$3\sum_{r=1}^{n} r^2 \ = n^3 + 3\sum_{r=1}^{n} r - n = n^3 + \frac{3}{2}n(n+1) - n$$

$$= \frac{2n^3 + 3n^2 + 3n - 2n}{2} \qquad \frac{2n^3 + 3n^2 + n}{2}$$

$$\sum_{r=1}^{n} r^2 = \frac{n(2n^2 + 3n + 1)}{6} = \frac{n}{6}(2n^2 + 2n + n + 1) = \frac{n}{6}[2n(n+1) + (n+1)]$$

$$\boxed{\sum_{r=1}^{n} r^2 = \frac{n(n+1)(2n+1)}{6}}$$

To find the summation $\sum_{r=1}^{n} r^3$

$$n^4 - (n - 1)^4 = n^4 - n^4 + 4n^3 - 6n^2 + 4n - 1 = 4n^3 - 6n^2 + 4n - 1$$

$$(n - 1)^4 - (n - 2)^4 = \qquad\qquad\qquad = 4(n - 1)^3 - 6(n - 1)^2 + 4(n - 1) - 1$$

$$\vdots \qquad\qquad\qquad\qquad\qquad\qquad\qquad \vdots$$

$$1^4 - 0^4 = \qquad\qquad\qquad = 4 \times 1^3 - 6 \times 1^2 + 4 \times 1 - 1$$

$$\rule{5cm}{0.4pt} \qquad\qquad \rule{6cm}{0.4pt}$$

$$n^4 = \qquad\qquad\qquad = 4 \sum_{r=1}^{n} r^3 - 6 \sum_{r=1}^{n} r^2 + 4 \sum_{r=1}^{n} r - n$$

but $\sum_{r=1}^{n} r^2 = \dfrac{n(n + 1)(2n + 1)}{6}$ $\qquad$ $\sum_{r=1}^{n} r = \dfrac{n(n + 1)}{2}$

$$4 \sum_{r=1}^{n} r^3 - 6 \sum_{r=1}^{n} r^2 + 4 \sum_{r=1}^{n} r - n = n^4$$

$$4 \sum_{r=1}^{n} r^3 = n^4 + (n^2 + n)(2n + 1) - 2(n^2 + n) + n$$

$$= n^4 + 2n^3 + 2n^2 + n^2 + n - 2n^2 - 2n + n$$

$$= n^4 + 2n^3 + n^2 = n^2(n^2 + 2n + 1)$$

$$\boxed{\sum_{r=1}^{n} r^3 = \dfrac{n^2(n + 1)^2}{4}.}$$

It is observed that $\boxed{\sum_{r=1}^{n} r^3 = \left(\sum_{r=1}^{n} r \right)^2 .}$

WORKED EXAMPLE 91

Determine the values of the following summations:-

(i) $\displaystyle\sum_{r=1}^{25} r(r+1)$ (ii) $\displaystyle\sum_{r=1}^{20} r(r-1)$.

SOLUTION 91

(i) $\displaystyle\sum_{r=1}^{25} r(r+1) = \sum_{r=1}^{25} r^2 + \sum_{r=1}^{25} r = \frac{25 \times 26 \times 51}{6} + \frac{25 \times 26}{2} = 5{,}850$

$\displaystyle\sum_{r=1}^{n} r^2 = \frac{n}{6}(n+1)(2n+1) \qquad \sum_{r=1}^{n} r = \frac{n(n+1)}{2}.$

(ii) $\displaystyle\sum_{r=1}^{20} r(r-1) = \sum_{r=1}^{20} r^2 - \sum_{r=1}^{20} r$

$= \dfrac{20 \times 21 \times 41}{6} - \dfrac{20 \times 21}{2} = 2{,}870 - 210 = 2{,}660.$

WORKED EXAMPLE 92

Prove the following summations:-

(i) $\displaystyle\sum_{r=1}^{n} r(r+1) = \frac{1}{3} n(n+1)(n+2)$.

(ii) $\displaystyle\sum_{r=1}^{n} \frac{1}{(2r-1)(2r+1)} = \frac{n}{2n+1}$

(iii) $\displaystyle\sum_{r=1}^{n} r(r+3) = \frac{n(n+1)(n+5)}{3}$.

SOLUTION 92

(i) $\displaystyle\sum_{r=1}^{n} r(r+1) = \sum_{r=1}^{n} r^2 + \sum_{r=1}^{n} r = \frac{n(n+1)(2n+1)}{6} + \frac{n(n+1)}{2}$

$$= \frac{n\,(n+1)\,(2n+1) + 3n\,(n+1)}{6} = \frac{n\,(n+1)\,[2n+1+3]}{6}$$

$$= \frac{n\,(n+1)\,(2n+4)}{6}$$

$$= \frac{n\,(n+1)\,2\,(n+2)}{6} = \frac{n\,(n+1)\,(n+2)}{3}.$$

(ii) $\displaystyle\sum_{r=1}^{n} \frac{1}{(2r-1)\,((2r+1)}$

$$\frac{1}{(2r-1)\,(2r+1)} \equiv \frac{A}{2r-1} + \frac{B}{2r+1}$$

$1 \equiv A\,(2r+1) + B\,(2r-1)$, if $r = -\dfrac{1}{2}$, $B = -\dfrac{1}{2}$ and if $r = \dfrac{1}{2}$, $A = \dfrac{1}{2}$

$$\frac{1}{(2r-1)\,(2r+1)} \equiv \frac{1}{2\,(2r-1)} - \frac{1}{2\,(2r+1)}$$

$$\sum_{r=1}^{n} \frac{1}{(2r-1)(2r+1)} = \frac{1}{2} \sum_{r=1}^{n} \frac{1}{2r-1} - \frac{1}{2} \sum_{r=1}^{n} \frac{1}{2r+1}$$

$$= \frac{1}{2}\left(\frac{1}{1} + \frac{1}{3} + \frac{1}{5} + \frac{1}{7} + \ldots + \frac{1}{2n-1}\right) - \frac{1}{2}\left(\frac{1}{3} + \frac{1}{5} + \frac{1}{7} + \ldots + \frac{1}{2n+1}\right)$$

let $\dfrac{1}{3} + \dfrac{1}{5} + \dfrac{1}{7} + \ldots + \dfrac{1}{2n-1} = S$, and the term before the $\dfrac{1}{2n+1}$ is

$$\frac{1}{2\,(n-1)+1} = \frac{1}{2n-1}, \text{ therefore}$$

$$\sum_{r=1}^{n} \frac{1}{(2r-1)\,(2r+1)} = \frac{1}{2}\left(\frac{1}{1} + S\right) - \frac{1}{2}\left(S + \frac{1}{2n+1}\right)$$

$$= \frac{1}{2} + \frac{1}{2}S - \frac{1}{2}S - \frac{1}{2\,(2n+1)} = \frac{1}{2} - \frac{1}{2\,(2n+1)}$$

$$= \frac{2n+1-1}{2\,(2n+1)} = \frac{n}{2n+1}.$$

(iii) $\displaystyle\sum_{r=1}^{n} r\,(r+3) = \sum_{r=1}^{n} r^2 + 3\sum_{r=1}^{n} r = \frac{n(n+1)(2n+1)}{6} + \frac{3n(n+1)}{2}$

$$= \frac{n(n+1)(2n+1) + 9n(n+1)}{6} = \frac{n(n+1)[(2n+1)+9]}{6}$$

$$= \frac{n(n+1)(2n+10)}{6}$$

$$= \frac{n(n+1)(n+5)}{3}.$$

A geometric progression $a + ar + ar + a\,r^2 + \ldots$ is convergent if $|r| < 1$, divergent if $|r| \geq 1$.

Proof

(i) If $|r| < 1$ $\quad S_n = a + ar + a\,r^2 + \ldots + a\,r^n = \dfrac{a(1 - r^n)}{1 - r}$

and $\displaystyle\lim_{n \to \infty} r^n \to 0$ for $|r| < 1$, therefore

$$\lim_{x \to 0} S_n \to \frac{a}{1 - r} \text{ and } \sum_{r=1}^{\infty} ar^n \text{ converges.}$$

(ii) If $|r| \geq 1$, $u_n = a\,r^n$ and $u_n \to \infty$ as $n \to \infty$ for $|r| > 1$, and $u_n = \pm a$

if $|r| = 1$ $\displaystyle\lim_{x \to 0} u_n \neq 0$, and thus $\displaystyle\sum_{r=1}^{\infty} ar^n$ cannot converge if $n \to \infty$

therefore $\displaystyle\sum_{r=1}^{\infty} ar^n$ diverges.

Using D'Alembert's ratio test, we have

$$\left| \frac{u_{n+1}}{u_n} \right| = \left| \frac{a\,r^{n+1}}{ar^n} \right| = |r|.$$

If $|r| > 1$ then the series diverges.

The series $\displaystyle\sum_{r=1}^{\infty} \frac{1}{r^k}$ is (i) convergent if $k > 1$ (ii) divergent if $k \leq 1$.

Proof.

(i) $\displaystyle\sum_{r=1}^{\infty}\frac{1}{r^k}=\frac{1}{1^k}+\frac{1}{2^k}+\frac{1}{3^k}+\ldots = \left(\frac{1}{1^k}\right)+\left(\frac{1}{2^k}+\frac{1}{3^k}\right)+\left(\frac{1}{4^k}+\frac{1}{5^k}+\frac{1}{6^k}+\frac{1}{7^k}\right)+\ldots +$

$$\left(\frac{1}{1^k}\right)+\left(\frac{1}{2^k}+\frac{1}{2^k}\right)+\left(\frac{1}{4^k}+\frac{1}{4^k}+\frac{1}{4^k}+\frac{1}{4^k}\right)+\ldots$$

$$=1+\frac{2}{2^k}+\frac{4}{4^k}+\ldots +\frac{2^r}{2^{rk}}$$

$$=1+\frac{1}{2^{k-1}}+\frac{1}{(2^{k-1})^2}+\ldots +\frac{1}{(2^{k-1})^r}=\frac{1-\dfrac{1}{(2^{k-1})^{r+1}}}{1-\dfrac{1}{2^{k-1}}}$$

assuming the G.P. with common ratio $\dfrac{1}{2^{k-1}}$.

$$\frac{1}{2^{k-1}}<\frac{1}{1-\dfrac{1}{2^{k-1}}}\qquad\left(0<\frac{1}{(2^{k-1})^r}<1 \text{ if } k>1\right)$$

(ii) $\displaystyle\sum_{r=1}^{2^r}\frac{1}{r}=\frac{1}{1}+\frac{1}{2}+\frac{1}{3}+\frac{1}{4}+\ldots +\frac{1}{2^r}$

$$=\left(\frac{1}{1}\right)+\left(\frac{1}{2}\right)+\left(\frac{1}{3}+\frac{1}{4}\right)+\left(\frac{1}{5}+\frac{1}{6}+\frac{1}{7}+\frac{1}{8}\right)+\ldots +\left(\frac{1}{2^{r-1}+1}+\ldots +\frac{1}{2^r}\right).$$

The $(r+1)^{\text{th}}$ bracket contains 2^{r-1} terms

$$>1+\frac{1}{2}+\left(\frac{1}{4}+\frac{1}{4}\right)+\left(\frac{1}{8}+\frac{1}{8}+\frac{1}{8}+\frac{1}{8}\right)+\left(\frac{1}{2^r}+\ldots +\frac{1}{2^r}\right)$$

$$=1+\frac{1}{2}+\frac{1}{2}+\frac{1}{2}+\frac{1}{2}+\ldots +\frac{1}{2}=1+\frac{r}{2}\text{ and }1+\frac{r}{2}\to\infty$$

as $r\to\infty$ $\displaystyle\sum_{r=1}^{\infty}\frac{1}{r}$ diverges. For $k<1$, each term of $\displaystyle\sum_{r=1}^{\infty}\frac{1}{r^k}$

is greater than the corresponding term of $\sum\limits_{r=1}^{\infty} \dfrac{1}{r}$ and hence $\sum\limits_{r=1}^{\infty} \dfrac{1}{r^k}$ diverges.

Therefore $\sum\limits_{r=1}^{\infty} \dfrac{1}{r^k}$ converges for $k > 1$ $\sum\limits_{r=1}^{\infty} \dfrac{1}{r^k}$ diverges for $k \leq 1$.

D'Alembert's ratio test

This test is particularly useful for power series.

Let $u_1 + u_2 + u_3 + \ldots + u_n + u_{n+1} + \ldots$ be a power series.

The ratio of any term to the preceding is given as $\dfrac{u_{n+1}}{u_n}$.

There are three cases to consider:-

(a) $\lim\limits_{n \to \infty} \left| \dfrac{u_{n+1}}{u_n} \right| < 1$ the series is convergent.

(b) $\lim\limits_{n \to \infty} \left| \dfrac{u_{n+1}}{u_n} \right| > 1$ the series is divergent.

(c) $\lim\limits_{n \to \infty} \left| \dfrac{u_{n+1}}{u_n} \right| = 1$ the series is inconclusive.

If inconclusive, then if $u_n = 0$ it may be convergent, if $u_n \neq 0$ it is certainly divergent.

Further

$$\dfrac{1}{1^k} + \dfrac{1}{2^k} + \dfrac{1}{3^k} + \ldots + \dfrac{1}{n^k} + \ldots,$$ if $k > 1$ the series coverges,

if $k \geq 1$ the series diverges.

WORKED EXAMPLE 93

Test the following power series for convergence or divergence.

(i) $\quad e = 1 + \dfrac{1}{1!} + \dfrac{1}{2!} + \dfrac{1}{3!} + \dfrac{1}{4!} + \ldots + \dfrac{1}{n!} + \dfrac{1}{(n+1)!} + \ldots \qquad = \displaystyle\sum_{r=0}^{\infty} \dfrac{1}{r!}.$

(ii) $\quad \dfrac{1}{1} + \dfrac{1}{2} + \dfrac{1}{3} + \dfrac{1}{4} + \dfrac{1}{5} + \ldots + \dfrac{1}{n} + \dfrac{1}{n+1} + \ldots \qquad = \displaystyle\sum_{r=0}^{\infty} \dfrac{1}{r}.$

(iii) $\quad 1 + x + x^2 + x^3 + \ldots + x^n + x^{n+1} + \ldots \qquad = \displaystyle\sum_{r=0}^{\infty} x^r.$

(iv) $\quad 1 + \dfrac{x}{1!} + \dfrac{x^2}{2!} + \dfrac{x^3}{3!} + \ldots + \dfrac{x^n}{n!} + \dfrac{x^{n+1}}{(n+1)!} + \ldots \qquad = \displaystyle\sum_{r=0}^{\infty} \dfrac{x^r}{r!} = e^x.$

(v) $\quad x - \dfrac{x^2}{2} + \dfrac{x^3}{3} - \ldots + (-1)^{n+1} \dfrac{x^n}{n} + (-1)^{n+2} \dfrac{x^{n+1}}{n+1} + \ldots \qquad = \displaystyle\sum_{r=0}^{\infty} (-1)^r \dfrac{x^r}{r}$

$$= \ln(1+x).$$

SOLUTION 93

(i) $\quad \dfrac{u_{n+1}}{u_n} = \dfrac{1/(n+1)!}{1/n!} = \dfrac{n!}{(n+1)!} = \dfrac{1}{n+1}$

if $n \to \infty$, then $\dfrac{1}{n+1} \to 0$ and the series is convergent, we know that

$$\sum_{r=0}^{\infty} \dfrac{1}{r!} = e = 2.71828 \ldots$$

(ii) $\quad \dfrac{u_{n+1}}{u_n} = \dfrac{1/(n+1)}{1/n} = \dfrac{n}{n+1} = \dfrac{n}{n(1+1/n)} = \dfrac{1}{1+1/n} \quad$ as $n \to \infty$,

then $\dfrac{n}{n+1} \to 1$ since $\dfrac{1}{n} \to 0.$

This of course is inconclusive since the ratio is neither less than unity nor more than unity. Further tests are necessary.

$u_n = \dfrac{1}{n} \to 0$ as $n \to \infty$, it may be convergent but the series is of the form

$$\dfrac{1}{1^k} + \dfrac{1}{2^k} + \dfrac{1}{3^k} + \ldots \quad \text{where } k = 1 \text{ and it is divergent.}$$

(iii) $\left| \dfrac{u_{n+1}}{u_n} \right| = \left| \dfrac{x^{n+1}}{x^n} \right| = |x|$ if $|x| < 1$, the series is convergent and if $|x| \geq 1$,

the series is divergent.

(iv) $\left| \dfrac{u_{n+1}}{u_n} \right| = \left| \dfrac{x^{n+1}}{(n+1)!} \dfrac{n!}{x^n} \right| = \left| \dfrac{x}{n+1} \right|$ which tends to zero as $n \to \infty$ for any finite value of x.

Therefore, the exponential series, e^x is always convergent, provided x is finite.

(v) The series is equal to $\ln(1 + x)$ and converges if $-1 < x \leq 1$.

WORKED EXAMPLE 94

Test whether the series $\displaystyle\sum_{n=1}^{\infty} \dfrac{n+1}{2n^2+1}$ is convergent or divergent.

SOLUTION 94

$$\left| \dfrac{u_{n+1}}{u_n} \right| = \left| \dfrac{(n+2)}{2(n+1)^2+1} \dfrac{2n^2+1}{(n+1)} \right| = \dfrac{n(1+2/n)\,n^2(2+1/n^2)}{n(1+1/n)\,2n^2\left(1 + \dfrac{2}{n} + \dfrac{1}{n^2} + \dfrac{1}{2n^2}\right)}$$

$$= \dfrac{(1+2/n)(2+1/n^2)}{(1+1/n)\,2\left(1 + \dfrac{2}{n} + \dfrac{1}{n^2} + \dfrac{1}{2\,n^2}\right)} \quad \text{as } n \to \infty \quad \left| \dfrac{u_{n+1}}{u_n} \right| = \dfrac{1 \times 2}{1 \times 2} = 1$$

$$\lim_{x \to \infty} \left| \dfrac{u_{n+1}}{u_n} \right| = 1.$$

Consider the u_n term $u_n = \dfrac{n+1}{2\,n^2+1} = \dfrac{n(1+1/n)}{n^2(2+1/n^2)} = \dfrac{1}{n}\dfrac{(1+1/n)}{(2+1/n^2)}$

as $n \to \infty$ $u_n \to 0$ and therefore the series may be convergent.

$$\sum_{n=1}^{\infty} \dfrac{n+1}{2\,n^2+1} = \dfrac{2}{2 \times 1^2+1} + \dfrac{3}{2 \times 2^2+1} + \dfrac{4}{2 \times 2^3+1} + \dots$$

and since this series is of the form $\dfrac{1}{1^k} + \dfrac{1}{2^k} + \dfrac{1}{3^k} + \dots$ where $k > 1$ the series converges.

EXERCISES 13

1. Express in Σ notation the following series.

   (i) $\sin x + \sin 2x + \sin 3x + \ldots + \sin nx$

   (ii) $\cos x + \cos 2x + \cos 3x + \ldots + \cos nx$

   (iii) $\operatorname{cosec} x + \operatorname{cosec} 3x + \operatorname{cosec} 5x + \ldots + \operatorname{cosec} (2n - 1)x$

   (iv) $1 + 2 + 3 + \ldots + n$

   (v) $1^2 + 2^2 + 3^2 + \ldots + n^2$

   (vi) $1.2.3 + 2.3.4 + 3.4.5 + \ldots + n(n + 1)(n + 2)$

   (vii) $2^1 + 2^2 + 2^3 + \ldots + 2^n$

   (viii) $\dfrac{1}{1.2} + \dfrac{1}{2.3} + \dfrac{1}{3.4} + \ldots + \dfrac{1}{n(n + 1)}$

   (ix) $1^3 + 2^3 + 3^3 + \ldots + n^3$

   (x) $2.3.4 + 3.4.5 + 4.5.6 + \ldots + (n +)(n + 2)(n + 3)$.

2. State the functions of the series.

   (i) $\displaystyle\sum_{r=0}^{\infty} \frac{x^r}{r!}$
   (ii) $\displaystyle\sum_{r=0}^{\infty} \frac{(-1)^r x^{2r+1}}{(2r + 1)!}$
   (iii) $\displaystyle\sum_{r=1}^{\infty} (-1)^r \frac{x^{2r}}{(2r)!}$

   (iv) $\displaystyle\sum_{r=1}^{\infty} (-1)^{r+1} \frac{x^r}{r}$
   (v) $\displaystyle\sum_{r=0}^{\infty} \frac{x^{2r}}{(2r)!}$
   (vi) $\displaystyle\sum_{r=0}^{\infty} \frac{x^{2r+1}}{(2r + 1)!}$.

3. Determine the summations:-

   (i) $\displaystyle\sum_{r=1}^{n} r$
   (ii) $\displaystyle\sum_{r=1}^{n} r^2$
   (iii) $\displaystyle\sum_{r=1}^{n} r^3$
   (iv) $\displaystyle\sum_{r=1}^{n} r^4$.

4. Evaluate the following:-

   (i) $\displaystyle\sum_{r=5}^{25} r$
   (ii) $\displaystyle\sum_{r=10}^{50} r^2$
   (iii) $\displaystyle\sum_{r=1}^{10} r^3$
   (iv) $\displaystyle\sum_{r=1}^{15} r^4$.

5. Determine the summations:-

   (i) $\displaystyle\sum_{r=5}^{n} r(r + 1)(r + 2)$
   (ii) $\displaystyle\sum_{r=1}^{n} \frac{1}{r(r + 1)(r + 2)}$

   (iii) $\displaystyle\sum_{r=1}^{n} \frac{1}{(r + 2)(r + 4)}$.

6. Test for convergence and divergence for the following:-

(i) $\sum_{r=1}^{\infty} \log\left(\dfrac{r}{r+1}\right)$ (ii) $\sum_{r=1}^{\infty} \dfrac{2r+1}{3r-1}$ (iii) $\sum_{r=1}^{\infty} \dfrac{1}{r(r+1)}$

Test each of the following series to decide whether or not it converges:-

7. $\sum_{n=1}^{\infty} \left(\dfrac{1}{n-1} - \dfrac{1}{2n^2} - \dfrac{1}{n+1}\right)$ 8. $\sum_{n=1}^{\infty} \dfrac{1}{n(n^2+1)}$

9. $\sum_{n=1}^{\infty} \dfrac{1}{n(n+1)}$ 10. $\sum_{n=1}^{\infty} \dfrac{1}{n}\left(\dfrac{1}{3}\right)^n$

11. $\sum_{n=1}^{\infty} \dfrac{\sin n\,\Theta}{3^n}$ 12. $\sum_{n=1}^{\infty} \dfrac{1}{(2n+1)(2n-1)}$

13. $\sum_{n=0}^{\infty} \dfrac{n^{1/2}}{n+1}$

14. If $\ln(1+x) = \sum_{r=0}^{\infty} (-1)^r \dfrac{x^r}{r}$ and $\ln(1-x) = -\sum_{r=1}^{\infty} \dfrac{x^r}{r}$.

Show that $\dfrac{\ln(1+x)}{(1-x)} = 2\sum_{r=0}^{\infty} \left(\dfrac{m-n}{m+n}\right)^{2r+1} \dfrac{1}{2r+1}$

where $1+x = m$ and $1-x = n$.

15. Investigate the convergence of (i) $\sum_{r=1}^{\infty} \dfrac{2r-3}{r^2-5r+2}$ (diverges)

(ii) $\sum_{r=1}^{\infty} \dfrac{4\sqrt{r}}{r^2+3r-7}$ (converges)

(iii) $\sum_{r=1}^{\infty} \dfrac{3r^2-5r+4}{2r\sqrt{r}-3}$. (diverges)

14. NON LINEAR TO LINEAR LAWS.

$$y = ax^2 + b$$

This equation is a non-linear one, since we have a term which is squared, x^2.

To make this a linear one, we have to plot y against x^2, thus comparing it with the gradient/intercept form of a straight line, $y = mx + c$.

$$y = \frac{a}{x} + b$$

This equation is also a non-linear one, since we have a term which is reciprocal of x.

To make this a linear one, we have to plot y against $\frac{1}{x}$, thus comparing it with the gradient/intercept form of a straight line, $y = mx + c$.

$$yx = bx + c$$

This non-linear equation can be transformed into a linear equation, if we plot yx

against x, or $yx = bx + c$, $y = b + \frac{c}{x}$; if we plot y against $\frac{1}{x}$.

$$y^2 = ax^2 + b$$

To transform this to a linear graph, y^2 is plotted against x^2.

$$y = ax^{2/3} + b$$

Similarly, if we plot y against $x^{2/3}$ the graph become a linear one.

How do we transform the following to a linear relationship?

$$y = ab^x$$

$$y = ax^n$$

$$T = T_o e^{\mu \theta}$$

Taking logarithms on both sides to the convenient base, we have:-

$\log y = x \log b$ + $\log a$ comparing with $y = mx + c$ we have $\log y$ to be plotted against, x $\log b$ is the gradient and $\log a$ is the intercept on the y-axis.

$\log y = n \log x$ + $\log a$ comparing with $y = mx + c$ we have $\log y$ to be plotted against $\log x$, n is the gradient and $\log a$ is the intercept on the y-axis.

$\log_e T = \mu\Theta + \ln T_o$ comparing with $y = mx + c$ we have $\log_e T$ to be plotted against Θ, μ is the gradient and $\ln T_o$ is the intercept on the y-axis.

Let us now consider some examples:-

WORKED EXAMPLE 95

To table below shows the values of the variables x and y which are believed to be related by the equation $y = A x^2 + B$ where A and B are constants.

x	1.73	2.00	2.24	2.50	2.65	2.83
y	100	90	80	70	60	50

Show graphically that, for these values, the equations is approximately satisfied. Use the graph to estimate:-

(i) the values A and B,   (b) the value of y when $x = 2.35$.

SOLUTION 95

$y = Ax^2 + B$

x	1.73	2.00	2.24	2.50	2.65	2.83
x^2	2.99	4.00	5.02	6.25	7.02	8.01
y	100	90	80	70	60	50

In order to obtain a linear graph the values of x are squared as shown in the table above and the graph of y against x^2 is plotted.

Equation (1) is compared with the linear graph $y = mx + c$ where $m = A$ = gradient and $c = B$ = intercept. Appropriate scales are chosen, on the x-axis 1 cm = 1, on the y-axis 1 cm = 10. To find the intercept on the y-axis when $x = 0$, $y = B = 130$.

To find the gradient from the graph $m = \dfrac{130 - 20}{0 - 11.2} = -\dfrac{110}{11.2}$.

The equation (1) may be written $y = -9.82\,x^2 + 130$.

(a) $A = -9.82$ and $B = 130$ (b) when $x = 2.35$, $x^2 = 5.52$, then $y = 75.1$

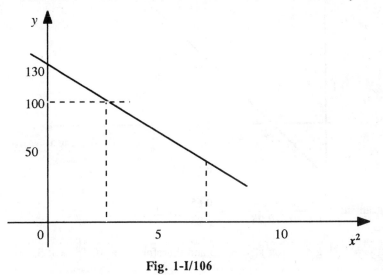

Fig. 1-I/106

WORKED EXAMPLE 96

The following table of values is thought to be connected by a law of the type $y = ax^n$

x	5623	3162	1000	316	173	100	31.6	10	3.16
y	2.82	2.51	2.00	1.59	1.41	1.26	1.00	0.794	0.631

By plotting a graph of $\log y$ (vertical) against $\log x$ (horizontal), determine the value of the constants a and n to three significant figures.

SOLUTION 96

Taking logarithms to the base ten on both sides of the equation, we have:-

$\log y = n \log x + \log a$. A new table of $\log y$ and $\log x$ is formed.

$\log x$	3.75	3.50	3.00	2.50	2.24	2.00	1.50	1.00	0.5
$\log y$	0.45	0.40	0.30	0.20	0.15	0.10	0	-0.10	-0.20

The graph of $\log y$ against $\log x$ is plotted which is a straight line.

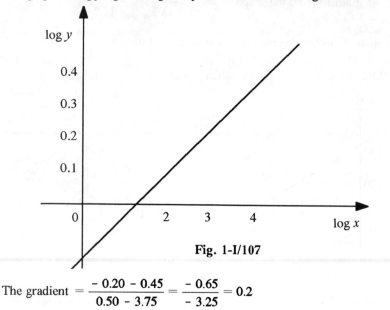

Fig. 1-I/107

The gradient $= \dfrac{-0.20 - 0.45}{0.50 - 3.75} = \dfrac{-0.65}{-3.25} = 0.2$

If $\log x = 0$, $\log a = \log y = -0.3$ and therefore $a = 10^{-0.3} = 0.5$.

The law is $y = 0.5\, x^{0.2}$, where $a = 0.5$ and $n = 0.2$.

WORKED EXAMPLE 97

The following equations are non-linear:-

(i) $y = ax^n$ (ii) $xy = a + bx$ (iii) $y = ax^{2/3} + b$.

State in each case which quantities should be plotted along the y-axis and which quantities along the x-axis in order to obtain straight line graphs.

SOLUTION 97

(i) $y = ax^n$, $\log y = n \log x + \log a$, $\log y$ against $\log x$ is plotted.

(ii) $xy = a + bx$, $y = \dfrac{a}{x} + b$, y against $\dfrac{1}{x}$ is plotted.

(iii) $y = ax^{3/2} + b$, y against $x^{3/2}$ is plotted.

EXERCISES 14

1. The following equations are non-linear:-

    (i) $y = ab^x$ (ii) $T = T_o e^{\mu\theta}$ (iii) $y = \dfrac{A}{x^n}$.

    State in each case which quantities should be plotted along the y-axis and which quantities along the x-axis in order to obtain straight line graphs.

2. The following table of values is thought to be connected by a law of the type.

    $y = ab^x$.

x	1.50	2.50	3.15	4.00	4.75
y	1.00	3.09	6.31	16.6	39.8

    By plotting a graph of $\log y$ (vertical), against x (horizontal), determine the value of the constant a and b to two signification figures.

3. T and θ are believed to be related by a law of the form:

$$T = T_o e^{\mu\theta}.$$

    The following pairs of values have been obtained:-

θ (radians)	5	10	15	20	25
T (kilograms)	66.7	181.3	492.7	1274.1	3641.0.

    Take 2 cm: 5 unit (for θ, with θ-axis parallel to the short edge of the paper).

    For the $ln\ T$ axis, parallel to the long edge of the paper, take 1 cm: 0.5 unit.

4. The following values of current and voltage were observed in a circuit.

I (amperes)	1	2	3	4	5
V (volts)	5	40	135	320	625

    The values are connected by a law of the form $V = KI^n$.

    Draw a graph of $\log V$ against $\log I$ and hence derive values of K and n.

    State the law connecting I and V.

1. ALGEBRA

SOLUTIONS 1

1. (i)

$$\begin{array}{r} -x^3 - x - 4 \\ x + 3 \enclose{longdiv}{-x^4 - 3x^3 - x^2 - 7x - 2} \\ -x^4 - 3x^3 \\ \hline -x^2 - 7x - 2 \\ -x^2 - 3x \\ \hline -4x - 2 \\ -4x - 12 \\ \hline \end{array}$$

10 The remainder

(ii)

$$\begin{array}{r} x^2 + 3x + 7 \\ x - 2 \enclose{longdiv}{x^3 + x^2 + x + 1} \\ x^3 - 2x^2 \\ \hline 3x^2 + x + 1 \\ 3x^2 - 6x \\ \hline 7x + 1 \\ 7x - 14 \\ \hline \end{array}$$

15 The remainder

(iii)

$$\begin{array}{r} -x^2 - x - 3 \\ x - 2 \enclose{longdiv}{-x^3 + x^2 - x + 1} \\ -x^3 + 2x^2 \\ \hline -x^2 - x + 1 \\ -x^2 + 2x \\ \hline -3x + 1 \\ -3x + 6 \\ \hline \end{array}$$

-5 The remainder

2. (i) $f(x) = -x^4 - 3x^3 - x^2 - 7x - 2$

$f(-3) = -(-3)^4 - 3(-3)^3 - (-3)^2 - 7(-3) - 2$

$= -81 + 81 - 9 + 21 - 2 = 10$

(ii) $f(x) = x^3 + x^2 + x + 1$

$f(2) = 8 + 4 + 2 + 1 = 15$

(iii) $f(x) = -x^3 + x^2 - x + 1$

$f(2) = -(2)^3 + (2)^2 - (2) + 1 = -8 + 4 - 2 + 1 = -5.$

3. (i) $x^3 + 2x^2 - 5x - 6 = 0$

$f(x) = x^3 + 2x^2 - 5x - 6 = 0$

$f(1) = 1 + 2 - 5 - 6 = -8$ $x - 1$ is not a factor

$f(2) = 8 + 8 - 10 - 6 = 0$ $x - 2$ is a factor

$f(3) = 27 + 18 - 15 - 6 = 24$ $x - 3$ is not a factor

$f(-2) = -8 + 8 + 10 - 6 = 4$ $x + 2$ is not a factor

$$
\begin{array}{r}
x^2 + 4x + 3 \\ \hline
x - 2 \enspace\big)\, x^3 + 2x^2 - 5x - 6 \\
x^3 - 2x^2 \\ \hline
4x^2 - 5x - 6 \\
4x^2 - 8x \\ \hline
3x - 6 \\
3x - 6 \\ \hline
0
\end{array}
$$

$f(x) = x^3 + 2x^2 - 5x - 6 = (x - 2)(x^2 + 4x + 3) = 0$

$$\boxed{x = 2}$$

or $x^2 + 4x + 3 = x^2 + 3x + x + 3 = x(x + 3) + x + 3$
$$= (x + 1)(x + 3) = 0$$

$$\boxed{x = -1} \text{ and } \boxed{x = -3}$$

(ii) $x^3 - 3x^2 - 4x + 12 = 0$

$f(x) = x^3 - 3x^2 - 4x + 12$

$f(1) = 1 - 3 - 4 + 12 = 6$ $x - 1$ is not a factor

$f(-1) = -1 - 3 + 4 + 12 = 12$ $x + 1$ is not a factor

$f(2) = 8 - 12 - 8 + 12 = 0$ $x - 2$ is a factor

$f(-2) = -8 - 12 + 8 + 12 = 0$ $x + 2$ is a factor

$f(3) = 27 - 27 - 12 + 12 = 0$ $x - 3$ is a factor

$f(x) = (x - 2)(x + 2)(x - 3) = 0$

$$\boxed{x = 2} \text{ or } \boxed{x = -2} \text{ or } \boxed{x = 3}$$

(iii) $x^4 - a^4 = 0$ $f(x) = x^4 - a^4$

$f(a) = a^4 - a^4 = 0,$ $x - a$ is a factor

$f(-a) = (-a)^4 - a^4 = 0,$ $\qquad\qquad$ $x + a$ is a factor

therefore $(x - a)(x + a)$ is a factor $f(x)$

$$
\begin{array}{r}
x^2 + a^2 \\[2pt]
x^2 - a^2 \overline{\big)\ x^4 - a^4} \\[2pt]
x^4 - a^2 x^2 \\ \hline
a^2 x^2 - a^4 \\
a^2 x^2 - a^4 \\ \hline
0
\end{array}
$$

therefore $f(x) = x^4 - a^4 = (x^2 + a^2)(x^2 - a^2) = (x^2 + a^2)(x - a)(x + a)$

(iv) $x^3 - 3x^2 + x + 2 = 0$

$f(x) \quad = x^3 - 3x^2 + x + 2$

$f(1) \quad = 1 - 3 + 1 + 2 = 1$ $\qquad$ $x - 1$ is not a factor

$f(2) \quad = 8 - 12 + 2 + 2 = 0$ $\qquad$ $x - 2$ is a factor

$f(-2) = -8 - 12 - 2 + 2 = -20$ $\qquad$ $x + 2$ is not a factor

$$
\begin{array}{r}
x^2 - x - 1 \\[2pt]
x - 2 \overline{\big)\ x^3 - 3x^2 + x + 2} \\[2pt]
x^3 - 2x^2 \\ \hline
-x^2 + x + 2 \\
-x^2 + 2x \\ \hline
-x + 2 \\
-x + 2 \\ \hline
0
\end{array}
$$

(v) $f(x) = 6x^3 + x^2 - x = 0,$ $x(6x^2 + x - 1) = 0,$ $x = 0$ or $6x^2 + x - 1 = 0$

$$x = \frac{-1 \pm \sqrt{1 + 24}}{12} = \frac{-1 \pm 5}{12} \Rightarrow x = -\frac{1}{2} \text{ or } \frac{-1 + 5}{12} = \frac{1}{3}$$

$2x + 1 = 0$ $\qquad$ $3x - 1 = 0$ $\qquad$ $f(x) = x(2x + 1)(3x - 1)$

$x = 0, \ x = -\dfrac{1}{2}, \ x = \dfrac{1}{3}.$

4. $\quad f(x) = x^{25} + x^{35}, \quad f(1) = 1 + 1 = 2$

5. $\quad f(x) = x^7 - x^5, \quad f(-1) = (-1)^7 - (-1)^5 = -1 - (-1) = -1 + 1 = 0$

6. $\quad f(x) = x^3 + x^2 + ax + 7 \qquad f(3) = 27 + 9 + 3a + 7 = 0$

$3a = -43$ $\qquad\qquad$ $\boxed{a = -\dfrac{43}{3}}$

7. $f(x) = -5x^3 + ax^2 + 7x - b$ $\quad f(2) = -5(8) + a(4) + 7(2) - b = 0$ or

$4a - b = 26$ $\qquad\qquad\qquad f(1) = -5 + a + 7 - b = 0$ or $a - b = -2$

$$4a - b = 26$$
$$\underline{a - b = -2}$$
$$3a = 28$$

$$a = \frac{28}{3}$$

$$b = a + 2 = \frac{28}{3} + 2 = \frac{28 + 6}{3} = \frac{34}{3}$$

$$\boxed{a = \frac{28}{3}} \text{ and } \boxed{b = \frac{34}{3}}$$

8. $f(x) \equiv ax^2 + bx + c$

$f(0) = c = 1, \qquad c = 1$

$f(1) = a + b + 1 = 2$ or $a + b = 1$

$f(-2) = 4a - 2b + 1 = -9$ or $4a - 2b = -10$

$a + b = 1$ $\qquad \boxed{a = -\dfrac{4}{3}}$ $b = 1 - a = 1 + \dfrac{4}{3} = \dfrac{7}{3}$

$$4a - 2b = -10 \qquad \boxed{b = \frac{7}{3}}$$
$$\underline{2a + 2b = 2}$$
$$6a = -8 \qquad\quad \boxed{c = 1}$$

9. $f(x) = ax^2 + bx + c$ $\qquad\qquad f(1) = a + b + c = 0$ $\quad a = 4, c = 1$

$4 + b + 1 = 0 \qquad b = -5 \qquad f(x) = 4x^2 - 5x + 1$

$$
\begin{array}{r}
4x - 1 \\
x - 1 \,\big|\, \overline{4x^2 - 5x + 1} \\
\underline{4x^2 - 4x} \\
-x + 1 \\
\underline{-x + 1} \\
0
\end{array}
$$

$f(x) = (x - 1)(4x - 1) = 0$ the other factor is $4x - 1$.

10. $f(x) = x^3 - 2x^2 + x + c$ $f(2) = 8 - 8 + 2 + c = 0$ or $c = -2$

$$
\begin{array}{r}
x^2 + 1 \\
x - 2 \ \overline{\big|\ x^3 - 2x^2 + x - 2} \\
\underline{x^3 - 2x^2} \\
x - 2 \\
\underline{x - 2} \\
0
\end{array}
$$

$f(x) = (x - 2)(x^2 + 1) = 0$, $x^2 + 1 = 0, x = \pm\, i$ the other roots are complex $x = i$, and $x = -i$.

11. $f(x)\quad = x^3 + ax^2 + bx - 5$

$f(1)\quad = 3 = 1 + a + b - 5 \Rightarrow a + b = 7$

$f(-1) = 4 = -1 + a - b - 5 \Rightarrow a - b = 10$

$2a = 17, a = \dfrac{17}{2}$ and $b = 7 - \dfrac{17}{2} = -\dfrac{3}{2}$.

12. $f(x)\quad = x^3 + ax^2 + bx - 5$

$f(-2) = -8 + 4a - 2b - 5 = 0 \ \Rightarrow 4a - 2b = 13$

$f(1)\quad = 1 + a + b - 5 = 50 \qquad \Rightarrow a + b = 54$

$$
\begin{array}{r}
4a - 2b = \ \ 13 \\
\underline{4a + 4b = 216} \\
6b = 203
\end{array}
$$

$$b = \frac{203}{6}$$

$$a = 54 - b = 54 - \frac{203}{6} = \frac{324 - 203}{6} = \frac{121}{6}$$

$a = \dfrac{121}{6}$ and $b = \dfrac{203}{6}$.

13. $f(x)\quad = ax^2 + bx + c$ $f(-1) = a - b + c = -1$

$f(1)\quad = a + b + c = 4$ $f(-2) = 4a - 2b + c = 9$

$2b = 5 \Rightarrow b = \dfrac{5}{2}$

$3a - 3b = 5 \Rightarrow 3a - \dfrac{15}{2} = 5 \Rightarrow 3a = \dfrac{10 + 15}{2} \Rightarrow a = \dfrac{25}{6}$

$$a + b + c = 4$$

$$\frac{25}{6} + \frac{5}{2} + c = 4 \Rightarrow c = 4 - \frac{25}{6} - \frac{15}{6} = 4 - \frac{40}{6}$$

$$c = -\frac{16}{6} = -\frac{8}{3} \qquad a = \frac{25}{6} \qquad b = \frac{5}{2} \qquad c = -\frac{8}{3}.$$

14. $f(x) = ax^2 + bx + c$ $\qquad\qquad$ $f(1) = a + b + c = 0$

$f(-1) = a - b + c = 5$ $\qquad\qquad$ $f(2) = 4a + 2b + c = -7$

$2b = -5 \Rightarrow b = -\dfrac{5}{2}$ $\qquad\qquad$ $3a + 3b = -12$

$a + b = -4$ $\qquad\qquad\qquad\qquad$ $a = -4 - b = -4 + \dfrac{5}{2} = -\dfrac{3}{2}$

$c = -a - b = \dfrac{3}{2} + \dfrac{5}{2} = 4$ $\qquad$ $a = -\dfrac{3}{2} \qquad b = -\dfrac{5}{2} \qquad c = 4$

$f(x) = -\dfrac{3}{2}x^2 - \dfrac{5}{2}x + 4$ $\qquad$ $P(x) = \left(-\dfrac{3}{2}x^2 - \dfrac{5}{2}x + 4\right)(dx + 1)^2$

$\dfrac{P(x)}{(x + 2)^2} = Q(x) + \dfrac{25x + 197}{(x + 2)^2}$ $\qquad$ $P(x) = Q(x)(x + 2)^2 + 25x + 197$

If $x = -2$, $P(-2) = 147 = \left(-\dfrac{3}{2}(4) + 5 + 4\right)(-2d + 1)^2$

$147 = (-6 + 5 + 4)(-2d + 1)^2$

$49 = (-2d + 1)^2 \Rightarrow (-2d + 1) = \pm 7$ or $-2d + 1 = -7 \Rightarrow \boxed{d = 4}$

$-2d + 1 = 7 \Rightarrow -2d = 6 \Rightarrow \boxed{d = -3}$

15. $f(x) = x^4 + ax^3 + bx^2 + cx + 1$

$$\frac{f(x)}{x^2 + 3x - 4} = Q(x) + \frac{-30x + 20}{x^2 + 3x - 4}$$

$x^2 + 3x - 4 = x^2 + 4x - x - 4 = x(x + 4) - (x + 4) = (x - 1)(x + 4)$

$f(x) = Q(x)(x - 1)(x + 4) + (-30x + 20), \qquad f(1) = -10, \qquad f(-4) = 140$

$$\frac{f(x)}{x^2 - 6x + 5} = F(x) + \frac{20x - 30}{x^2 - 6x + 5}$$

$x^2 - 6x + 5 = x^2 - 5x - x + 5 = x\,(x - 5) - (x - 5) = (x - 5)\,(x - 1)$

$f(x) \quad = F(x)\,(x - 5)\,(x - 1) + 20x - 30, \qquad f(1) = -10, \qquad f(5) = 70$

$f(1) \quad = 1 + a + b + c + 1 = -10$

$f(-4) = 256 - 64a + 16b - 4c + 1 = 140$

$f(5) \quad = 625 + 125a + 25b + 5c + 1 = 70$

$a + b + c = -12$ $\qquad\qquad a + b + c = -12 \ldots$ (i)

$-64a + 16b - 4c = 140 - 257 = -117$ $\quad -64a + 16b - 4c = -117 \ldots$ (ii)

$125a + 25b + 5c = 70 - 1 - 625$ $\qquad 125a + 25b + 5c = -556 \ldots$ (iii)

(ii) + 4(i) $\quad -64a + 16b - 4c\ = -117$
$\qquad\qquad\qquad\quad 4a + 4b + 4c\ = -48$

$\qquad\qquad\qquad \overline{\quad -60a + 20b\ = -165 \quad \ldots \text{(iv)}}$

(iii) $-$ 5(i) $\quad 125a + 25b + 5c\ = -556$
$\qquad\qquad\qquad\quad 5a + 5b + 5c\ = -60$

$\qquad\qquad\qquad \overline{\quad 120a + 20b\ = -496}$
$\qquad\qquad\qquad\quad\ 30a + \ 5b\ = -214 \quad \ldots \text{(v)}$

(iv) + 2(v) $\quad -60a + 20b = -165$
$\qquad\qquad\qquad\ 60a + 10b = -248$

$\qquad\qquad\qquad \overline{\quad 30b\ = -413}$

$$b = \frac{413}{30}$$

$$30a = -124 - 5\left(-\frac{413}{30}\right) = -124 + \frac{413}{6}$$

$$a = -\frac{331}{180}.$$

$$c = -12 - a - b = -12 + \frac{331}{180} + \frac{413}{30}$$

$$= -12 + \frac{2809}{180} = \frac{649}{180}.$$

16. $F(3) = 1$, $F(-1) = -15$ $\dfrac{F(x)}{(x-3)(x+1)} = Q(x) + \dfrac{ax+b}{(x-3)(x+1)}$

$F(3) = 3a + b = 1$, $F(-1) = -a + b = -15$

$$\begin{array}{r} 3a + b = 1 \\ \hline 4a = 16 \\ a = 4 \\ b = -15 + 4 = -11 \end{array}$$

17. $\dfrac{P(x)}{x^2 + 4x + 4} = Q(x) + \dfrac{2x+3}{x^2 + 4x + 4}$ $P(x) = Q(x)(x+2)^2 + (2x+3)$ ... (1)

$P(-2) = -4 + 3 = -1$

$P(-2) = -8 + 4a - 2b + c = -1 \ \Rightarrow \ \boxed{4a - 2b + c = 7}$ ... (i)

$P(-1) = 0 = -1 + a - b + c = 0 \ \Rightarrow \ \boxed{a - b + c = 1}$ ... (ii)

differentiating (1) w.r.t. x

$P'(x) = Q'(x)(x+2)^2 + Q(x)\, 2(x+2) + 2$

$3x^2 + 2ax + b = Q'(x)(x+2)^2 + Q(x)(2x+4) + 2$ $x = -2$

$12 - 4a + b = 2$, $b - 4a = -10$ ... (iii)

(i) − (ii) $\underline{3a - b = 6}$ ... (iv)

(iii) + (iv) $-a = -4$ $\boxed{a = 4}$

$b = -10 + 4a = -10 + 16$ $\boxed{b = 6}$

$c = 7 + 2b - 4a = 7 + 12 - 16 = 3$ $\boxed{c = 3}$

18. See proofs in the text.

19. $F(x) = x^3 + ax^2 + bx + c$

$F(1) = 27 = 1 + a + b + c$ $\Rightarrow \quad a + b + c = 26$ ... (i)

$F(-2) = -30 = -8 + 4a - 2b + c$ $\Rightarrow \quad 4a - 2b + c = -22$ ... (ii)

$F(2) = -30 = 8 + 4a + 2b + c$ $\Rightarrow \quad 4a + 2b + c = -38$ ... (iii)

(ii) – (iii) $4a + 2b + c = -38$
$4a - 2b + c = -22$

$4b = -16$ $\boxed{b = -4}$

(ii) – (i) $4a - 2b + c = -22$
$a + b + c = 26$

$3a - 3b = -48$

$a - b = -16$

$a + 4 = -16$ $\boxed{a = -20}$

$a + b + c = 26 \Rightarrow -20 - 4 + c = 26 \Rightarrow c = 26 + 24$ $\boxed{c = 50}$

20. $f(x) = x^3 + ax^2 + bx + c$

$f(-4) = 5 = -64 + 16a - 4b + c \quad \Rightarrow \quad 16a - 4b + c = 69 \quad \ldots \text{(i)}$

$f(3) = 0 = 27 + 9a + 3b + c \quad \Rightarrow \quad 9a + 3b + c = -27 \ldots \text{(ii)}$

$f(-3) = 0 = -27 + 9a - 3b + c \quad \Rightarrow \quad 9a - 3b + c = 27 \quad \ldots \text{(iii)}$

$7a - 7b = 96$ from (i) – (ii)

$6b = -54$ from (ii) – (iii)

$$\boxed{b = -9}$$

$7a = 96 + 7b = 96 - 63 = 33$

$$\boxed{a = \dfrac{33}{7}}$$

$9a + 3b + c = -27 \Rightarrow c = -27 - 9a - 3b = -27 - 9\left(\dfrac{33}{7}\right) + 27$

$$= -\dfrac{297}{7} + 27 = -\dfrac{297}{7}.$$

$$\boxed{c = -\dfrac{297}{7}}$$

SOLUTIONS 2

1. $-\dfrac{1}{3-x} + \dfrac{5}{3+x} = \dfrac{5(3-x)-(3+x)}{(3-x)(3+x)} = \dfrac{15-5x-3-x}{9-x^2}$

$$= \dfrac{12-6x}{9-x^2} = \dfrac{6(2-x)}{9-x^2}.$$

2. $\dfrac{1}{1} - \dfrac{1}{5} = \dfrac{5-1}{5} = \dfrac{4}{5}.$

3. $\dfrac{3}{x+3} + \dfrac{5}{x-4} = \dfrac{3(x-4)+5(x+3)}{(x+3)(x-4)} = \dfrac{8x+3}{(x+3)(x-4)}.$

4. $\dfrac{2}{x} - \dfrac{3}{x+3} = \dfrac{2(x+3)-3x}{x(x+3)} = \dfrac{2x+6-3x}{x(x+3)} = \dfrac{6-x}{x(x+3)}.$

5. $\dfrac{1}{x^2} - \dfrac{1}{x+2} = \dfrac{x+2-x^2}{x^2(x+2)} = \dfrac{2+x-x^2}{x^2(x+2)}.$

6. $\dfrac{1}{x} + \dfrac{2}{x+1} + \dfrac{3}{x+3} = \dfrac{(x+1)(x+3)+2x(x+3)+3x(x+1)}{x(x+1)(x+3)}.$

$$= \dfrac{x^2+4x+3+2x^2+6x+3x^2+3x}{x(x+1)(x+3)}$$

$$= \dfrac{6x^2+13x+3}{x(x+1)(x+3)}$$

7. $\dfrac{1}{2} - \dfrac{1}{3} + \dfrac{1}{5} = \dfrac{15-10+6}{30} = \dfrac{11}{30}.$

8. $\dfrac{x+1}{x-3} + \dfrac{1}{x+2} - \dfrac{3}{x-5}$

$$= \dfrac{(x+1)(x+2)(x-5)+(x-3)(x-5)-3(x-3)(x+2)}{(x-3)(x+2)(x-5)}$$

$$= \frac{(x + 1)(x^2 - 3x - 10) + x^2 - 8x + 15 - 3x^2 + 3x + 18}{(x + 2)(x - 3)(x - 5)}$$

$$= \frac{x^3 - 3x^2 - 10x + x^2 - 3x - 10 - 2x^2 - 5x + 33}{(x + 2)(x - 3)(x - 5)}$$

$$= \frac{x^3 - 4x^2 - 18x + 23}{(x + 2)(x - 3)(x - 5)}$$

9. $1 - \dfrac{1}{x + 1} = \dfrac{x + 1 - 1}{x + 1} = \dfrac{x}{x + 1}.$

10. $1 + \dfrac{x}{x + 2} = \dfrac{x + 2 + x}{x + 2} = \dfrac{2x + 2}{x + 2}.$

11. $\dfrac{x + 1}{x - 1} + \dfrac{3}{x} = \dfrac{x^2 + x + 3x - 3}{x(x - 1)} = \dfrac{x^2 + 4x - 3}{x(x - 1)}.$

12. $\dfrac{1}{(x + 1)^3} - \dfrac{1}{(x + 1)^2} + \dfrac{1}{x + 1} + \dfrac{1}{2x + 1}$

$$= \frac{(2x + 1) - (x + 1)(2x + 1) + (x + 1)^2(2x + 1) + (x + 1)^3}{(x + 1)^3(2x + 1)}$$

$$= \frac{2x + 1 - 2x^2 - 2x - x - 1 + 2x^3 + 4x^2 + 2x + x^2 + 2x + 1 + x^3 + 3x^2 + 3x + 1}{(x + 1)^3(2x + 1)}$$

$$= \frac{3x^3 + 6x^2 + 6x + 2}{(x + 1)^3(2x + 1)}.$$

13. $\dfrac{1}{(x^2 + 1)} + \dfrac{1}{x - 1} = \dfrac{x - 1 + x^2 + 1}{(x^2 + 1)(x - 1)} = \dfrac{x^2 + x}{(x^2 + 1)(x - 1)} = \dfrac{x(x + 1)}{(x^2 + 1)(x - 1)}.$

14. $\dfrac{1}{2x - 1} - \dfrac{1}{2x^2 - 3} = \dfrac{2x^2 - 3 - 2x + 1}{(2x - 1)(2x^2 - 3)} = \dfrac{2x^2 - 2x - 2}{(2x - 1)(2x^2 - 3)}.$

15. $\dfrac{1}{x + 2} + \dfrac{1}{(x + 3)^2} - \dfrac{1}{x^2 - 5} = \dfrac{(x + 2)(x^2 - 5) + x^2 - 5 - (x + 2)^2}{(x + 2)^2(x^2 - 5)}$

$$= \frac{x^3 - 5x + 2x^2 - 10 + x^2 - 5 - x^2 - 4x - 4}{(x + 2)^2(x^2 - 5)} = \frac{x^3 + 2x^2 - 9x - 19}{(x + 2)^2(x^2 - 5)}.$$

16.
$$\frac{x + 7}{(x - 3)(x + 4)} \equiv \frac{A}{x - 3} + \frac{B}{x + 4}$$

$$x + 7 \equiv A(x + 4) + B(x - 3)$$

If $x = -4$, $\quad -4 + 7 = -7B \quad$ or $\quad B = -\frac{3}{7}$

If $x = 3$, $\quad\quad 3 + 7 = A7 \quad$ or $\quad A = \frac{10}{7}$, therefore

$$\frac{x + 7}{(x - 3)(x + 4)} \equiv \frac{10}{7(x - 3)} - \frac{3}{7(x + 4)}.$$

17.
$$\frac{2x + 1}{(x - 1)(x + 2)} \equiv \frac{A}{x - 1} + \frac{B}{x + 2}$$

$$2x + 1 \equiv A(x + 2) + B(x - 1).$$

If $x = 1$, $\quad\quad 3 = A3 \quad\quad$ or $\quad A = 1$.

If $x = -2$, $\quad -3 = B(-3) \quad$ or $\quad B = 1$, therefore

$$\frac{2x + 1}{(x - 1)(x + 2)} \equiv \frac{1}{x - 1} + \frac{1}{x + 2}.$$

18.
$$\frac{2x + 5}{(2x + 1)(3x - 1)} \equiv \frac{A}{2x + 1} + \frac{B}{3x - 1}$$

$$2x + 5 \equiv A(3x - 1) + B(2x + 1).$$

If $x = \frac{1}{3}, \frac{2}{3} + 5 = B\frac{5}{3}$ or $B = \frac{17}{5}$

If $x = -\frac{1}{2}, 4 = A\left(-\frac{3}{2} - 1\right) \Rightarrow A = -\frac{8}{5}$, therefore

$$\frac{2x + 5}{(2x + 1)(3x - 1)} \equiv -\frac{8}{5(2x + 1)} + \frac{17}{5(3x - 1)}$$

19.
$$\frac{x^2 + x - 5}{(x + 2)(x + 3)} = \frac{x^2 + x - 5}{x^2 + 5x + 6} = \frac{(x^2 + 5x + 6) - (4x + 11)}{x^2 + 5x + 6}$$

$$= 1 - \frac{4x + 11}{(x + 2)(x + 3)} \quad \text{check with long division}$$

$$\frac{4x + 11}{(x + 2)(x + 3)} \equiv \frac{A}{x + 2} + \frac{B}{x + 3}$$

$$4x + 11 \equiv A(x + 3) + B(x + 2).$$

If $x = -3$, $-1 = -B$ or $\boxed{B = 1}$

If $x = -2$, $\boxed{A = 3}$

$$\frac{4x + 11}{(x + 2)(x + 3)} = \frac{3}{x + 2} + \frac{1}{x + 3}$$

therefore $\dfrac{x^2 + x - 5}{(x + 2)(x + 3)} = 1 - \dfrac{3}{x + 2} - \dfrac{1}{x + 3}.$

20. $\dfrac{3x^2 - x - 7}{(x - 1)(x + 3)} = \dfrac{3x^2 - x - 7}{x^2 + 2x - 3} = \dfrac{3(x^2 + 2x - 3) - 7x + 2}{(x^2 + 2x - 3)}$

$$= 3 - \frac{7x - 2}{(x - 1)(x + 3)} \qquad \frac{7x - 2}{(x - 1)(x + 3)} \equiv \frac{A}{x - 1} + \frac{B}{x + 3}$$

$$7x - 2 \equiv A(x + 3) + B(x - 1).$$

If $x = 1$, $4A = 5$ or $A = \dfrac{5}{4}$, if $x = -3$, $B = \dfrac{23}{4}$

$$\frac{3x^2 - x - 7}{(x - 1)(x + 3)} \equiv 3 - \frac{5}{4(x - 1)} - \frac{23}{4(x + 3)}.$$

21. $\dfrac{x^3}{(x + 4)(x - 5)} \equiv \dfrac{x^3}{(x^2 - x - 20)} = x + 1 + \dfrac{21x + 20}{(x + 4)(x + 5)}.$

By long division

$$
\begin{array}{r}
x + 1 \\
x^2 - x - 20 \overline{\smash{\big)}\ x^3 } \\
x^3 - x^2 - 20x \\
\hline
x^2 + 20x \\
x^2 - x - 20 \\
\hline
21x + 20
\end{array}
$$

$$\frac{21x + 20}{(x + 4)(x - 5)} \equiv \frac{A}{x + 4} + \frac{B}{x - 5}$$

$$21x + 20 \equiv A\,(x - 5) + B\,(x + 4).$$

If $x = -4$, $9A = -64$ or $A = \dfrac{64}{9}$. If $x = 5$, $9B = 125$ or $B = \dfrac{125}{9}$

therefore $\dfrac{x^3}{(x + 4)(x - 5)} \equiv x + 1 + \dfrac{64}{9(x + 4)} + \dfrac{125}{9(x - 5)}$.

22. $\dfrac{x + 3}{x^2 - 49} = \dfrac{x + 3}{(x - 7)(x + 7)}$

$\qquad = \dfrac{A}{x - 7} + \dfrac{B}{x + 7} \Rightarrow x + 3 \equiv A\,(x + 7) + B\,(x - 7)$

If $x = 7$, $14A = 10$ or $A = \dfrac{5}{7}$. If $x = -7$, $-14B = -4$ or $B = \dfrac{2}{7}$

therefore $\dfrac{x + 3}{x^2 - 49} \equiv \dfrac{5}{7(x - 7)} + \dfrac{2}{7(x + 7)}$.

23. $\dfrac{2x - 1}{81 - x^2} \equiv \dfrac{21 - 1}{(9 - x)(9 + x)}$

$\qquad \equiv \dfrac{A}{9 - x} + \dfrac{B}{9 + x} \Rightarrow 2x - 1 \equiv A\,(9 + x) + B\,(9 - x).$

If $x = 9$, $18A = 17$ or $A = \dfrac{17}{18}$. If $x = -9$, $18B = -19$ or $B = -\dfrac{19}{18}$

$\dfrac{2x - 1}{81 - x^2} \equiv \dfrac{17}{18(9 - x)} - \dfrac{19}{18(9 + x)}$.

24. $\dfrac{3x + 7}{x^2 - 36} \equiv \dfrac{3x + 7}{(x - 6)(x + 6)}$

$\qquad \equiv \dfrac{A}{x - 6} + \dfrac{B}{x + 6} \Rightarrow 3x + 7 \equiv A\,(x + 6) + B\,(x - 6).$

If $x = 6$, $12A = 25$ or $A = \dfrac{25}{12}$. If $x = -6$, $-12B = -11$ or $B = \dfrac{11}{12}$

therefore $\dfrac{3x + 7}{x^2 - 36} \equiv \dfrac{25}{12(x - 6)} + \dfrac{11}{12(x + 6)}$.

25. $$\frac{x^2 - 3x + 5}{(x + 1)(x - 2)(x + 3)} \equiv \frac{A}{x + 1} + \frac{B}{x - 2} + \frac{C}{x + 3}$$

$$x^2 - 3x + 5 \equiv A(x - 2)(x + 3) + B(x + 1)(x + 3) + C(x + 1)(x - 2)$$

If $x = 2$, $4 - 6 + 5 = B15$ or $B = \dfrac{1}{5}$

If $x = -1$, $1 + 3 + 5 = A(-3)$ or $A = -\dfrac{3}{2}$

If $x = -3$, $9 + (+ 5 = C(-2)(-5)$ or $C = \dfrac{23}{10}$

therefore, $$\frac{x^2 + 3x - 5}{(x + 1)(x - 2)(x + 3)} = -\frac{3}{2(x + 1)} + \frac{1}{5(x - 2)} + \frac{23}{10(x + 3)}.$$

26. $$\frac{5x^2 + 25x - 7}{(x + 3)(x + 5)(x - 7)} \equiv \frac{A}{x + 3} + \frac{B}{x + 5} + \frac{C}{x - 7}$$

$$5x^2 + 25x - 7 \equiv A(x + 5)(x - 7) + B(x + 3)(x - 7) + C(x + 3)(x + 5).$$

If $x = 7$, $5(49) + 25(7) - 7 = C(10)(12)$ or $C = \dfrac{413}{120}$

If $x = -3$, $45 - 75 - 7 \equiv A(-20)$ or $A = \dfrac{37}{20}$.

If $x = -5$, $125 - 125 - 7 = B24$ or $B = -\dfrac{7}{24}$

$$\frac{5x^2 + 25x - 7}{(x + 3)(x + 5)(x - 7)} \equiv \frac{37}{20(x + 3)} - \frac{7}{24(x + 5)} + \frac{413}{120(x - 7)}.$$

27. $$\frac{6(2 - x)}{(3 - x)(3 + x)} \equiv \frac{A}{3 - x} + \frac{B}{3 + x} \qquad 6(2 - x) \equiv A(3 + x) + B(3 - x)$$

If $x = -3$, $6(2 - (-3)) = B(3 - (-3))$ $30 = 6B$ or $B = 5$.

If $x = 3$ $-6 = 6A$ or $A = -1$

Therefore, $$\frac{6(2 - x)}{(3 - x)(3 + x)} \equiv \frac{-1}{3 - x} + \frac{5}{3 + x} \quad \text{check}$$

$$\frac{6(2-x)}{(3-x)(3+x)} = \frac{-3-x+15-5x}{(3-x)(3+x)} = \frac{-6x+12}{(3-x)(3+x)}$$

$$= \text{R.H.S.} = \frac{6(2-x)}{(3-x)(3+x)}$$

L.H.S. = R.H.S.

28. $\dfrac{6(2-x)}{x(x+3)} \equiv \dfrac{A}{x} + \dfrac{B}{x+3}$ $\qquad 6-x \equiv A(x+3) + Bx.$

If $x=0$, $6 = 3A$ or $A = 2$. If $x = -3$, $9 = -3B$ or $B-3$

Therefore, $\dfrac{6-x}{x(x+3)} \equiv \dfrac{2}{x} - \dfrac{3}{x+3}.$

29. $\dfrac{6x^2 + 13x + 3}{x(x+1)(x+3)} \equiv \dfrac{A}{x} + \dfrac{B}{x+1} + \dfrac{C}{x+3}$

$6x^2 + 13x + 3 \equiv A(x+3)(x+1) + Bx(x+3) + Cx(x+1).$

If $x-1$, $\qquad 6 - 13 + 3 = B(-1)2$ $\qquad$ or $\qquad B = 2.$

If $x = 0$, $\qquad 3 = 3A$ $\qquad\qquad\qquad$ or $\qquad A = 1.$

If $x = -3$, $\qquad 54 - 39 + 3 = C(-3)(-2)$ or $\qquad C = 3.$

Therefore, $\dfrac{6x^2 + 13x + 3}{x(x+1)(x+3)} \equiv \dfrac{1}{x} + \dfrac{2}{x+1} + \dfrac{3}{x+3}.$

30. $\dfrac{x^3 - 3x^2 - 11x + 30}{(x+2)(x-3)(x-5)} = \dfrac{x^3 - 3x^2 - 11x + 30}{x^3 - 6x^2 - x + 30}$

$$= 1 + \frac{3x^2 - 10x}{(x+2)(x-3)(x-5)}.$$

Divide numerator by denominator

$$
\begin{array}{r}
1 \\
x^3 - 6x^2 - x + 30 \;\overline{\smash{)}\; x^3 - 3x^2 - 11x + 30} \\
\underline{x^3 - 6x^2 - x + 30} \\
3x^2 - 10x
\end{array}
$$

therefore $\dfrac{x^3 - 3x^2 - 11x + 30}{x^3 - 6x^2 - x + 30} = 1 + \dfrac{3x^2 - 10x}{x^3 - 6x^2 - x + 30}.$

Express $\dfrac{3x^2 - 10x}{(x + 2)(x - 3)(x - 5)}$ in partial fractions since this is a

proper function.

$$\frac{3x^2 - 10x}{(x + 2)(x - 3)(x - 5)} \equiv \frac{A}{x + 2} + \frac{B}{x - 3} + \frac{C}{x - 5}$$

$$3x^2 - 10x \equiv A(x - 3)(x - 5) + B(x + 2)(x - 5) + C(x + 2)(x - 3).$$

If $x = 3$, $27 - 30 = B5\,(-2)$ or $B = \dfrac{3}{10}$.

If $x = -2$, $12 + 20 = A\,(-5)(-7)$ or $A = \dfrac{32}{35}$.

If $x = 5$, $75 - 50 = C\,(7)(2)$ or $C = \dfrac{25}{14}$.

Therefore $\dfrac{3x^3 - 3x^2 - 11x + 30}{(x + 2)(x - 3)(x - 5)} = 1 + \dfrac{32}{35\,(x + 2)} + \dfrac{3}{10\,(x - 3)} + \dfrac{25}{14\,(x - 5)}.$

31. $\dfrac{x}{x + 1} = \dfrac{x + 1 - 1}{x + 1} = 1 - \dfrac{1}{x + 1}.$

32. $\dfrac{2(x + 1)}{x + 2} = \dfrac{2(x + 2 - 1)}{x + 2} = 2 - \dfrac{2}{x + 2}.$

SOLUTIONS 3

1.   (i)   Maximum   (ii)   Minimum

            $a < 0$ $a > 0$

2. $x = -\dfrac{b}{2a}.$

3.   See text.

4.   See text.

5.   (a) $x = -\dfrac{b}{2a} = -2,\ b = 4a$ when $x = 0$, that is,

          $f(0) = 7 = c.\ \ y_{min} = a\,(-2)^2 + b\,(-2) + 7 = 3$

          $4a - 2b = -4,\ 4a - 8a = -4,\ -4a = -4$

$$\boxed{a = 1} \qquad \boxed{b = 4}\ \text{and}\ \boxed{c = 7}$$

          $f(x) = x^2 + 4x + 7.$

   (b) $x = -\dfrac{b}{2a} = -3,\ b = 6a$

          $a\,(-3)^2 + b\,(-3) + c = -5 = y_{min}$ $9a - 3b = -5 - 2 = -7$

          $f(0) = 2 = c$ $9a - 3b = -7$ $9a - (6a)\,3 = -7$

          $9a - 18a = -7$ $-9a = -7$ $a = \dfrac{7}{9},\ b = 6 \times \dfrac{7}{9} = \dfrac{14}{3}.$

          $f(x) = \dfrac{7}{9}x^2 + \dfrac{14}{3}x + 2$

   (c) $x = -\dfrac{b}{2a} = 3,\ b = -6a$ $f(0) = c = 5$

          $f(3) = a\,(3)^2 + b\,(3) + 5 = 1$ $9a + 3b = -4$

          $9a - 18a = -4$ $-9a = -4$ $a = \dfrac{4}{9},\ b = -\dfrac{8}{3}$

          $f(x) = \dfrac{4}{9}x^2 - \dfrac{8}{3}x + 5.$

(d) $x = -\dfrac{b}{2a} = 5,\ b = -10a$ $f(5) = a\,(5)^2 + b\,(5) + c = -1$

$f(0) = -10 = c,$ $25a + 5b - 10 = -1,$ $25a - 50a = 9$

$-25a = 9,\ a = -\dfrac{9}{25},$

$b = -10\left(-\dfrac{9}{25}\right) = \dfrac{90}{25}$ $f(x) = -\dfrac{9}{25}x^2 + \dfrac{90}{25}x - 10.$

6.   (i) $x = -\dfrac{b}{2a} = -\dfrac{4}{2\,(-1)} = 2$ $y_{max} = -(2)^2 + 4\,(2) - 1 = 3$

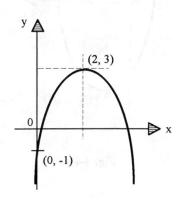

Fig. 1-II/1

(ii) $x = -\dfrac{b}{2a} = -\dfrac{5}{2\,(-2)} = 1.25$ $f(0) = 7$

$y_{max} = -2(1.25)^2 + 5(1.25) + 7 = 10.125$

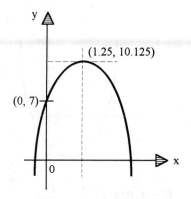

Fig. 1-II/2

(iii) $\quad x = -\dfrac{b}{2a} = -\dfrac{(-2)}{2\,(3)} = \dfrac{1}{3}$ $\qquad$ $f(0) = -4$

$$y_{\min} = 3\left(\dfrac{1}{3}\right)^2 - 2\left(\dfrac{1}{3}\right) - 4 = \dfrac{1}{3} - \dfrac{2}{3} - 4 = -4\dfrac{1}{3} = -\dfrac{13}{3}.$$

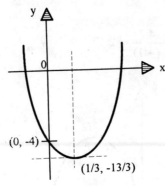

$(0, -4)$

$(1/3, -13/3)$

Fig. 1-II/3

(iv) $\quad x = -\dfrac{b}{2a} = -\dfrac{2}{2\,(5)} = -\dfrac{1}{5}$ $\qquad$ $f(0) = -2$

$$y_{\min} = 5\left(-\dfrac{1}{5}\right)^2 + 2\left(-\dfrac{1}{5}\right) - 2 = \dfrac{1}{5} - \dfrac{2}{5} - 2 = -\dfrac{1}{5} - 2 = -2\dfrac{1}{5} = -\dfrac{11}{5}.$$

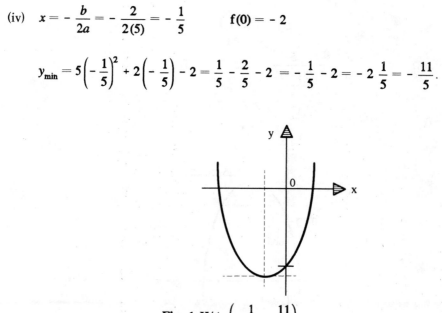

Fig. 1-II/4 $\left(-\dfrac{1}{5}, -\dfrac{11}{5}\right)$

7. If $a > 0, D = 0$ minimum

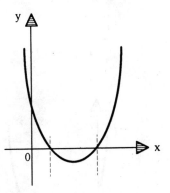

Fig. 1-II/5

8. If $a > 0, D > 0$.

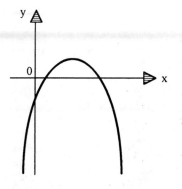

Fig. 1-II/6

9. $a < 0$ $D > 0$

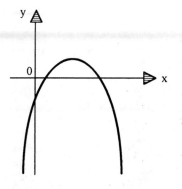

Fig. 1-II/7

10. $a < 0$ $D = 0$

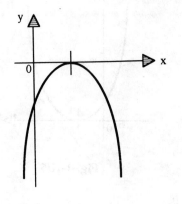

Fig. 1-II/8

11. $a > 0$ $D < 0$

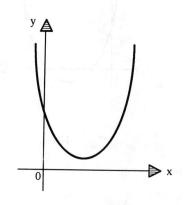

Fig. 1-II/9

12. $a < 0$ $\qquad$ $D < 0$

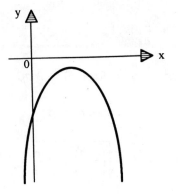

Fig. 1-II/10

13. For real and unequal roots, $D > 0$ $\qquad$ $5^2 - 4 \times 3 (k + 1) > 0,$

$25 - 12k - 12 > 0$ $\qquad$ $\boxed{k = 1}$ $\qquad$ $- 12k > - 13, k < \dfrac{13}{12}.$

14. (i) $D = 0$ (ii) $D < 0$ (iii) $D > 0.$

SOLUTIONS 4

1. (i) $\alpha + \beta = -\dfrac{b}{a} \quad \alpha\beta = \dfrac{c}{a}$.

   (ii) $(\alpha - \beta)^2 = \alpha^2 + \beta^2 - 2\alpha\beta = (\alpha + \beta)^2 - 2\alpha\beta - 2\alpha\beta$

   $\alpha - \beta = \pm\sqrt{(\alpha + \beta)^2 - 4\alpha\beta}$, since $\alpha > \beta$

   $\alpha - \beta = \sqrt{(\alpha + \beta)^2 - 4\alpha\beta} = \sqrt{\left(-\dfrac{b}{a}\right)^2 - 4\dfrac{c}{a}} = \sqrt{\dfrac{b^2 - 4ac}{a^2}}$.

   (iii) $(\alpha - \beta)^2 = \dfrac{b^2 - 4ac}{a^2}$.   (iv) $(\alpha + \beta)^2 = \left(-\dfrac{b}{a}\right)^2 = \dfrac{b^2}{a^2}$.

   (v) $\alpha^2 + \beta^2 = (\alpha + \beta)^2 - 2\alpha\beta = \dfrac{b^2}{a^2} - 2\left(-\dfrac{b}{a}\right) = \dfrac{b^2 + 2ba}{a^2}$.

   (vi) $(\alpha + \beta)^3 = \alpha^3 + \beta^3 + 3\alpha^2\beta + 3\alpha\beta)^2$

   $\alpha^3 + \beta^3 = (\alpha + \beta)^3 - 3\alpha\beta(\alpha + \beta)$

   $= \left(-\dfrac{b}{a}\right)^3 - 3\dfrac{c}{a}\left(-\dfrac{b}{a}\right) = -\dfrac{b^3}{a^3} + 3\dfrac{bc}{a^2} = \dfrac{3abc - b^3}{a^3}$.

   (vii) $\alpha^3 - \beta^3 = (\alpha - \beta)(\alpha^2 + \alpha\beta + \beta^2) = (\alpha - \beta)(\alpha^2 + \beta^2 + \alpha\beta)$

   $= \sqrt{\dfrac{b^2 - 4ac}{a^2}}\left[\dfrac{b^2 + 2ab}{a^2} + \dfrac{c}{a}\right]$.

   (viii) $\alpha^2 - \beta^2 = (\alpha - \beta)(\alpha + \beta) = \sqrt{\dfrac{b^2 - 4ac}{a^2}}\left(-\dfrac{b}{a}\right)$.

   (ix) $(\alpha^2)^2 + (\beta)^2 = (\alpha^2 + \beta^2)^2 - 2\alpha^2\beta^2 = \left(\dfrac{b^2 + 2ab}{a^2}\right)^2 - 2\dfrac{c^2}{a^2}$.

   (x) $\dfrac{1}{\alpha^2} + \dfrac{1}{\beta^2} = \dfrac{\alpha^2 + \beta^2}{\alpha^2\beta^2} = \dfrac{(b^2 + 2ab)/a^2}{c^2/a^2} = \dfrac{b^2 + 2ab}{c^2} = \dfrac{b(b + 2a)}{c^2}$.

2. $n + m = \dfrac{5}{3}$, $nm = \dfrac{7}{3}$

(i) $\dfrac{1}{n} + \dfrac{1}{m} = \dfrac{m + n}{nm} = \dfrac{5/3}{7/3} = \dfrac{5}{7}$

(ii) $\dfrac{1}{n^3} - \dfrac{1}{m^3} = \dfrac{m^3 - n^3}{n^3 m^3} = \dfrac{(m - n)(m^2 + nm + n^2)}{n^3 m^3}$

where $(m - n)^2 = m^2 - 2mn + n^2 = m^2 + n^2 - 2mn$

$$= (m + n)^2 - 2mn - 2mn = (m + n)^2 - 4mn$$

$(m - n) = \pm\sqrt{(m + n)^2 - 4mn}$

$$= \pm\sqrt{\left(\frac{5}{3}\right)^2 - 4\left(\frac{7}{3}\right)} = \pm\sqrt{\frac{25}{9} - \frac{28}{3}}$$

$$= \pm\sqrt{\frac{25 - 84}{9}} = \pm\frac{\sqrt{-59}}{3} = \pm\frac{\sqrt{59}}{3}i$$

and $m^2 + nm + n^2 = m^2 + n^2 + nm = (m + n)^2 - 2mn + nm$

$$= (m + n)^2 - mn = \left(\frac{5}{3}\right)^2 - \frac{7}{3} = \frac{25}{9} - \frac{21}{9} = \frac{4}{9}$$

and $\dfrac{1}{n^3} - \dfrac{1}{m^3} = \dfrac{(m - n)(m^2 + nm + n^2)}{(nm)^3}$

$$= \frac{\pm\dfrac{\sqrt{59}}{3}i\left(\dfrac{4}{9}\right)}{\left(\dfrac{7}{3}\right)^3} = \pm\frac{\sqrt{59}}{3} \times \frac{4}{9} \times \frac{27}{343}i = \pm\,0.09\,i.$$

3.   If α and β are the roots of the quadratic equation, then $\alpha = \dfrac{1}{\beta}$ or $\beta = \dfrac{1}{\alpha}$.

$$S = \alpha + \beta = -\frac{b}{a} = \alpha + \frac{1}{\alpha} = \frac{\alpha^2 + 1}{\alpha}$$

$$P = \alpha\beta = \frac{c}{a} = \alpha\,\frac{1}{\alpha} = 1, \qquad \boxed{c = a}$$

$$\alpha^2 + 1 + \alpha\left(\frac{b}{a}\right) = 0 \qquad \alpha^2 + \frac{b}{a}\alpha + 1 = 0$$

$$\alpha = -\frac{b/a \pm \sqrt{(b/a)^2 - 4}}{2} = \frac{-b/a \pm \sqrt{(b^2 - 4a^2)/a^2}}{2} \qquad \boxed{b^2 \geq 4a^2}.$$

4. $\quad \alpha + \beta = -7 \qquad\qquad \alpha^3 + \beta^3 = 125$

$$\alpha^3 + \beta^3 = (\alpha + \beta)^3 - 3\alpha^2\beta - 3\alpha\beta^2 = (\alpha + \beta)^3 - 3\alpha\beta(\alpha + \beta)$$

$$125 = -343 - 3\alpha\beta(-7)$$

$$125 + 343 = 21\alpha\beta \qquad\qquad\qquad \alpha\beta = \frac{156}{7}$$

$$x^2 - (\alpha + \beta)x + \alpha\beta = 0 \qquad\qquad x^2 - (-7)x + \frac{156}{7} = 0$$

$$\boxed{7x^2 + 49x + 156 = 0}$$

5. If α and β are the roots of the equation then if $\alpha = 3\beta$ or $\beta = 3\alpha$.

$$S = \alpha + \beta = 3\beta + \beta = 4\beta = -\frac{b}{a} \qquad\qquad P = \alpha\beta = 3\beta\beta = 3\beta^2 = \frac{c}{a}$$

$$ax^2 + bx + c = 0$$

$$3\beta^2 = \frac{c}{a} \qquad\qquad\qquad\qquad\qquad\qquad 4\beta = -\frac{b}{a} = \pm 4\sqrt{\frac{c}{3a}}$$

$$\beta^2 = \frac{c}{3a} \qquad\qquad\qquad\qquad\qquad\qquad \text{squaring up both sides}$$

$$\beta = \pm\sqrt{\frac{c}{3a}} \qquad\qquad\qquad\qquad\qquad\qquad \frac{b^2}{a^2} = 16\,\frac{c}{3a}$$

$$\boxed{3b^2 = 16ac}$$

6. (i) $\quad \dfrac{\alpha}{\beta} + \dfrac{\beta}{\alpha} = \dfrac{\alpha^2 + \beta^2}{\alpha\beta} = \dfrac{(\alpha + \beta)^2 - 2\alpha\beta}{\alpha\beta} = \dfrac{\left(\frac{9}{7}\right)^2 - 2}{1}$ where $\alpha + \beta = \dfrac{9}{7}$, $\alpha\beta = \dfrac{-7}{-7} = 1$

$$\frac{\alpha}{\beta} + \frac{\beta}{\alpha} = \frac{81}{49} - 2 = \frac{81 - 98}{49} = -\frac{17}{49}$$

(ii) $\dfrac{1}{\alpha^4} + \dfrac{1}{\beta^4} = \dfrac{\beta^4 + \alpha^4}{\alpha^4 \beta^4} = \dfrac{(\beta^2)^2 + (\alpha^2)^2}{(\alpha^4 \beta^4)} = \dfrac{(\beta^2 + \alpha^2)^2 - 2\alpha^2\beta^2}{(\alpha\beta)^4}$

$$= \dfrac{[(\alpha + \beta)^2 - 2\alpha\beta]^2 - 2(\alpha\beta)^2}{(\alpha\beta)^4} = \dfrac{\left(\dfrac{81}{49} - 2\right)^2 - 2}{1}$$

$$= \left(\dfrac{81 - 98}{49}\right)^2 - 2 = \dfrac{289}{2401} - 2 = \dfrac{289 - 4802}{2401} = -\dfrac{4513}{2401}.$$

7.   Let α be one of the roots and the other root is 2α.

$\alpha + 2\alpha = \dfrac{k + 1}{k} = $ the sum of the roots

$\alpha \cdot 2\alpha = \dfrac{9}{k}, \ \alpha = \pm \dfrac{3}{\sqrt{2k}}$ $\qquad 3\alpha = \dfrac{k + 1}{k} = \pm \dfrac{9}{\sqrt{2k}}$ ... (1)

squaring up both sides of (1)

$\left(\dfrac{k + 1}{k}\right)^2 = \left(\pm \dfrac{9}{\sqrt{2k}}\right)^2 \Rightarrow \dfrac{k^2 + 2k + 1}{k^2} = \dfrac{81}{2k}$

$2k^3 + 4k^2 + 2k = 81k^2 \Rightarrow 2k^2 - 77k + 2 = 0.$

$k = \dfrac{77 \pm \sqrt{5929 - 16}}{4}, \ k = 38.47 \text{ or } 0.026$

$3\alpha = \dfrac{k + 1}{k} \Rightarrow \alpha = \dfrac{1}{3}\left(1 + \dfrac{1}{k}\right)$

$\alpha = \dfrac{1}{3}\left(1 + \dfrac{1}{38.47}\right) \text{ or } \alpha = \dfrac{1}{3}\left(1 + \dfrac{1}{0.026}\right)$

$\alpha = 0.342 \quad \alpha = 13.158.$

Therefore the roots are 0.342 and 0.684 or 13.158 amd 26.316.

8.   For the quadratic equation to have real roots, the discriminant, $D \geq 0$.

$(k + 1)^2 - 36k \geq 0$ $\qquad\qquad k^2 - 34k + 1 \geq 0$

$$k = \frac{34 \pm \sqrt{34^2 - 4}}{2} = \frac{34 \pm 33.94}{2} \qquad k = 33.97 \text{ or } 0.03$$

$k < 0.003$ and $k > 33.97$.

9. If α is one root, then the other root would be 4α.

$$\alpha + 4\alpha = 5\alpha = \frac{-k}{-3} = \frac{k}{3}, \qquad \alpha \cdot 4\alpha = \frac{-4}{-3} = \frac{4}{3} \qquad \alpha = \pm \frac{1}{\sqrt{-3}}$$

$$k = 3(5\alpha) = \pm \frac{15}{\sqrt{3}} = \pm 5\sqrt{3}.$$

The roots are $\dfrac{1}{\sqrt{3}}$ or $\dfrac{4}{\sqrt{3}}$, and $-\dfrac{1}{\sqrt{3}}$ or $\dfrac{-4}{\sqrt{3}}$ the values of k

are $5\sqrt{3}$ or $-5\sqrt{3}$.

10. (i) $\quad S = \alpha + \beta = -\dfrac{b}{a} = -\dfrac{(-1)}{-2)} = -\dfrac{1}{2}, \quad P = \alpha\beta = \dfrac{c}{a} = \dfrac{1}{2}.$

(ii) $\quad S = \alpha + \beta = -\dfrac{5}{3}, P = \alpha\beta = \dfrac{9}{3} = 3.$

(iii) $S = \alpha + \beta = 2, P = \alpha\beta = 7.$

(iv) $S = 4, P = -2.$ $\qquad\qquad$ (v) $S = 1, P = -\dfrac{1}{5}.$

11. (i) $\quad x^2 + 3x + 5 = 0$ $\quad$ (ii) $x^2 - 25x - 39 = 0$ $\quad$ (iii) $x^2 - 37x + 2 = 0.$

12. $ax^3 + bx^2 + cx + d = 0,$

$$x^3 + \frac{bx^2}{a} + \frac{cx}{a} + \frac{d}{a} = 0 = (x - \alpha)(x - \beta)(x - \gamma)$$

$$= [x^2 - (\alpha + \beta) x + \alpha\beta] (x - \gamma)$$

$$= x^3 - (\alpha + \beta) x^2 + \alpha\beta x - \gamma x^2 + (\alpha + \beta) \gamma x - \alpha\beta\gamma$$

$$= x^3 - (\alpha + \beta + \gamma) x^2 + (\alpha\beta + \alpha\gamma + \beta\gamma) x - \alpha\beta\gamma.$$

Equating coefficients $-(\alpha + \beta + \gamma) = \dfrac{b}{a},$ $\qquad$ $\boxed{\alpha + \beta + \gamma = -\dfrac{b}{a}}$

$\boxed{\alpha\beta + \alpha\gamma + \beta\gamma = \dfrac{c}{a}}$ $\qquad\qquad$ $\boxed{\alpha\beta\gamma = -\dfrac{d}{a}}$

SOLUTIONS 5

1.   (i) $3x + 2 < 5$ $3x < 5 - 2$

                $3x < 3$

                $x < 1$ or $x : 1 > x$

   (ii) $-5x - 3 < 5$ $-5x < 8$

                $x > -\dfrac{8}{5}$ or $x : -\dfrac{8}{5} < x.$

   (iii) $\dfrac{3x - 2}{x} \geq 3$

                multiplying both sides by the squared denominator x^2

                $\dfrac{(3x - 2)\, x^2}{x} \geq 3\, x^2$

                $(3x - 2)\, x - 3x^2 \geq 0$

                $3x^2 - 2x - 3x^2 \geq 0$ $-2x \geq 0$

                $x \leq 0$ or $x : 0 \geq x$

   (iv) $\dfrac{3}{x - 1} > 1$ $\dfrac{3\,(x - 1)^2}{x - 1)} > (x - 1)^2$

                $3(x - 1) > (x - 1)^2$ $(x - 1)\, [3 - (x - 1)] > 0$

                $(x - 1)\, (3 - x + 1) > 0$ $(x - 1)\, (4 - x) > 0$

                $(x - 1)\, (x - 4) < 0$

                $1 < x < 4$ or $\{x : 1 < x\} \cap \{x : x < 4\}$

   (v) $\dfrac{3 + 2x}{3x - 4} < -5$ $\dfrac{(3 + 2x)\,(3x - 4)^2}{(3x - 4)} < 5\,(3x - 4)^2$

                $(3 + 2x)\,(3x - 4) + 5\,(3x - 4)^2 < 0$

                $(3x - 4)\, [3 + 2x + 5\,(3x - 4)] < 0$

                $(3x - 4)\, (17x - 17) < 0$ or $17\,(3x - 4)\,(x - 1) < 0$

                $(3x - 4)\,(x - 1) < 0$

                $1 < x < \dfrac{4}{3}$ or $\{x : 1 < x\} \cap \{x : x < \dfrac{4}{3}\}$

(vi) $\dfrac{2x - 5}{x} \geq 1$ or $\dfrac{(2x - 5) x^2}{x} \geq x^2$

$x (2x - 5) - x^2 \geq 0$ or $2x^2 - 5x - x^2 \geq 0$

$x^2 - 5x \geq 0$ or. $x (x - 5) \geq 0$

$x > 5$ and $x < 0$ or $\{x : 5 < x\} \cap \{x : x < 0\}$.

(vii) $\dfrac{1}{x + 1} \leq 1$ $\dfrac{(x + 1)^2}{(x + 1)} \leq (x + 1)^2$

$x + 1 - (x + 1)^2 \leq 0$ $(x + 1) (1 - x - 1) \leq 0$

$(x + 1) (- x) \leq 0$ $x (x + 1) \geq 0$

$x < - 1$ $x > 0$

$\{x : - 1 < x\} \cup \{x : x < 0\}$.

(viii) $\dfrac{5x - 1}{5x} < 1$ $\dfrac{(5x - 1) x^2}{5x} < x^2$

$x (5x - 1) < 5x^2$ $5x^2 - x - 5x^2 < 0$

$- x < 0$ $x > 0$ or $\{x : 0 < x\}$.

2. (i) $- x^2 + 2x - 1 < 0$ $- x^2 + x + x - 1 < 0$

$- x(x - 1) + x - 1 < 0$ $(x - 1) (- x + 1) < 0$

$(x - 1) (x - 1) > 0$ $(x - 1)^2 > 0$

Taking square roots on both sides.

$\pm (x - 1) > 0$ $x - 1 > 0$ and $- (x - 1) > 0$

$x > 1$ and $x < 1$ or $x \neq 1$.

(ii) $x^2 - 3x - 4 > 0$ $x^2 - 4x + x - 4 > 0$

$x (x - 4) + (x - 4) > 0$ $(x - 4) (x + 1) > 0$

$x > 4$ $x < - 1$.

3. (i) $| 2x + 1 | > 1$

squaring up both sides

$(2x + 1)^2 > 1^2$ $(2x + 1)^2 - 1^2 > 0$

$[2x + 1 - 1] (2x + 1) + 1 > 0$ $2x (2x + 2) > 0$

$x (x + 1) > 0$ $x < - 1, x > 0$

(ii) $| x - 2 | \le 1$ $(x - 2)^2 \le 1^2$

$(x - 2)^2 - 1^2 \le 0$ $(x - 2 - 1)(x - 2 + 1) \le 0$

$(x - 3)(x - 1) \le 0$ $1 \le x \le 3.$

4. $\dfrac{x - 1}{x(x + 1)} < 0$ multiplying both sides by the squares of the denominator, namely,

$x^2(x + 1)^2$, we have $\dfrac{(x - 1)x^2(x + 1)^2}{x(x + 1)} < 0$ cancelling down $x(x - 1)(x + 1) < 0$

	$1 > x > 0$	$0 > x > -1$	$x > 1$	$x < -1$
x	+	−	+	−
$x - 1$	−	−	+	−
$x + 1$	+	+	+	−
$x(x - 1)(x + 1)$	−	+	+	−

From the table, we have $0 < x < 1$ and $x < -1$.

5.   (i) $(x - 1)(x + 2)(x - 3) < 0$

	$3 > x > 1$	$-2 < x < 1$	$x < -2$	$x > 3$
$x - 1$	+	−	−	+
$x + 2$	+	+	−	+
$x - 3$	−	−	−	+
$(x - 1)(x + 2)(x - 3)$	−	+	−	+

From the table, we have $x < -2$ and $1 < x < 3$.

(ii) $x(x + 1)(x - 2) > 0$

	$2 > x > 0$	$-1 < x < 0$	$x < -1$	$x > 2$
x	+	−	−	+
$x + 1$	+	+	−	+
$x - 2$	−	−	−	+
$x(x + 1)(x - 2)$	−	+	−	+

From the table, we have $-1 < x < 0$ and $x > 2$.

6.   (i) $-2x^2 + 11x - 5 > 0$ $-2x^2 + 10x + x - 5 > 0$

                $-2x\,(x - 5) + (x - 5) > 0$ $(x - 5)\,(-2x + 1) > 0$

                multiplying both sides by -1 $(x - 5)\,(2x - 1) < 0$

                therefore $\dfrac{1}{2} < x < 5$ $\left\{ x : \dfrac{1}{2} < x \right\} \cap \{x : x < 5\}.$

   (ii) $(2x - 1)\,(x + 5) < 0$ $-5 < x < \dfrac{1}{2}.$ in set notation

                $\{x : -5 < x\} \cap \left\{ x : x < \dfrac{1}{2} \right\}.$

   (iii) $4x^2 - 5x + 1 < 0$ $4x^2 - 4x - x + 1 < 0$

                $4x\,(x - 1) - (x - 1) < 0$ $(x - 1)\,(4x - 1) < 0$

                $\dfrac{1}{4} < x < 1$ $\left\{ x : \dfrac{1}{4} < x \right\} \cap \{x : x < 1\}$

7.   (i) $|x - 2| < 3$ squaring up both sides $(x - 2)^2 < 3^2$

                $(x - 2)^2 - 3^2 < 0$ $[(x - 2) - 3]\,[(x - 2) + 3] < 0$

                $(x - 5)\,(x + 1) < 0,\ -1 < x < 5,\ \{x : -1 < x\} \cap \{x : x < 5\}$

   (ii) $|2x + 3| \le 11$ squaring up both sides $(2x + 3)^2 \le 11^2$

                $(2x + 3)^2 - 11^2 \le 0$ $[(2x + 3) - 11]\,[(2x + 3) + 11] \le 0$

                $(2x - 8)\,(2x + 14) \le 0$ $2(x - 4)\,2\,(x + 7) \le 0$

                $(x - 4)\,(x + 7) \le 0$ $-7 \le x \le 4$

                $\{x : -7 \le x\} \cup \{x \le\ : x \le 4\}.$

   (iii) $-1 < x < 5$ $-7 < x < 4$

                $-1 < x < 4$

                $\{x : -1 < x\} \cup \{x : x < 4\}$

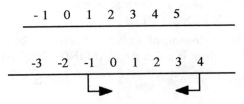

Fig. 1-II/11

8. (i) $|x - 1| > 3|2x - 3|$ squaring up both sides

$(x - 1)^2 > 3^2 (2x - 3)^2$

$(x - 1)^2 - 3^2 (2x - 3)^2 > 0$

$[(x - 1) - 3(2x - 3)][(x - 1) + 3(2x - 3)] > 0$

$(x - 1 - 6x + 9)(x - 1 + 6x - 9) > 0$

$(-5x + 8)(7x - 10) > 0$

$(5x - 8)(7x - 10) < 0$

$\dfrac{7}{10} < x < \dfrac{8}{5}$ $\left\{x : \dfrac{7}{10} < x\right\} \cap \left\{x : x < \dfrac{8}{5}\right\}.$

SOLUTIONS 6

1. If $y = 3x$, x is called the independent variable and y is the dependent variable. Giving values of x such as, 1, 2, 3, 4, we can find the values of y, y depends on the values of x. The set of elements for x are 1, 2, 3, 4, and this set is called

    (i)   THE DOMAIN the corresponding set of elements of y are 3, 6, 9, 12 and is called

    (ii)   the CO-DOMAIN OR RANGE

    (iii)   one value of x results in one value of y as in $y = 3x$,
            ONE TO ONE FUNCTION.

    (iv)   The two sets of elements of domain and range can be mapped as following in a diagram which is called the MAPPING DIAGRAM.

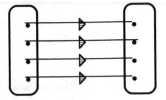

THE DOMAIN   **THE CO-DOMAIN**

Fig. 1-II/12

    (v)   MANY-TO-ONE MAPPING DIAGRAM

$$f: x\ 1 \mapsto 4x^2$$

| for $x = 1$, | $y = 4$ | for $x = 2, y = 16$ |
| for $x = -1$ | $y = 4$ | for $x = -2, y = 16$ |

for two values of x (or many values), y has the same value (one value).

Two arrowed lines arrive at one of the elements of the range.

This is a function.

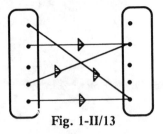

Fig. 1-II/13

1-II/34

2. (i) f: $x \mapsto 5x - 4$, f is such that x is mapped onto $5x - 4$.

(ii) $f^{-1}: x \mapsto \dfrac{1}{5}(x + 4)$ the inverse function of f is such that x is mapped

onto $\dfrac{1}{5}(x + 4)$.

3. A FUNCTION is a relation or mapping in which <u>one</u> and only <u>one</u>, arrowed line leaves each element or member of the domain.

(i) $y = mx + c$ and (ii) $y = x^2$ are functions.

(iii) $y^2 = x$ <u>is not</u> a function

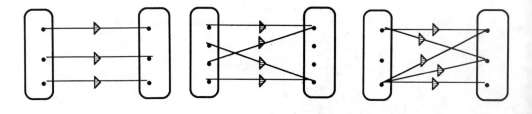

FUNCTION	FUNCTION	NOT A FUNCTION
(i) **Fig. 1-II/14**	(ii) **Fig. 1-II/15**	(iii) **Fig. 1-II/16**

4. (i) {2, 3, 4, 6} set of element of the domain {5, 8, 11, 17} set of elements of the range.

This is a one-to-one function.

(ii) and (iii) are not functions.

5. $x = 0, y = 2; \quad x = 1, y = 7; \quad x = 2, y = 12; \quad x = 3, y = 17;$
$x = -1, y = -3; \quad x = -2, y = -8; \quad x = -3, y = -13.$

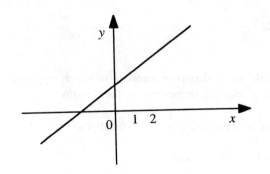

Fig. 1-II/17

(i) When $x = 0$, $y = 2$, $g(0) = 2$, g cuts y-axis when $x = 0$,

$$x = -\frac{2}{5}, \; g\left(-\frac{2}{5}\right) = 0 \text{ g cuts the } x\text{-axis.}$$

(ii) $g\left(\dfrac{1}{2}\right) = 5\left(\dfrac{1}{2}\right) + 2 = 4.5.$

(iii) $g(k) = 0$, $5k + 2 = 0$, $k = -\dfrac{2}{5}$.

(iv) The set of elements of the range are: $\{- 13, -8, -3, 2, 7, 12, 17\}$.

6. The domain $\{1, 2, 3, 4, 5\}$ when $x = 1$, $y = 2 \times 1 + 1 - 3 = 0$; $x = 2$,

$y = 2 \times 2^2 + 2 - 3 = 7$; $x = 3$, $y = 2 \times 3^2 + 3 - 3 = 18$; $x = 4$,

$y = 2 \times 4^2 + 4 - 3 = 33$; $x = 5$, $y = 2 \times 5^2 + 5 - 3 = 52$.

The corresponding elements are $\{0, 7, 18, 33, 52\}$.

7. f: $x \mapsto 5\sqrt{5}$ $\qquad$ $y = 5\sqrt{x}$, $0 = 5\sqrt{5}$, $x = 0$ when $y = 0$;

$1 = 5\sqrt{5}$, $1 = 25x$, $x = \dfrac{1}{25}$ when $y = 1$;

$2 = 5\sqrt{5}$, $4 = 25 \times x$, $x = \dfrac{4}{25}$ when $y = 2$;

$3 = 5\sqrt{5}$, $9 = 25x$, $x = \dfrac{9}{25}$ when $y = 3$.

The corresponding elements of the domain are: $\left\{0, \dfrac{1}{25}, \dfrac{4}{25}, \dfrac{9}{25}\right\}$.

8. If h: $x \mapsto 4x^3 + 5x^2 - 3x + 5$,

$h(-2) = 4(-2)^3 + 5(-2)^2 - 3(-2) + 5 = -32 + 20 + 6 + 5 = -1$.

$4x^3 + 5x^2 - 3x + 5 = 5$, $4x^3 + 5x^2 - 3x = 0$, $x(4x^2 + 5x - 3) = 0$

$x = 0$, $x = \dfrac{-5 \pm \sqrt{25 + 48}}{8} = \dfrac{-5 \pm 8.54}{8}$

$x = 0$, $x = 0.443$, $x = -1.69$.

9. f: $x \mapsto \dfrac{1}{x + 1}$

(a) Sketch.

There is an asymptote when $x = -1$, that is when $x = -1$, $y \mapsto \infty$

$y = \dfrac{1}{x + 1} = (x + 1)^{-1}$, $\dfrac{dy}{dx} = -(x + 1)^{-2} = -\dfrac{1}{(x + 1)^2}$

the gradient is always negative for all values of x.

(b) $x = \dfrac{1}{y + 1}$ $\qquad$ f: $x \mapsto \dfrac{1}{x + 1}$ $\qquad$ $y + 1 = \dfrac{1}{x}$, $y = \dfrac{1}{x} - 1$

$y = \dfrac{1 - x}{x}$ $\qquad$ f^{-1}: $x \mapsto \dfrac{1 - x}{x}$ $\qquad$ $\dfrac{dy}{dx} = -\dfrac{1}{x^2}$

$x = 0$, $y \mapsto \infty$ an asymptote. $x \mapsto \infty$, $y = -1$ an asymptote.

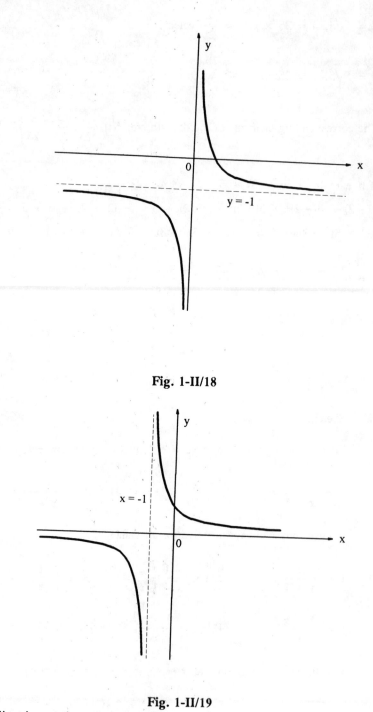

Fig. 1-II/18

Fig. 1-II/19

The gradient is negative.

(c) The domain for f^{-1} is $-\infty < x < 0$ and $0 < x < 0$.

   The range for f^{-1} is $-\infty < y < -1$ and $-1 < y < \infty$.

(d) (i) $f^{-1}(-1) = \dfrac{1 - (-1)}{-1} = -2$

   (ii) $f(2) = \dfrac{1}{3}$

   (iii) $fff(3) = ff\left(\dfrac{1}{4}\right) = f\left(\dfrac{1}{5/4}\right) = f\left(\dfrac{4}{5}\right) = \dfrac{1}{\dfrac{4}{5} + 1} = \dfrac{5}{9}$

   (iv) $f^{-1}(2) = \dfrac{1 - 2}{2} = -\dfrac{1}{2}$.

(e) f and f^{-1} are one-to-one functions.

SOLUTIONS 7

1. (i) $2^{-6} = \dfrac{1}{2^6} = \dfrac{1}{64}$ (ii) $81^{1/2} = (9^2)^{1/2} = 9^1 = 9$

(iii) $2^{-3} = \dfrac{1}{2^3} = \dfrac{1}{8}$ (iv) $64^{-1/2} = (2^6)^{-1/2} = 2^{-3} = \dfrac{1}{8}$

(v) $125^{-3} = \dfrac{1}{125^3} = \dfrac{1}{(5^3)^3} = \dfrac{1}{5^9}$

(vi) $125^{3/2} = (5^3)^{3/2} = 5^{9/2} = 625\sqrt{5}$

(vii) $16^{3/4} = (2^4)^{3/4} = 2^3 = 8$

(viii) $16^{5/3} \times 2^3 \times 32^{-4/3} = (2^4)^{5/3} \times 2^3 \times (2^5)^{-4/3}$

$$= 2^{20/3} \times 8 \times 2^{-20/3} = 8$$

(ix) $81^{1/4} \times 3^5 \times 9^{-3/5} = (3^4)^{1/4} \times 3^5 \times 3^{-6/5}$

$$= 3^1 \times 3^5 \times 3^{-6/5} = 3^{6-6/5} = 3^{24/5}.$$

(x) $128^{3/7} = (2^7)^{3/7} = 2^3 = 8.$

2. (i) $64^{-1/x} = 2$ $(2^6)^{-1/x} = 2^1$ $2^{-6/x} = 2^1$ $-\dfrac{6}{x} = 1$

$x = -6$

(ii) $125^x = 5$ $(5^3)^x = 5^1$ $5^{3x} = 5^1$ $3x = 1$

$x = \dfrac{1}{3}.$

(iii) $\left(\dfrac{49}{81}\right)^{-x} = \dfrac{9}{7}$ $\left(\dfrac{7^2}{9^2}\right)^{-x} = \dfrac{9}{7}$ $\left(\dfrac{7}{9}\right)^{-2x} = \left(\dfrac{9}{7}\right)^1 = \left(\dfrac{7}{9}\right)^{-1}$

$-2x = -1$ $x = \dfrac{1}{2}.$

3. (i) $\left(\dfrac{625}{144}\right)^{-3/2} \times \left(\dfrac{12}{25}\right)^{-4/3} = \left(\dfrac{25^2}{12^2}\right)^{-3/2} \times \dfrac{12^{-4/3}}{25^{-4/3}} = \dfrac{25^{-3}}{12^{-3}} \times \dfrac{12^{-4/3}}{25^{-4/3}}$

$$= \dfrac{25^{-3+4/3}}{12^{-3+4/3}} = \dfrac{25^{-5/3}}{12^{-5/3}} = \dfrac{12^{5/3}}{25^{5/3}} = \left(\dfrac{12}{25}\right)^{5/3}$$

(ii) $\left(\dfrac{729}{169}\right)^{-1/2} = \left(\dfrac{27^2}{13^2}\right)^{-1/2} = \left(\dfrac{13^2}{27^2}\right)^{1/2} = \dfrac{13}{27}$

(iii) $\left(\dfrac{125}{49}\right)^{-1} = \dfrac{49}{125}$

(iv) $1000^{-1/3} = \left(10^3\right)^{-1/3} = 10^{-1} = \dfrac{1}{10}$

(v) $\left(\dfrac{81}{125}\right)^{-1/3} \times 3^{4/3} = \dfrac{\left(3^4\right)^{-1/3}}{\left(5^3\right)^{-1/3}} \times 3^{4/3} = \dfrac{3^{-4/3} \times 3^{4/3}}{5^{-1}} = \dfrac{1}{5^{-1}} = 5.$

4. (i) $\left(e^2\right)^x - e^x - 2 = 0$

$e^{2x} - e^x - 2 = 0$

let $W = e^x$ then $W^2 = e^{2x}$

$W^2 - W - 2 = 0$

$W = \dfrac{1 \pm \sqrt{1 + 8}}{2}$

$W = \dfrac{1 + 3}{2} = 2$ or $W = \dfrac{1 - 3}{2} = -1$

$e^x = 2$

taking logarithms on both sides to the base e

$x \ln e = \ln 2 \qquad x = \ln 2 \qquad x = 0.693$
$e^x = -1$ this does not exist since log
of negative number is complex.

(ii) $6e^{2x} + e^x - 1 = 0$

Let $W = e^x$ then $W^2 = e^{2x}$

$6W^2 + W - 1 = 0$

$W = \dfrac{-1 \pm \sqrt{1 + 24}}{12}$

$W = \dfrac{-1 \pm 5}{12}$

$W = -\dfrac{1}{2}$ or $W = \dfrac{1}{3}$

$e^x = -\dfrac{1}{2}$ does not exist

$e^x = \dfrac{1}{3}$, $\ln e^x = \ln \dfrac{1}{3}$

$x \ln e = -\ln 3$
$x = -\ln 3 = -1.19$

(iii) $\quad 1 - e^{-2x} = 0 \qquad e^{-2x} = 1 \qquad -2x = \ln 1 = 0$

$$\boxed{x = 0}$$

5. Simplify $45 \times 5^{6x+7} - 25 \times 125^{2x+2} = 5 \times 9 \times 5^{6x+7} - 5^2 \times (5^3)^{2x+2}$

$$= 9 \times 5^{6x+8} - 5^{6x+8}$$

$$= (9-1) \times 5^{6x+8} = 8 \times 5^{6x+8}.$$

6. $\quad 25^x - 5^{x+1} - 6 = 0 \qquad W = 5^x \qquad 5^{2x} - 5 \times 5^x - 6 = 0$

$W^2 - 5W - 6 = 0 \qquad W = \dfrac{5 \pm \sqrt{25 + 24}}{2} = \dfrac{5 \pm 7}{2} \qquad x = 6 \text{ or } x = -1$

$5^x = 6 \Rightarrow x = \dfrac{\log 6}{\log 5} = 1.11 \qquad\qquad 5^x = -1 \text{ is not defined.}$

$$\boxed{x = 1.11}$$

7. (i) $\quad 3^{x+5} = 1 \Rightarrow 3^{x+5} = 3^\circ \Rightarrow x + 5 = 0 \Rightarrow \boxed{x = -5}$

(ii) $\quad 27^x = \dfrac{1}{\sqrt[3]{3}} \to (3^3)^x = \dfrac{1}{3^{1/3}} = 3^{-1/3} \to 3^{3x} = 3^{-1/3} \to 3x = -\dfrac{1}{3} \qquad x = -\dfrac{1}{9}$

(iii) $\quad 8^{6x+7} = 16^{-x-5} \Rightarrow (2^3)^{6x+7} = (2^4)^{-x-5} \Rightarrow 2^{18x+21} = 2^{-4x-20}$

$18x + 21 = -4x - 20 \Rightarrow 22x = -41 \Rightarrow \boxed{x = -\dfrac{41}{22}}$

(iv) $\quad x^{-7/5} = 81 \times 125^{3/4} \Rightarrow x^{-7/5} = 3^4 \times (5^3)^{3/4}$

$x^{-7/5} = 3^4 \times 5^{9/4} \Rightarrow \boxed{x = 3^{-20/7} \times 5^{-45/28}} \qquad = 3.26 \times 10^{-3}$

(v) $\quad 4^{2x+2} = 2^{x-1} - 1 \Rightarrow (2^2)^{2x+2} = 2^{x-1} \qquad 4x + 4 = x - 1 \qquad 3x = -5$

$$\boxed{x = -\dfrac{5}{3}}$$

8. (i) $\dfrac{3^x \, 9^{x+1}}{8^{x+2}} = \dfrac{3^x \, (3^2)^{(x+1)}}{2^{3\,(x+2)}} = \dfrac{3^x \, 3^{2x+2}}{2^{3x+6}} = \dfrac{3^{3x+2}}{2^{3x+6}}$

(ii) $\dfrac{4^{-x} \times 16^{2x}}{4^{(-1+x)} \times 2^{3x-2}} = \dfrac{(2^2)^{-x} \times (2^4)^{2x}}{(2^2)^{(-1+x)} \times 2^{3x-2}} = \dfrac{2^{-2x+8x}}{2^{-2+2x+3x-2}} = 2^{x+4}$

(iii) $\dfrac{36^{2x+1} \times 6^3}{216^2 \times 6^0} = \dfrac{(6^2)^{(2x+1)} \times 6^3}{(6^3)^2 \times 6^0} = \dfrac{6^{4x+2+3}}{6^6 \times 1} = 6^{4x-1}$

9. (i) $\dfrac{x^{-1} + y^{-1}}{x^{-2} + y^{-2}} = \dfrac{\dfrac{1}{x} + \dfrac{1}{y}}{\dfrac{1}{x^2} + \dfrac{1}{y^2}} = \dfrac{\dfrac{y+x}{xy}}{\dfrac{x^2+y^2}{x^2 y^2}} = \dfrac{xy\,(y+x)}{(y^2+x^2)}$

(ii) $\left(\dfrac{1}{\sqrt{x}} + \sqrt{x} \right)^2 = \dfrac{1}{x} + x + 2$

(iii) $\dfrac{xy^{-1} + yx^{-1}}{x^3 - y^3} = \dfrac{\dfrac{x}{y} + \dfrac{y}{x}}{x^3 - y^3} = \dfrac{x^2 + y^2}{xy\,(x^3 - y^3)}\,.$

10. (i) $3^{x-y} = 27 \Rightarrow 3^{x-y} = 3^3 \quad \Rightarrow \quad \boxed{x - y = 3} \qquad \dots \text{(1)}$

$5^{y+x} = 1 \Rightarrow 5^{y+x} = 5^0 \quad \Rightarrow \quad \boxed{x + y = 0} \qquad \dots \text{(2)}$

adding (1) and (2) $x = \dfrac{3}{2}, \, y = -\dfrac{3}{2}\,.$

(ii) $5^x \times 25^y = 1 \Rightarrow 5^x \times 5^{2y} = 5^0 \Rightarrow 5^{x+2y} = 5^0.$

$$\boxed{x + 2y = 0} \quad \dots \text{(1)}$$

$6^x = 36^y \, 216 \Rightarrow 6^x = 6^{2y} \times 216 \Rightarrow 6^{x-2y} = 6^3 \text{ hence } \boxed{x - 2y = 3} \; \dots \text{(2)}$

adding (1) and (2)

$$\boxed{x = \dfrac{3}{2}} \qquad\qquad 2y = -\dfrac{3}{2} \Rightarrow \boxed{y = -\dfrac{3}{4}}$$

SOLUTIONS 8

1. (i) $\log_5 625 = 4 \Rightarrow 5^4 = 625$

   (ii) $\log_{12} 144 = 2 \Rightarrow 12^2 = 144$

   (iii) $\log_2 128 = 7 \Rightarrow 2^7 = 128$

   (iv) $\log_{13} 169 = 2 \Rightarrow 13^2 = 169$

   (v) $\log_{1/5} 25 = -2 \Rightarrow (1/5)^{-2} = 25$

   (vi) $\log_{1/7} 49 = -2 \Rightarrow (1/7)^{-2} = 49$

   (vii) $\log_{1/11} 121 \Rightarrow (1/11)^{-2} = 121$

   (viii) $\log_M N = P \Rightarrow M^P = N$

   (ix) $\log_y x^2 = 2 \Rightarrow y^2 = x^2$

   (x) $\log_B A = C \Rightarrow B^C = A$

   (xi) $z \log_y x = w \Rightarrow y^w = x^z$

   (xii) $\log_e 625 = 4 \log_e 5 \Rightarrow 5^4 = 625.$

2. (i) $2^{10} = 1024 \Rightarrow \log_2 1024 = 10$

   (ii) $3^5 = 243 \Rightarrow \log_3 243 = 5$

   (iii) $2^{10} = 1024 \Rightarrow 10 \log_{1024} 2 = 1$

   (iv) $3^5 = 243 \Rightarrow 5 \log_{243} 3 = 1$

   (v) $i = I e^{-t/T} \Rightarrow \dfrac{i}{I} = e^{-t/T} \rightarrow e^{t/T} = \dfrac{I}{i} \rightarrow \dfrac{t}{T} = \log_e \dfrac{I}{i}$

   (vi) $v = V e^{-t/T} \Rightarrow \dfrac{v}{V} = e^{-t/T} \rightarrow \dfrac{V}{v} = e^{t/T} \rightarrow \dfrac{t}{T} = \ln \dfrac{V}{v}$

   (vii) $q = Q e^{-t/T} \Rightarrow \dfrac{q}{Q} = e^{-t/T} \qquad e^{t/T} = \dfrac{Q}{q} \rightarrow \dfrac{t}{T} = \ln \dfrac{Q}{q}$

   (viii) $24^2 = 576 \Rightarrow \log_{24} 576 = 2$

   (ix) $143^2 = 20449 \Rightarrow \log_{143} 20449 = 2$

   (x) $8^4 = 4096 \Rightarrow \log_8 4096 = 4.$

3. (i) $2^{10} = 1024 \Rightarrow \log 1024 = 10 \log 2$

   (ii) $3^5 = 243 \Rightarrow \log_{10} 243 = 5 \log_{10} 3$

(iii) $2^{10} = 1024 \quad \Rightarrow \log_{10} 1024 = 10 \log_{10} 2$

(iv) $3^5 = 243 \quad \Rightarrow \log_{10} 243 = 5 \log_{10} 3$

(v) $i = I e^{-t/T} \quad \Rightarrow \dfrac{i}{I} = e^{-t/T} \rightarrow \dfrac{I}{i} = e^{t/T} \rightarrow \dfrac{t}{T} \log e = \log \dfrac{I}{i}$

(vi) $v = V e^{-t/T} \quad \Rightarrow \dfrac{v}{V} = e^{-t/T} \rightarrow \dfrac{V}{v} = e^{t/T} \rightarrow \dfrac{t}{T} \log e = \log \dfrac{V}{v}$

(vii) $q = Q e^{-t/T} \quad \Rightarrow \dfrac{q}{Q} = e^{-t/T} \rightarrow \dfrac{Q}{q} = e^{t/T} \rightarrow \dfrac{t}{T} \log e = \log \dfrac{Q}{q}$

(viii) $24^2 = 576 \quad \Rightarrow \log 576 = 2 \log 24$

(ix) $143^2 = 20449 \Rightarrow \log 20449 = 2 \log 143$

(x) $8^4 = 4096 \quad \Rightarrow \log 4096 = 4 \log 8.$

4. (i) $e^{\ln x} = X \Rightarrow \ln e^{\ln x} = \ln X \Rightarrow \ln x \ln e = \ln X \Rightarrow x = X$ therefore

$$\boxed{e^{\ln x} = x}$$

(ii) $e^{\ln 1/3} = 1/3$ (iii) $e^{\ln y} = y$ (iv) $e^{\ln 1/e} = \dfrac{1}{e}$

(v) $e^{\ln x^2} = x^2$ (vi) $\log_a a = 1$ (vii) $\log_{1/a} \dfrac{1}{a} = 1$

(viii) $\log_x x = 1$ (ix) $\log_a a^2 = 2$ (x) $\log_{1/3} \dfrac{1}{27} = -3$

(xi) $\log_{25} \dfrac{1}{625^2} = \log_{25} \left(\dfrac{1}{25}\right)^4 = \log_{25} 25^{-4} = -4$

(xii) $\log_4 \dfrac{1}{64} = \log_4 \left(\dfrac{1}{4}\right)^3 = \log_4 4^{-3} = -3$

(xiii) $e^{e^{\ln x}} = e^x$ (xiv) $a^{\log_a 7} = 7$

(xv) $10^{\log 25} = 25$ (xvi) $5^{\log_5 5^2} = 25$

(xvii) $75^{\log_{75} 3} = 3$

(xviii) $10^{\ln x} = X \Rightarrow \ln x \log 10 = \log X \Rightarrow \log X = \ln x \Rightarrow 10^{\ln x} = $ antilog $\ln x$

(xix) $y^{\log_y b} = b$

(xx) $\left(\dfrac{1}{2}\right)^{\frac{1}{2}\log_{1/2} 2} = \left(\dfrac{1}{2}\right)^{\log_{1/2} 2\sqrt{2}} = \sqrt{2}.$

5. $5 \log 64 - \log 36 - 3 \log (1/8) + 3 \log 100$

     $= 5 \log 4^3 - \log 6^2 - 3 \log (1/2)^3 + 3 \log 10^2$

     $= \log 4^{15} - \log 6^2 - \log (1/2)^9 + \log 10^6$

     $= \log \dfrac{4^{15}\, 10^6}{6^2 \left(\dfrac{1}{2}\right)^9} = \log \left(4^{15} \times 10^6 \times 2^9 \times 6^{-2}\right) \approx 16.2.$

6. $\dfrac{\log 8 - \log 4}{3 \log 2 + \log 32} = \dfrac{\log (8/4)}{\log (2^3 \times 32)} = \dfrac{\log 2}{\log 256} = \dfrac{\log_2 2/\log_2 10}{\log_2 256/\log_2 10} = \dfrac{\log_2 2}{\log_2 256} = \dfrac{1}{8}.$

7.   (i) $e^{\log y} = X \Rightarrow \log_e e^{\log y} = \log_e X \Rightarrow \log y = \log_e x$

        $X = $ antilog to the base e of $\log y$

   (ii) $10^{\ln x} = $ antilog to the base 10 of $\ln x$.

   (iii) $z^{\log_z 10} = 10$ (iv) $5^{\log_5 5} = 5$ (v) $7^{2 \log_7 3} = 7^{\log_7 3^2} = 9.$

8. $3 \log_2 1/8 \Rightarrow 3 \log_2 (1/2)^3 = \log_2 (1/2)^9 = \log_2 2^{-9} = -9$

     $3 \log_{1/2} 1/8 \Rightarrow 3 \log_{1/2} (1/2)^3 = \log_{1/2} (1/2)^9 = 9$

     $3 \log_2 (1/8) - 3 \log_{1/2} (1/8) = -9 - 9 = -18.$

9. $x^3 = y$

     $x \log 8 = (x + y) \log 2 \Rightarrow 3x \log 2 = (x + y) \log 2 \Rightarrow 3x = x + y$

     $\Rightarrow 2x = y \Rightarrow 2x = x^3 \Rightarrow x (2 - x^2) = 0$

     $x = 0$ or $x = \pm \sqrt{2}$ are the solutions.

10.   (i) $5^x = 7 \Rightarrow x \log 5 = \log 7 \Rightarrow x = \dfrac{\log 7}{\log 5} = 1.21$

(ii) $3^x = 8^2 \Rightarrow x \log 3 = \log 64 \quad \Rightarrow \quad x = \dfrac{\log 64}{\log 3} = 3.79$

(iii) $2^{x-1} = 8^{2+x} \Rightarrow 2^{x-1} = \left(2^3\right)^{2+x} \Rightarrow \quad 2^{x-1} = 2^{6+3x}$

$x - 1 = 6 + 3x \Rightarrow 2x = -7 \quad \Rightarrow \quad \boxed{x = -\dfrac{7}{2}}$

(iv) $3^{x-2} = 3^{2x} \Rightarrow 2x = x - 2 \qquad \Rightarrow \quad \boxed{x = -2}$

(v) $4^{1/x} = 7 \Rightarrow \left(\dfrac{1}{x}\right) \log 4 = \log 7 \Rightarrow \quad x = \dfrac{\log 4}{\log 7} \qquad\qquad \boxed{x = 0.712}$

(vi) $5^{1/x-1} = 25 \Rightarrow 5^{1/x-1} = 5^2 \qquad \Rightarrow \quad \dfrac{1}{x} - 1 = 2 \qquad\qquad \boxed{x = \dfrac{1}{3}}$

(vii) $3^x \times 5^{x+1} = 9^2 \qquad \log 3^x + \log 5^{x+1} = \log 81$

$x \log 3 + (x + 1) \log 5 = \log 81$

$0.477x + 0.699x + 0.699 = 1.9 \qquad\qquad 1.176x = 1.211 \qquad \boxed{x \approx 1.03}$

(viii) $3.76^x = 7.95 \Rightarrow x \log 3.76 = \log 7.95 \qquad x = \dfrac{\log 7.95}{\log 3.76} \qquad \boxed{x = 1.565}$

(ix) $11^x = 4 \Rightarrow x \log 11 = \log 4 \qquad\qquad x = \dfrac{\log 4}{\log 11} = 0.578 \qquad \boxed{x = 0.578}$

(x) $3.6^{-x} = 25 \Rightarrow -x \log 3.6 = \log 25 \qquad x = -\dfrac{\log 25}{\log 3.6} \qquad \boxed{x = -2.513}$

(xi) $\left(\dfrac{1}{3.9}\right)^{x-1} = 37.37 \Rightarrow (x - 1) \log \dfrac{1}{3.9} = \log 37.37$

$(x - 1)(-0.591) = 1.573 \qquad\qquad x - 1 = -2.661 \qquad \boxed{x = -1.661}$

(xii) $7.3^x = 9.9 \Rightarrow x \log 7.3 = \log 9.9 \qquad x = \dfrac{\log 9.9}{\log 7.3} = 1.153 \qquad \boxed{x = 1.153}$

(xiii) $\left(\dfrac{1}{5.9}\right)^x = \dfrac{1}{25.25} \Rightarrow 5.9^x = 25.25 \qquad x = \dfrac{\log 25.25}{\log 5.9} = 1.819 \qquad \boxed{x = 1.819}$

(xiv) $4.7^x = \dfrac{1}{3.9} \Rightarrow x = \dfrac{\log 1/3.9}{\log 4.7} = -0.879 \qquad\qquad \boxed{x = -0.879}$

(xv) $(3900)^x = 47 \Rightarrow x = \dfrac{\log 47}{\log 3900} = 0.466$ $\boxed{x = 0.466}$

(xvi) $(81000)^x = 39000 \Rightarrow x = \dfrac{\log 39000}{\log 81000}$ $\boxed{x = 0.935}$

(xvii) $680^x = 3.9 \Rightarrow x = \dfrac{\log 3.9}{\log 680} = 0.209$ $\boxed{x = 0.209}$

11. $5^{x+3} + 5^{x+1} = 100$, $5^x 5^3 + 5^x 5 = 100$.

Let $w = 5^x$ then $125w + 5w = 100 \Rightarrow 130w = 100 \Rightarrow w = \dfrac{100}{130}$,

$w = 0.7692307 = 5^x \Rightarrow x = \dfrac{\log 0.7692307}{\log 5} = -0.163$ $\boxed{x = -0.163}$

12. $2^{3x} - 6 \times 2^{2x+1} + 41 \times 2^x = 30$. Let $2^x = w$, $2^{2x} = w^2$, $2^{3x} = w^3$

$w^3 - 6 \times 2 \times w^2 + 41w - 30 = 0$, $w^3 - 12w^2 + 41w - 30 = 0$.

Let $w = 1$, $f(1) = 1 - 12 + 41 - 30 = 0$, therefore $w - 1$ is a factor.

By long division

$$
\begin{array}{r}
w^2 - 11w + 30 \\
w - 1 \enclose{longdiv}{w^3 - 12w^2 + 41w - 30} \\
\underline{w^3 - w^2} \\
-11w^2 + 41w - 30 \\
\underline{-11w^2 + 11w} \\
30w - 30 \\
\underline{30w - 30} \\
0 \text{ remainder}
\end{array}
$$

$f(w) = (w - 1)(w^2 - 11w + 30) = 0$

$w = 1$, or $w = \dfrac{11 \pm \sqrt{121 - 120}}{2} = \dfrac{11 \pm 1}{2}$

$x = 6$ or $x = 5$ $\qquad w = 1, w = 5, w = 6$ $\qquad 2^x = 1 \Rightarrow$ $\boxed{x = 0}$

$2^x = 5 \Rightarrow x = \dfrac{\log 5}{\log 2} = 2.32$ $\qquad 2^x = 6 \Rightarrow x = \dfrac{\log 6}{\log 2} = 2.59$

$\boxed{x = 0}$ $\qquad\qquad\qquad$ $\boxed{x = 2.32}$ and $\boxed{x = 2.59}$

13. (i) $e^y - e^{-y} - 2x = 0$ multiplying by e^y each term $e^{2y} - 2x\,e^y - 1 = 0$

$$e^y = \frac{2x \pm \sqrt{4\,x^2 + 4}}{2} = x \pm \sqrt{x^2 + 1}$$ taking logarithms to the base e on both

sides $y = \ln\left(x + \sqrt{x^2 + 1}\right)$ since $x - \sqrt{x^2 + 1}$ is negative and the logarithm

is not defined.

(ii) $e^y + e^{-y} - 2x = 0$ multiplying by e^y each term $e^{2y} - 2x\,e^y + 1 = 0$

$$e^y = \frac{2x \pm \sqrt{4\,x^2 - 4}}{2} = x \pm \sqrt{x^2 - 1}$$ taking logarithms to the base e on both

sides $y = \ln\left(x \pm \sqrt{x^2 - 1}\right)$ $y = \ln\left(x + \sqrt{x^2 - 1}\right)$ or $y = \ln\left(x - \sqrt{x^2 - 1}\right)$

both quantities inside the brackets are positive and the logarithms exist, but

$$x + \sqrt{x^2 - 1} = \frac{1}{x - \sqrt{x^2 - 1}}$$ since $\left(x + \sqrt{x^2 - 1}\right)\left(x - \sqrt{x^2 - 1}\right) = 1$

$x^2 - \left(x^2 - 1\right) = 1$ therefore $\boxed{y = \pm \ln\left(x + \sqrt{x^2 - 1}\right)}$

14. (i) $5 \log x = \log 10 \Rightarrow x^5 = 10$.

(ii) $4 \log x^{1/2} - 3 \log x^2 + 2 \log x^3 - \log x^4 + \log 10 = 0$

$$\log_{10} \frac{x^2 \times x^6}{x^6 \times x^4} = -1 \qquad x^{-2} = 10^{-1} \Rightarrow x^2 = 10 \Rightarrow \qquad \boxed{x = \sqrt{10}}$$

(iii) $3 \log x + 4 \log y + 5 \log z + 7 \log w = 3$

$\log x^3 + \log y^4 + \log z^5 + \log w^7 = 3$ $\log_{10} x^3\,y^4\,z^5\,w^7 = 3$

$x^3\,y^4\,z^5\,w^7 = 10^3 = 1000$.

(iv) $\log y + 1 = 3 \log x$ $\log y + \log 10 = \log x^3$ $\log 10y = \log x^3$

$$\boxed{y = \frac{1}{10}\,x^3}$$

(v) $\log y + 2 = \log x$ $\log y + \log 100 = \log x$ $\boxed{100y = x}$

SOLUTIONS 9

1. (i) $e^{1/2} = 1 + \dfrac{\left(\frac{1}{2}\right)}{1!} + \dfrac{\left(\frac{1}{2}\right)^2}{2!} + \dfrac{\left(\frac{1}{2}\right)^3}{3!} + \dfrac{\left(\frac{1}{2}\right)^4}{4!}$

$= 1 + \dfrac{1}{2} + \dfrac{1}{8} + \dfrac{1}{48} + \dfrac{1}{384} = 1.65$

(ii) $e^{-1} = 1 + \dfrac{(-1)}{1!} + \dfrac{(-1)^2}{2!} + \dfrac{(-1)^3}{3!} + \dfrac{(-1)^4}{4!}$

$= 1 - 1 + \dfrac{1}{2} - \dfrac{1}{6} + \dfrac{1}{24} = \dfrac{9}{24} = 0.375$

(iii) $e^{-y} = 1 + \dfrac{(-y)}{1!} + \dfrac{(-y)^2}{2!} + \dfrac{(-y)^3}{3!} + \dfrac{(-y)^4}{4!}$

$= 1 - y + \dfrac{y^2}{2} - \dfrac{y^3}{6} + \dfrac{y^4}{24}$

(iv) $e^2 = 1 + \dfrac{2}{1!} + \dfrac{2^2}{2!} + \dfrac{2^3}{3!} + \dfrac{2^4}{4!} = 1 + 2 + 2 + \dfrac{8}{6} + \dfrac{16}{24} = 7.$

(v) $e^{x/2} = 1 + \dfrac{x}{2} + \dfrac{(x/2)^2}{2!} + \dfrac{(x/2)^3}{3!} + \dfrac{(x/2)^4}{4!}.$

2. $e^{2x} = 1 + \dfrac{2x}{1!} + \dfrac{(2x)^2}{2!} + \dfrac{(2x)^3}{3!} + \ldots = 1 + 2x + 2x^2 + \dfrac{4}{3}x^3 + \ldots$

3. $e^{3x} = 1 + 3x + \dfrac{(3x)^2}{2!} + \dfrac{(3x)^3}{3!} + \ldots = 1 + 3x + \dfrac{9}{2}x^2 + \dfrac{9}{2}x^3 + \ldots$

4. (i) $\dfrac{e^x + e^{-x}}{2} = \dfrac{1}{2}\left(1 + \dfrac{x}{1!} + \dfrac{x^2}{2!} + \dfrac{x^3}{3!} + \dfrac{x^4}{4!} + \ldots + 1 - \dfrac{x}{1!} + \dfrac{x^2}{2!} - \dfrac{x^3}{3!} + \dfrac{x^4}{4!} + \ldots\right)$

$= 1 + \dfrac{x^2}{2!} + \dfrac{x^4}{4!} + \ldots$

(ii) $$\frac{e^x - e^{-x}}{2} = \frac{1}{2}\left(1 + \frac{x}{1!} + \frac{x^2}{2!} + \frac{x^3}{3!} + \ldots - 1 + \frac{x}{1!} - \frac{x^2}{2!} + \frac{x^3}{3!} - \ldots\right)$$

$$= \frac{x}{1!} + \frac{x^3}{3!} + \frac{x^5}{5!} + \ldots$$

5. Graphs are shown in the text.

6. Graphs are shown in the text.

7. (i) $\lim\limits_{x \to \infty} e^{-ky} = \frac{1}{e^{\infty}} = \frac{1}{\infty} = 0.$

(ii) $\lim\limits_{x \to -\infty} e^{kx} = \frac{1}{e^{\infty}} = \frac{1}{\infty} = 0.$

8. See text.

9. See text.

10. (i)

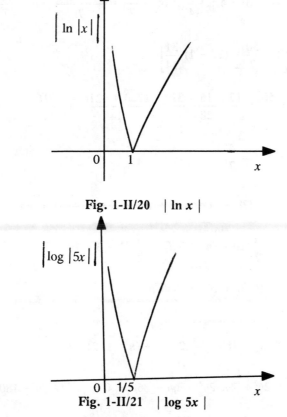

Fig. 1-II/20 $| \ln x |$

(ii)

Fig. 1-II/21 $| \log 5x |$

SOLUTIONS 10

1. $1 + 3 + 5 + \ldots + 199$

$$S_n = \frac{n}{2}[2a + (n - 1)\, d], \; l = a + (n - 1)\, d$$

$$a = 1, l = 199 = 1 + (n - 1)\, 2, \; n - 1 = 99, \; n = 100$$

$$S_{100} = \frac{100}{2}[2 \times 1 + 99 \times 2] = 50 \times 200 = 10{,}000.$$

2. $l_5 = a + (5 - 1)\, d, \; l_{19} = a + (19 - 1)\, d$

$l_5 = 16, \; l_{19} = 47 \qquad 16 = a + 4d, \; 47 = a + 18d$

$$47 - 16 = 14d \qquad d = \frac{31}{14}$$

$$a = 16 - 4d = 16 - 4 \times \frac{31}{14} = 16 - \frac{62}{7} = \frac{112 - 62}{7} = a = \frac{50}{7}.$$

$$S_{17} = \frac{17}{2}\left[2 \times \frac{50}{7} + (17 - 1)\,\frac{31}{14}\right]$$

$$S_{17} = 17 \times \frac{50}{7} + \frac{17 \times 16 \times 31}{28} = \frac{1700 + 4216}{14} = \frac{5916}{14}$$

$$S_{17} = \frac{2958}{7} = 422\,\frac{4}{7}.$$

3. (a) $\quad l_{28} = a + (28 - 1)\, d = 3 + 27 \times 3 = 3 + 81 = 84$

   (b) $\quad S_n \quad = \frac{n}{2}[2a + (n - 1)\, d] = \frac{20}{2}[2 \times 3 + 19 \times 3]$

   $\qquad S_{20} \quad = 10\,(6 + 57) = 630.$

4. $a = 4, d = 2, S_n = 180 = \frac{n}{2}[2 \times 4 + (n - 1)\, 2]$

   $360 = 8n + 2n^2 - 2n, \; 2n^2 + 6n - 360 = 0 \qquad n^2 + 3n - 180 = 0$

$$n = \frac{-3 \pm \sqrt{9 + 4 \times 180}}{2} = \frac{-3 \pm 27}{2}$$

$n = 12$ or $n = -15$ which is disregarded.

5. $a = 199, d = 194 - 199 = -5$

$$S_n = \frac{n}{2}[2a + (n - 1)d]$$

$$= \frac{n}{2}[2 \times 199 + (n - 1)(-5)] = \frac{n}{2} \, 398 - \frac{n}{2}(n - 1) \, 5$$

$$= 398 \frac{n}{2} - \frac{5n^2}{2} + 5 \frac{n}{2} < 0$$

$$-\frac{5}{2} n^2 + 403 \frac{n}{2} < 0, \text{ or } 5n^2 - 403n > 0$$

$$n \, (5n - 403) > 0$$

$$n < 0 \text{ or } n > \frac{403}{5} = 80 \frac{3}{5} \qquad \therefore \boxed{n = 81}$$

6.   If (a) is the first term, $a + d$, is the second term, $a + 2d$ is the third term, $a + (n - 1) \, d$ is the nth term, therefore the last or n^{th} term is given by $l = a + (n - 1) \, d$.

7. $S_n = \frac{n}{2}[2N + (n - 1) \, M]$ see text, substitute $a = N$ and $d = M$.

8. $x = \frac{100 + y}{2}$ and $y = \frac{82 + x}{2}$ $2x = 100 + y, \, 2y = 82 + x$ $x = 2y - 82$

$$100 + y = 4y - 164, \, 3y = 264, \, y = \frac{264}{3}$$

$$y = 88, \, x = 2 \times 88 - 82 = 176 - 82 = 94.$$

9. 2, 4, 6 ..... 1998 $d = 2, a = 2, n = 999$

$$S_n = \frac{n}{2}[2a + (n - 1) d] = S_{999} = \frac{999}{2}[4 + 998 \times 2]$$

$$= 1000 \times 999 = 999000.$$

10. $\log 12 - \log 3 = \log \dfrac{12}{3} = \log 4 = d$

$a + (n - 1) d = \log 12 + (n - 1) \log 4 = \log 12 + \log 4^{n - 1}$

$$= \log 12 \times 4^{n - 1} = \log 3 \times 4^n.$$

$$S_n = \frac{n}{2}[2a + (n - 1) d] = \frac{n}{2}[2 \log 3 + (n - 1) \log 4]$$

$$= \frac{n}{2}\left[\log 3^2 \, 4^{n - 1}\right] = \log (9 \times 4^{n - 1})^{n/2}.$$

11. $S_n = \dfrac{n}{2}[a + l]$ see text.

12. $S_n = \dfrac{n}{2}[a + N]$ $2S_n = na + nN$ $\dfrac{2S_n - nN}{n} = a.$

13. $l_{27} = 1 + (27 - 1) 1 = 27$, where $a = 1, d = 1$.

14. $l_{35} = - 3 + (35 - 1) 2 = - 3 + 68 = 65, a = - 3, d = 2$.

15. $l_5 = \dfrac{1}{4} + (5 - 1) \left(\dfrac{5}{8} - \dfrac{1}{4}\right) = \dfrac{1}{4} + 4 \times \dfrac{3}{8} = \dfrac{1}{4} + \dfrac{3}{2} = \dfrac{7}{4}, a = \dfrac{1}{4}, d = \dfrac{3}{8}$

16. $l_{12} = - 7 + (12 - 1) (- 5) = - 7 - 55 = - 62, a = - 7, d = - 5$.

17. $l_{50} = - \dfrac{1}{2} + (50 - 1) \left(- 1 + \dfrac{1}{2}\right) = - \dfrac{1}{2} + 49 \left(- \dfrac{1}{2}\right) = - 25, a = - \dfrac{1}{2}, d = - \dfrac{1}{2}.$

18. (i) $l_n = 1 + (n - 1) 5 = 1 + 5n - 5 = 5n - 4$

    (ii) $l_n = 1 + (n - 1) (- 4) = 1 - 4n + 4 = 5 - 4n$

    (iii) $l_n = \dfrac{3}{8} + (n - 1) \left(\dfrac{1}{2} - \dfrac{3}{8}\right) = \dfrac{3}{8} + (n - 1) \dfrac{1}{8} = \dfrac{1}{4} + \dfrac{1}{8}n.$

19. $l_n = 27, a = 5, l_n = a + (n - 1) d, d = \dfrac{l_n - a}{(n - 1)} = \dfrac{27 - 5}{n - 1} = \dfrac{22}{n - 1}$

$d = \dfrac{22}{4} = \dfrac{11}{2}.$

20. $l_{37} = 3 + (37 - 1) 5 = 3 + 36 \times 5 = 183.$

21. $2 \times 1 - 1, 2 \times 2 - 1, 2 \times 3, - 1, \ldots, 2 \times n - 1 = 1, 3, 5, \ldots 2n - 1.$

22. $2 \times 1, 2 \times 2, 2 \times 3, \ldots, 2n \qquad 2, 4, 6, \ldots, 2n.$

23. $S_{45} = \dfrac{1}{2} + (45 - 1) \left(\dfrac{1}{4} - \dfrac{1}{2} \right) = \dfrac{1}{2} + 44 \left(- \dfrac{1}{4} \right) = \dfrac{1}{2} - 11 = - 10 \dfrac{1}{2}, a = \dfrac{1}{2},$

$d = - \dfrac{1}{4}.$

24. $S_n = 0.1 + (n - 1) (0.3 - 0.1) = 0.1 + (n - 1) (0.2) = 0.2n - 0.1.$

25. $S_{25} = \dfrac{25}{2} \left[2 \times \left(- \dfrac{1}{4} \right) + (25 - 1) \left(- \dfrac{1}{2} + \dfrac{1}{4} \right) \right] = \dfrac{25}{2} \left(- \dfrac{1}{2} - \dfrac{24}{4} \right)$

$= - \dfrac{25 \times 26}{8} = - 81 \dfrac{1}{4}.$

26. $S_{33} = \dfrac{33}{2} [2 \times 0.125 + (33 - 1) (0.25 - 0.125)] = \dfrac{33}{2} [0.25 + 32 \times 0.125]$

$= \dfrac{33}{2} \times 4.25 = 70 \dfrac{1}{8}.$

27. $a = 1, d = 6, l_n = 247 = a + (n - 1) d = 1 + (n - 1) 6$

$\dfrac{247 - 1}{6} = n - 1, n = \dfrac{246}{6} + 1 = 42.$

28. $l_n = x + (n - 1) y.$

29. $l_n = N + (n - 1) D.$

30. $S_p = \dfrac{P}{2} [2A + (P - 1) Q]$ see text

replace $n = P, a = A, d = Q$.

31.

$\dfrac{n(n+1)}{2}$	$n = 1$	$\dfrac{1 \times 1}{2} = 1$	the sum of the first term
	$n = 2$	$\dfrac{2 \times 3}{2} = 3$	the sum of the first two terms
	$n = 3$	$\dfrac{3 \times 4}{2} = 6$	the sum of the first three terms

therefore 1, 2, 3, 4, 5.

32.

$n^2 - 7n$	$n = 1$	$1 - 7 = -6$	the sum of the first term
	$n = 2$	$4 - 14 = -10$	the sum of the first two terms
	$n = 3$	$9 - 21 = -12$	the sum of the first three terms

$-6, -4, -2$

33. $a, b, c \quad b - a = c - b, 2b = c + a, \quad b = \dfrac{c + a}{2}.$

34. $1, x, 51, y$

$x = \dfrac{1 + 51}{2} = 26, 51 = \dfrac{26 + y}{2}, y = 102 - 26 = 76$

35. $5(1 + 1), 5(2 + 1), 5(3 + 1), \ldots$ or 10, 15, 20, ...

$S_{25} = \dfrac{25}{2} (20 + 24 \times 5) = 25 \times 70 = 1750.$

SOLUTIONS 11

1. (i) 2, 4, 8, 16, 32, 64, 128 ... 2^n the common ratio is 2, therefore 8 x 2 = 16 which is the next term 16 x 2 = 32, after 16 and so on, the nth term is 2^n.

(ii) $r = \dfrac{1}{2}$ $1, \dfrac{1}{2}, \dfrac{1}{4}, \dfrac{1}{8}, \dfrac{1}{16}, \dfrac{1}{32}, \dfrac{1}{64}, ... , \left(\dfrac{1}{2}\right)^{n-1}$.

(iii) $r = \dfrac{-x}{x} = -1$ $x, -x, x, -x, x, -x, ... (-1)^{n-1} x$

(iv) 1, 3, 9, 27, 81, 243, 729, ..., 3^{n-1}.

(v) $a, ar, ar^2, ar^3, ar^4, ar^5, ar^6, ..., ar^{n-1}$

(vi) 729, 243, 81, 27, 9, 3, 1, ..., $\left(\dfrac{1}{3}\right)^{n-1}$. $r = \dfrac{243}{729} = \dfrac{1}{3}$

(vii) $-2, 4, -8, 16, -32, 64, -128, ..., (-2)^n$ $r = \dfrac{4}{-2} = -2$

(viii) 1, 7, 49, 343, 2401, 16807, 117649, ..., 7^{n-1} $r = \dfrac{7}{1}$

(ix) 3, 6, 12, 24, 48, 96, 192, ..., $3 \times 2^{n-1}$ $\dfrac{6}{3} = r = 2$

(x) 1, 5, 25, 125, 625, 3125, 15625, ..., 5^{n-1} $\dfrac{5}{1} = r$.

2. (i) 2^{15} (ii) $\left(\dfrac{1}{2}\right)^{14}$ (iii) x (iv) 3^{14} (v) ar^{14}

(vi) $\left(\dfrac{1}{3}\right)^{14}$ (vii) -2^{15} (viii) 7^{14} (ix) 3×2^{14} (x) 5^{14}.

3. $S_n = \dfrac{2(1 - 2^n)}{1 - 2} = 2 \times \dfrac{2^n - 1}{1} = 2^{n+1} - 2 > 500$

$a = 2$ $r = 2$ $2^{n+1} - 2 > 500$ $2^{n+1} > 502$

$(n + 1) > \dfrac{\log 502}{\log 2} = 8.97$ $n > 7.97$ $n = 8$.

4. 729,243,81, ... $a = 729$

$$r = \frac{243}{729} = \frac{1}{3}$$ $$S_n = \frac{a(1-r^n)}{1-r} > 1093$$

$$S_n = \frac{729\left(1 - \dfrac{1}{3^n}\right)}{1 - \dfrac{1}{3}} > 1093$$

$$729\left(1 - \frac{1}{3^n}\right) > 1093 \times \frac{2}{3}$$ $$1 - \frac{1}{3^n} > \frac{1093 \times 2}{729 \times 3}$$

$$1 - \frac{1}{3^n} > 0.999542752$$ $$1 - 0.999542752 > \frac{1}{3^n}$$

$$\frac{1}{3^n} < 4.57247374 \times 10^{-4}$$

$$3^n > 2186.999985 \quad \boxed{n = 7}$$

5. $$\frac{a(1-r^n)}{1-r} > 10000$$ $$\frac{1(1-3^n)}{1-3} > 10000$$

$$\frac{3^n - 1}{2} > 10000$$ $$3^n - 1 > 20000$$

$$3^n > 20001$$ $$\boxed{\text{If } n = 10}$$

$$3^{10} = 59049 \qquad \text{if } n = 9 \qquad 3^9 = 19683$$

6. The geometric mean $a = \sqrt{3 \times 2187} = 81$.

The geometric mean $b = \sqrt{3a} = \sqrt{3 \times 81} = \sqrt{243}$.

The geometric mean $c = \sqrt{2187a} = \sqrt{177147}$.

Where a, b and c are the three geometric means between 3 and 2187.

Therefore, the three geometric means are $\sqrt{243}$, 81, $\sqrt{177147}$ and the series is 3, $\sqrt{243}$, 81, $\sqrt{177147}$, 2187.

7. n^{th} term $= 7 \times 3^{n-3}$. If $n = 1$, $7 \times 3^{-2} = \dfrac{7}{9}$ is the first term.

If $n = 2$, $7 \times 3^{-1} = \dfrac{7}{3}$ is the second term and 7 the third term.

$$S_n = \left(\frac{7}{3^2}\right)\frac{(1 - 3^n)}{1 - 3} \qquad\qquad r = \frac{7/3}{7/9} = 3$$

$$S_n = \frac{7}{9} \times \frac{3^n - 1}{2} = \frac{7}{18}(3^n - 1) \qquad\qquad S_{25} = \frac{7}{18}(3^{25} - 1).$$

8. n^{th} term $= \dfrac{1}{3} 5^{2n-2}$.

If $n = 1$, $a = \dfrac{1}{3}5^0 = \dfrac{1}{3}$.

If $n = 2$, $ar = \dfrac{1}{3}5^2$ therefore $r = 25$

$$\frac{1}{3}, \frac{1}{3} \times 5^2, \frac{1}{3} \times 5^4, ... \frac{1}{3} \times 5^{2n-2} \qquad\qquad S_n = \frac{\frac{1}{3}(1 - (5^2)^n)}{1 - 5^2}$$

$$S_{35} = \frac{1}{3}\frac{(5^2)^{35} - 1}{5^2 - 1} = \frac{1}{72}(5^{70} - 1).$$

9. (i) $a = 2, r = 2$ $\qquad\qquad S_{30} = 2\dfrac{(2^{30} - 1)}{2 - 1} = 2(2^{30} - 1)$

(ii) $a = 1, r = \dfrac{1}{2}$ $\qquad\qquad S_{30} = \dfrac{(1/2^{30} - 1)}{\dfrac{1}{2} - 1} = 2\left(1 - \dfrac{1}{2^{30}}\right)$

(iii) $a = x, r = -1$ $\qquad\qquad S_{30} = \dfrac{x(1 - (-1)^{30})}{[1 - (-1)]} = \dfrac{x(1 - 1)}{2} = 0$

(iv) $a = 1, r = 3$ $\qquad\qquad S_{30} = \dfrac{3^{30} - 1}{2}$

(v) $S_{30} = \dfrac{a(1 - r^{30})}{1 - r}$

(vi) $a = 729, r = \dfrac{243}{729} = \dfrac{1}{3}$ $S_{30} = 729 \dfrac{\left(1 - \dfrac{1}{3^{30}}\right)}{1 - 1/3} = 729 \times \dfrac{3}{2}\left(1 - \dfrac{1}{3^{30}}\right)$

(vii) $a = -2, r = -2$ $S_{30} = \dfrac{-2\left(1 - (-2)^{30}\right)}{1 - (-2)} = -\dfrac{2}{3}\left(1 + 2^{30}\right)$

(viii) $1, 7, 49, \ldots$

$a = 1, r = 7$ $S_{30} = \dfrac{1 - 7^{30}}{1 - 7} = \dfrac{7^{30} - 1}{6} = \dfrac{1}{6}\left(7^{30} - 1\right)$

(ix) $a = 3, r = 2$ $S_{30} = 3\dfrac{\left(2^{30} - 1\right)}{2 - 1} = 3\left(2^{30} - 1\right)$

(x) $a = 1, r = 5$ $S_{30} = \dfrac{1}{4}\left(5^{30} - 1\right)$

---

10. (i) $0.\dot{3}\dot{3} = 0.333333\ldots = 0.3 + 0.03 + 0.003 + 0.0003 + \ldots$

$= 0.3\,(1 + 0.1 + 0.01 + 0.001 + \ldots)$

$= \dfrac{3}{10}\dfrac{1}{1 - 0.1} = \dfrac{3}{10}\dfrac{1}{0.9} = \dfrac{3}{9} = \dfrac{1}{3}$

$S_\infty = \dfrac{a}{1 - r} = \dfrac{1}{1 - 0.1} = \dfrac{1}{0.9}$ $a = 1, r = 0.1$ $0.\overline{33} = \dfrac{1}{3}.$

(ii) $3.767676 = 3 + 0.767676\ldots = 3 + 0.76 + 0.0076 + 0.000076 + \ldots$

$= 3 + 0.76\,(1 + 0.01 + 0.01^2 + \ldots)$

$= 3 + \dfrac{76}{100}\dfrac{1}{1 - 0.01} = 3 + \dfrac{76}{99} = \dfrac{297 + 76}{99} = \dfrac{373}{99}.$

(iii) $2.169169169\ldots\ 2 + 0.169 + 0.000169 + 0.000000169\ldots$

$= 2 + 0.169\,(1 + 0.001 + 0.001^2 + \ldots)$

$= 2 + \dfrac{169}{1000}\dfrac{1}{1 - 0.001} = 2 + \dfrac{169}{999} = \dfrac{2167}{999}$

$2.\dot{1}6\dot{9} = \dfrac{2167}{999}.$

11. $ar^{n-1} = n^{th}$ term, $ar^6 = 7^{th}$ term

$ar^6 = 250 \ldots (1)$ $ar^{16} = 1525 \ldots (2)$

dividing (2) by (1) $\dfrac{ar^{16}}{ar^6} = \dfrac{1525}{250}$

$$r^{10} = \frac{1525}{250} = \frac{305}{50} = \frac{61}{10}$$

$$r = \left(\frac{61}{10}\right)^{1/10}$$

$$ar^6 = 250 = a\left(\frac{61}{10}\right)^{6/10}$$

$$a = 250\left(\frac{10}{61}\right)^{3/5}$$

$$250\left(\frac{10}{61}\right)^{3/5}, \ 250\left(\frac{10}{61}\right)^{3/5}\left(\frac{61}{10}\right)^{1/10}, \ 250\left(\frac{10}{61}\right)^{3/5}\left(\frac{61}{10}\right)^{2/10}$$

are the first three terms or

$$250\left(\frac{10}{61}\right)^{3/5}, \ 250\,\frac{10^{3/5-1/10}}{61^{3/5-1/10}}, \ 250\,\frac{10^{3/5-2/10}}{61^{3/5-2/10}} \ \text{or}$$

$$250\left(\frac{10}{61}\right)^{3/5}, \ 250\left(\frac{10}{61}\right)^{1/2}, \ 250\left(\frac{10}{61}\right)^{2/5}.$$

12. $S_x = P + PR + PR^2 + \ldots + PR^{x-1}$ $\ldots (1)$

$RS_x = PR + PR^2 + \ldots + PR^{x-1} + PR^x$ $\ldots (2)$

(1) − (2) $S_x(1 - R) = P - PR^x$

$$S_x = P\,\frac{1 - R^x}{1 - R} \qquad R^x \to 0 \text{ as } |R| < 1 \text{ and}$$

$$X \to \infty \qquad S_\infty = \frac{P}{I - R}.$$

13. $l_n = ar^{n-1}$ $\qquad S_n = l_1 + l_2 + l_3 + \dots + l_n$

$l_1 = ar^{1-1} = ar^0 = a,\ l_2 = ar,\ l_3 = ar^2,\ \dots\ l_n = ar^{n-1}$

$S_n = a + ar + ar^2 + \dots + ar^{n-1}$

(i) $\quad S_n = \dfrac{a(1 - r^n)}{1 - r}$

(ii) $\quad l_1\, l_2\, l_3 \dots l_n\ = a.\,ar.\,ar^2 \dots ar^{n-1} = a^n\, r^{0 + 1 + 2 + \dots + (n-1)}$

$$= a^n\, r^{n(n-1)/2}$$

where $1 + 2 + \dots + (n - 1) = \dfrac{n-1}{2}\,[2 + (n - 2)] = \dfrac{(n-1)\,n}{2}$

14. $\quad a,\, b,\, c \qquad r = \dfrac{b}{a} = \dfrac{c}{b} \Rightarrow b = \sqrt{ac}$

$$S_n = \frac{a\left[1 - \left(\dfrac{\sqrt{ac}}{a}\right)^n\right]}{1 - \dfrac{\sqrt{ac}}{a}} = \frac{a\left(1 - a^{n/2}\,\dfrac{c^{n/2}}{a^n}\right)}{1 - \dfrac{a^{1/2}\,c^{1/2}}{a}} = \frac{a\left(1 - \dfrac{c^{n/2}}{a^{n/2}}\right)}{\left(1 - \dfrac{c^{1/2}}{a^{1/2}}\right)}.$$

15. $\qquad\qquad a \qquad\qquad\qquad b \qquad\qquad\qquad c$

First $\qquad\qquad\qquad$ third $\qquad\qquad\qquad$ fifth $\qquad\qquad b = \sqrt{ac}$

$a,\ \sqrt{a\sqrt{ac}},\ b,\ \sqrt{c\sqrt{ac}},\ c.$

The second and fourth terms are $\sqrt{a\sqrt{ac}}$ and $\sqrt{c\sqrt{ac}}$ respectively.

16. $\quad S_{30} = 1 + 1.01 + 1.01^2 + \dots$

$$S_{30} = \frac{1 - 1.01^{30}}{1 - 1.01} = \frac{1.01^{30} - 1}{1.01 - 1} = \frac{1.01^{30} - 1}{0.01}$$

$$\boxed{S_{30} = 100\,(1.01^{30} - 1)}$$

17. $\dfrac{(a+1)}{b^0}, \dfrac{(a+1)^2}{b^1}, \dfrac{(a+1)^3}{b^2}, \dots \dfrac{(a+1)^n}{b^{n-1}}$

$$S_n = (a+1)\,\dfrac{\left[1-\left(\dfrac{a+1}{b}\right)^n\right]}{\left[1-\dfrac{a+1}{b}\right]} = \dfrac{(a+1)}{b^{n-1}}\,\dfrac{[(a+1)^n - b^n]}{[a+1-b]}.$$

18. (i) $\quad 0.4\dot{6}\dot{5} \quad = 0.4 + 0.065 + 0.00065 + 0.0000065 + \dots$

$\qquad\qquad\quad = 0.4 + 0.065\,(1 + 0.01 + 0.01^2 + \dots)$

$$= \dfrac{4}{10} + \dfrac{65}{1000}\,\dfrac{1}{1-0.01} = \dfrac{4}{10} + \dfrac{65}{990} = \dfrac{4\times 99 + 65}{990} = \dfrac{461}{990}$$

(ii) $\quad 1.\dot{2}3\dot{5} \quad = 1.235235\dots = 1 + 0.235 + 0.000235 + \dots$

$\qquad\qquad\quad = 1 + 0.235\,(1 + 0.001 + 0.001^2 + \dots)$

$$= 1 + \dfrac{235}{1000}\cdot\dfrac{1}{1-0.001} = 1 + \dfrac{235}{999} = \dfrac{1234}{999}$$

(iii) $\quad 2.35656.. \quad = 2.3 + 0.056 + 0.00056 + \dots$

$\qquad\qquad\quad = 2.3 + 0.056\,(1 + 0.01 + 0.01^2 + \dots)$

$$= \dfrac{23}{10} + \dfrac{56}{1000}\,\dfrac{1}{1-0.01} = \dfrac{23}{10} + \dfrac{56}{990} = \dfrac{23\times 99 + 56}{990} = \dfrac{2333}{990}$$

19. $1, x^2, x^4, \dots \qquad S_n = \dfrac{1-x^{2n}}{1-x^2}.$

The sum to infinity, $\quad S_\infty = \dfrac{1}{1-x^2}$

$$1 + x^2 + x^4 + x^6 + \dots = \dfrac{1}{1-x^2}$$

Let $S = 1 + 2x^2 + 3x^4 + 4x^6 + 5x^8 + \dots$ multiplying both sides by $(1-x^2)$,

we have $S\,(1-x^2) = 1 + 2x^2 + 3x^4 + 4x^6 + \dots - x^2 - 2x^4 - 3x^6 - 4x^8 - \dots$

$$= 1 + x^2 + x^4 + x^6 + \dots = \dfrac{1}{1-x^2}$$

$$S_\infty = \dfrac{1}{(1-x^2)^2} = 1 + 2x^2 + 3x^4 + 4x^6 + \dots$$

20. $1, x, x^2, x^3, \ldots$ $\qquad S_\infty = \dfrac{1}{1-x} = 5$ $\qquad 1, x^2, x^4, x^6, \ldots$

$$S_\infty = \dfrac{1}{1-x^2} = 4 \qquad\qquad \dfrac{(1-x)(1+x)}{(1-x)} = \dfrac{5}{4} \;\Rightarrow\; 1+x = \dfrac{5}{4}$$

$$x = \dfrac{1}{4}$$

the corresponding series are $\;1, \dfrac{1}{4}, \dfrac{1}{4^2}, \ldots \qquad\qquad 1, \dfrac{1}{4^2}, \dfrac{1}{4^4}, \ldots$

21. $0.7\dot{2}\dot{5} = 0.72525\ldots = 0.7 + 0.025 + 0.00025 + \ldots$

$$= \dfrac{7}{10} + 0.025\,(1 + 0.01 + 0.01^2 + \ldots) = \dfrac{7}{10} + \dfrac{25}{1000} \times \dfrac{1}{1 - 0.01}$$

$$= \dfrac{7}{10} + \dfrac{25}{990} = \dfrac{7 \times 99 + 25}{990} = \dfrac{718}{990} = \dfrac{359}{495}.$$

22. a, b, c is an $A.P$, $2a, 2b, 2c$ is a G.P.

The common difference $= d = b - a = c - b$, the common ratio $=$

$$r = \dfrac{2b}{2a} = \dfrac{b}{a} \quad d = b - a = \dfrac{a^2}{a-1} - a = \dfrac{a^2 - a^2 + a}{a-1} = \dfrac{a}{a-1}$$

$$r = \dfrac{b}{a} = \dfrac{a^2}{a(a-1)} = \dfrac{a}{a-1} \quad \text{therefore } d = r.$$

The nth term of the A.P. $= a + (n-1)\,\dfrac{a}{a-1}$

the nth term of the G.P. $= 2a \left(\dfrac{a}{a-1}\right)^{n-1}$.

The sum of nth terms of the G.P. $S_n = \dfrac{2a\left[1 - \left(\dfrac{a}{a-1}\right)^{n}\right]}{1 - \dfrac{a}{a-1}} = \dfrac{2a\left[\left(\dfrac{a}{a-1}\right)^{n} - 1\right]}{\dfrac{a}{a-1} - 1}$

$$= \dfrac{2a\left[\left(\dfrac{a}{a-1}\right)^{n} - 1\right]}{\dfrac{a - a + 1}{a-1}} = 2a\,(a-1)\left[\left(\dfrac{a}{a-1}\right)^{n} - 1\right].$$

23. $S_n = a + ar + ar^2 + \dots ar^{n-1} = \dfrac{a(1-r^n)}{1-r}$

$P_n = a(ar)(ar^2) \dots (ar^{n-1}) = a^n r^{1+2+3+\dots(n-1)} = a^n \dfrac{r^{n(n-1)/2}}{2}$

$\dfrac{1}{a} + \dfrac{1}{ar} + \dfrac{1}{ar^2} + \dots + \dfrac{1}{ar^{n-1}} = \dfrac{1}{a}\left(\dfrac{r^{n-1} + r^{n-2} + \dots + r^0}{r^{(n-1)(n-2)\dots 3.2.1}} \right)$

$= \dfrac{1}{a} \dfrac{\left(1 + r + \dots r^{n-1}\right)}{r^{n(n-1)/2}}$

$= \dfrac{1}{a} \dfrac{n(n-1)/2}{r^{n(n-1)/2}}$

$= \dfrac{1}{a} \dfrac{n(n-1)/2}{P_n/a^n} = \dfrac{a^{n-1} n(n-1)}{2P_n}$

$\dfrac{1}{a(ar)(ar^2)\dots(ar^{n-1})} = \dfrac{1}{P_n} = \dfrac{1}{a^n\, r^{n(n-1)/2}}$

24. $\dfrac{1}{2}, \dfrac{1}{6}, \dfrac{1}{8}, \dots \qquad a = \dfrac{1}{2}, r = \dfrac{1/6}{1/2} = 1/3$

$S_n = \dfrac{1}{2} \dfrac{\left(1 - \dfrac{1}{3^n}\right)}{1 - 1/3} = \dfrac{3}{4}\left(1 - \dfrac{1}{3^n}\right) \qquad S_\infty = \dfrac{3}{4}$ since $\left(\dfrac{1}{3^n}\right) \to 0$

$S_\infty - S_n > 0.0001 \qquad\qquad \dfrac{3}{4} - \dfrac{3}{4} + \dfrac{1}{3^n} > 0.0001 \qquad\qquad \dfrac{1}{3^n} > 0.0001.$

$.3^n < \dfrac{1}{0.0001} = 10000 \qquad 3^n < 10000 \qquad n = 8$

since $3^8 = 6561$ and $3^9 = 19683$.

SOLUTIONS 12

1. (i) $(1 - 5x)^{-3}$ $= 1 + (-3)(-5x) + (-3)(-4)(-5x)^2 \dfrac{1}{2} = 1 + 15x + 150x^2$

   (ii) $(1 + 3x)^{3/4}$ $= 1 + \left(\dfrac{3}{4}\right)(3x) + \left(\dfrac{3}{4}\right)\left(-\dfrac{1}{4}\right)(3x)^2 \dfrac{1}{2} = 1 + \dfrac{9}{4}x - \dfrac{27}{32}x^2$

   (iii) $(1 - 4x)^{-1/3}$ $= 1 + \left(-\dfrac{1}{3}\right)(-4x) + \left(-\dfrac{1}{3}\right)\left(-\dfrac{4}{3}\right)(-4x)^2 \dfrac{1}{2}$

   $= 1 + \dfrac{4}{3}x + \dfrac{32}{9}x^2$

   (iv) $(1 - x)^{1/2}$ $= 1 + \dfrac{1}{2}(-x) + \left(\dfrac{1}{2}\right)\left(-\dfrac{1}{2}\right)(-x)^2 \dfrac{1}{2} = 1 - \dfrac{1}{2}x - \dfrac{1}{8}x^2$

   (v) $(1 + x)^{-1/2}$ $= 1 + \left(-\dfrac{1}{2}\right)x + \left(-\dfrac{1}{2}\right)\left(-\dfrac{3}{2}\right)x^2 \dfrac{1}{2} = 1 - \dfrac{1}{2}x + \dfrac{3}{8}x^2.$

2. (i) $(1 + px)^n$ $= 1 + npx + n(n - 1)p^2x^2 \dfrac{1}{2}$

   $= 1 + npx + \dfrac{1}{2}n(n - 1)p^2x^2$

   (ii) $(1 - px)^{-n}$ $= 1 + (-n)(-px) + (-n)(-n - 1)(-px)^2 \dfrac{1}{2}$

   $= 1 + npx + \dfrac{1}{2}n(n + 1)p^2x^2$

   (iii) $(1 + 3ax)^{-n}$ $= 1 + (-n)(3ax) + (-n)(-n - 1)(3ax)^2 \dfrac{1}{2}$

   $= 1 - 3anx + \dfrac{9}{2}n(n + 1)a^2x^2$

   (iv) $(1 - 2bx)^n$ $= 1 + n(-2bx) + n(n - 1)(-2bx)^2 \dfrac{1}{2}$

   $= 1 - 2nbx + 2n(n - 1)b^2x^2$

(v) $(1 - bx)^n = 1 + n(-bx) + n(n-1)(-bx)^2 \dfrac{1}{2}$

$$= 1 - nbx + b^2 n(n-1)\dfrac{x^2}{2}.$$

3. (i) $\sqrt{\dfrac{1-y}{1+y}} = (1-y)^{1/2}(1+y)^{-1/2}$

$$= \left[1 + \dfrac{1}{2}(-y) + \dfrac{1}{2}\left(-\dfrac{1}{2}\right)(-y)^2 \dfrac{1}{2}\right]\left[1 - \dfrac{1}{2}y + \left(-\dfrac{1}{2}\right)\left(-\dfrac{3}{2}\right)y^2 \dfrac{1}{2}\right]$$

$$= \left(1 - \dfrac{1}{2}y - \dfrac{1}{8}y^2\right)\left(1 - \dfrac{1}{2}y + \dfrac{3}{8}y^2\right)$$

$$= 1 - \dfrac{1}{2}y + \dfrac{3}{8}y^2 - \dfrac{1}{2}y + \dfrac{1}{4}y^2 - \dfrac{1}{8}y^2 = 1 - y + \dfrac{1}{2}y^2.$$

(ii) $\dfrac{1}{\sqrt{1-y^2}} = (1-y^2)^{-1/2} = 1 + \left(-\dfrac{1}{2}\right)(-y^2) + \left(-\dfrac{1}{2}\right)\left(-\dfrac{3}{2}\right)(-y^2)^2 \dfrac{1}{2}$

$$= 1 + \dfrac{1}{2}y^2 + \dfrac{3}{8}y^4.$$

(iii) $\sqrt{9 + ax} = \sqrt{9\left(1 + \dfrac{ax}{9}\right)} = 3\left(1 + \dfrac{ax}{9}\right)^{1/2}$

$$= 3\left[1 + \dfrac{1}{2}\dfrac{ax}{9} + \dfrac{1}{2}\left(-\dfrac{1}{2}\right)\dfrac{a^2 x^2}{81}\dfrac{1}{2}\right] = 3 + \dfrac{1}{6}ax - \dfrac{1}{216}a^2 x^2$$

(iv) $\dfrac{1}{\sqrt{16 - bx}} = (16 - bx)^{-1/2} = 16^{-1/2}\left(1 - \dfrac{bx}{16}\right)^{-1/2}$

$$= \dfrac{1}{4}\left(1 + \left(-\dfrac{1}{2}\right)\left(-\dfrac{bx}{16}\right) + \left(-\dfrac{1}{2}\right)\left(-\dfrac{3}{2}\right)\left(-\dfrac{bx}{16}\right)^2 \dfrac{1}{2}\right)$$

$$= \dfrac{1}{4} + \dfrac{bx}{128} + \dfrac{3}{8192}b^2 x^2.$$

4. $(25 + x)^{1/2} = 5\left(1 + \dfrac{x}{25}\right)^{1/2} = 5\left(1 + \dfrac{1}{2}\dfrac{x}{25} + \dfrac{1}{2}\left(-\dfrac{1}{2}\right)\left(\dfrac{x}{25}\right)^2 \times \dfrac{1}{2}\right)$

$$= 5 + \dfrac{x}{10} - \dfrac{x^2}{2 \times 500} = 5 + \dfrac{x}{10} - \dfrac{x^2}{1000}$$

5. (i) $(1 + 2x)^{1/3} = 1 + \dfrac{1}{3}(2x) + \dfrac{1}{3}\left(-\dfrac{2}{3}\right)(2x)^2 \dfrac{1}{2} + \dfrac{1}{3}\left(-\dfrac{2}{3}\right)\left(-\dfrac{5}{3}\right)(2x)^3 \dfrac{1}{6}$

$$= 1 + \dfrac{2}{3}x - \dfrac{4}{9}x^2 + \dfrac{40}{81}x^3.$$

(ii) $(1 - 3x)^{-1/5} = 1 + \left(-\dfrac{1}{5}\right)(-3x) + \left(-\dfrac{1}{5}\right)\left(-\dfrac{6}{5}\right)(-3x)^2 \dfrac{1}{2} +$

$$\left(-\dfrac{1}{5}\right)\left(-\dfrac{6}{5}\right)\left(-\dfrac{11}{5}\right)(-3x)^3 \dfrac{1}{6}$$

$$= 1 + \dfrac{3}{5}x + \dfrac{27}{25}x^2 + \dfrac{297}{125}x^3$$

$(1 + 2x)^{1/3} + 25(1 - 3x)^{-1/5} = a + bx + cx + dx^3 + \ldots$

$1 + \dfrac{2}{3}x - \dfrac{4}{9}x^2 + \dfrac{40}{81}x^3 + 25 + 15x + 27x^2 + \dfrac{297}{5}x^3 = a + bx + cx^2 + dx^3$

The constant terms $\boxed{a = 26}$

Equating the coefficients of x:-

$\dfrac{2}{3} + 15 = b$ $\boxed{b = \dfrac{47}{3}}$

Equating the coefficients of x^2:

$-\dfrac{4}{9} + 27 = c$ $\boxed{c = \dfrac{239}{9}}$

Equating the coefficients of x^3:

$\dfrac{40}{81} + \dfrac{297}{5} = d$ $\boxed{d = \dfrac{24{,}257}{405}}$

6. $(1 + 2x)^{1/2} (1 - 3x)^{-1/2}$

$$= \left(1 + x + \frac{1}{2}\left(-\frac{1}{2}\right)4x^2\frac{1}{2} + \frac{1}{2}\left(-\frac{1}{2}\right)\left(-\frac{3}{2}\right)8x^3\frac{1}{6}\right) \times$$

$$\left(1 + \left(-\frac{1}{2}\right)(-3x) + \left(-\frac{1}{2}\right)\left(-\frac{3}{2}\right)9x^2 + \left(-\frac{1}{2}\right)\left(-\frac{3}{2}\right)\left(-\frac{5}{2}\right)(-27x^3)\frac{1}{6}\right)$$

$$= \left(1 + x - \frac{1}{2}x^2 + \frac{1}{2}x^3\right)\left(1 + \frac{3}{2}x + \frac{27}{4}x^2 + \frac{135}{16}x^3\right)$$

$$= 3\left(1 + x - \frac{1}{2}x^2 + \frac{1}{2}x^3\right)\left(1 + \frac{3}{2}x + \frac{27}{4}x^2 + \frac{135}{4}x^3\right) + \left(-\frac{1}{2}\right)\left(-\frac{3}{2}\right)(-27x^3)\frac{1}{6}$$

The coefficient of x^3

$$\frac{135}{16} + \frac{27}{4} - \frac{3}{4} + \frac{1}{2} = \frac{135 + 108 - 12 + 8}{16} = \frac{239}{16}$$

7. $(1 - 7x)^{-1/3} = 1 + \left(-\frac{1}{3}\right)(-7x) + \left(-\frac{1}{3}\right)\left(-\frac{4}{3}\right)(-7x)^2\frac{1}{2} +$

$$\left(-\frac{1}{3}\right)\left(-\frac{4}{3}\right)\left(-\frac{7}{3}\right)(-7x)^3\frac{1}{6}$$

$$= 1 + \frac{7}{3}x + \frac{98}{9}x^2 + \frac{4802}{81}x^3.$$

8. $(a + b)^n = a^n\left(1 + \frac{b}{a}\right)^n$

$$= a^n\left\{1 + n\frac{b}{a} + n(n - 1)\frac{b^2}{a^2}\frac{1}{2} + \ldots + n(n - 1)\ldots(n - (r - 1))\frac{b^r}{a^r}\frac{1}{r!} + . \right\}$$

The term containing $b^r = \frac{a^{n-r}n(n - 1)\ldots(n - r + 1)}{r!}\frac{b^r}{a^r}$

$$= a^{n-r}\frac{n(n - 1)\ldots(n - r + 1)}{r!}b^r.$$

9. The coefficient of x^{25} in the expansion $(1 + 3x)^{37}$ is

$$^{37}C_{25}(-3)^{25} = \frac{37!}{25!\,12!}(-3)^{25}.$$

10. $T = 2\pi\sqrt{\dfrac{l}{g}}$ $\qquad T^2 = 4\pi^2\dfrac{l}{g}$ $\qquad g = \dfrac{kl}{T^2}$ where $k = 4\pi^2$

$T' = T + \dfrac{1}{100}T = T(1 + 0.01)$ $\qquad l' = l - \dfrac{0.5}{100}l = l(1 - 0.005).$

$g' = \dfrac{kl'}{T'^2} = kl'T'^{-2} = kl(1 - 0.005)(1 + 0.01)^{-2}\,T^{-2}$

$g' = klT^{-2}(1 - 0.005)(1 + 0.01)^{-2}$

$g' = g(1 - 0.005)(1 + 0.001)^{-2} = g(1 - 0.005)(1 - 0.02)$

$\qquad = g(1 - 0.02 - 0.005 + 0.0001) = g(1 - 0.0249).$

The error in g is $- 0.0249$ or $- 2.5\%$.

11. $(1 + x)^{1/2} = 1 + \dfrac{1}{2}x + \dfrac{1}{2}\left(-\dfrac{1}{2}\right)x^2\dfrac{1}{2} = 1 + \dfrac{1}{2}x - \dfrac{1}{8}x^2$

$(1 - 2x)^{-1} = 1 + (-1)(-2x) + (-1)(-2)(-2x)^2\dfrac{1}{2} = 1 + 2x + 4x^2$

$f = \dfrac{k\sqrt{w}}{l}$, $f' = k(w')^{1/2}(l')^{-1} = k(w + 0.01w)^{1/2}(l - 0.02l)^{-1}$

$f' = kw^{1/2}\,l^{-1}(1 + 0.01)^{1/2}(1 - 0.02)^{-1}$

$\qquad = f\left(1 + \dfrac{1}{2}0.01 - \dfrac{1}{8}0.01^2\right)(1 + 0.02 + 0.0004)$

$f' = f(1 + 0.005 - 0.0000125)(1 + 0.02 + 0.0004)$

$\qquad = f(1.0049875)(1.0204) = 1.0254892f$

The error in f is 0.0255 or $+ 2.55\%$.

12. $(1 + x)^n \ = 1 + nx + \dfrac{1}{2} n(n - 1) x^2 + \dfrac{n(n - 1)(n - 2)}{1 \times 2 \times 3} x^3$

$= 1 + nx + \dfrac{1}{2} n(n - 1) x^2 + \dfrac{n(n - 1)(n - 2) x^3}{6}.$

If $n = 3$ $\quad (1 + x)^3 = 1 + 3x + 3x^2 + x^3.$

If $n = -3$ $\quad (1 + x)^{-3} = 1 - 3x + 6x^2 - 10x^3.$

If $n = -\dfrac{1}{3}$ $\quad (1 + x)^{-1/3}$

$= 1 - \dfrac{1}{3}x + \dfrac{1}{2}\left(-\dfrac{1}{3}\right)\left(-\dfrac{4}{3}\right)x^2 + \left(-\dfrac{1}{3}\right)\left(-\dfrac{4}{3}\right)\left(-\dfrac{7}{3}\right)\dfrac{x^3}{1 \times 2 \times 3}$

$= 1 - \dfrac{1}{3}x + \dfrac{2}{9}x^2 - \dfrac{14}{81}x^3$

13. (i) $\dfrac{1}{(1.005)^3} = (1.005)^{-3} = (1 + 0.005)^{-3}$

$= 1 + (-3)(0.005) + (-3)(-4)(0.005)^2 \dfrac{1}{2}$

$= 1 - 0.015 + 0.000125 \approx 0.9850.$

(ii) $\sqrt[3]{27.003} \ = (27 + 0.003)^{1/3} = 3\left(1 + \dfrac{0.003}{27}\right)^{1/3}$

$= 3\left(1 + \dfrac{1}{3}\dfrac{0.001}{9} + \dfrac{1}{3}\left(-\dfrac{2}{3}\right)\left(\dfrac{0.001}{9}\right)^2 \dfrac{1}{2}\right)$

$\approx 3\left(1 + \dfrac{0.001}{27} - \dfrac{1}{729} 0.000001\right) \approx 3 + \dfrac{0.001}{9} \quad \approx 3.0001.$

(iii) $(1.05)^{1/5} \ = (1 + 0.05)^{1/5} \approx 1 + \dfrac{1}{5}0.05 + \dfrac{1}{5}\left(-\dfrac{4}{5}\right)(0.05)^2 \dfrac{1}{2}$

$= 1 + 0.01 - \dfrac{4}{50} 0.0025 \approx 1.0098.$

(iv) $0.995^{-\frac{1}{3}} = (1 - 0.005)^{-1/3} \approx 1 + \frac{1}{3}\,0.005 + \frac{1}{3}\left(-\frac{2}{3}\right)0.005^2 \times \frac{1}{2} \approx 1.0017$

14. (i) $(1 + x)^{+\,1/2} = 1 + \frac{1}{2}x + \frac{1}{2}\left(-\frac{1}{2}\right)x^2\,\frac{1}{2} = 1 + \frac{1}{2}x - \frac{1}{8}x^2$

(ii) $(1 - x)^{-3} = 1 + (-3)(-x) + (-3)(-4)(-x)^2\,\frac{1}{2} = 1 + 3x + 6x^2$

$$\frac{(1 + x)^{1/2}}{(1 - x)^3} = (1 + x)^{1/2}(1 - x)^{-3} = \left(1 + \frac{1}{2}x - \frac{1}{8}x^2\right)(1 + 3x + 6x^2)$$

$$= 1 + 3x + 6x^2 + \frac{1}{2}x + \frac{3}{2}x^2 - \frac{1}{8}x^2 = 1 + \frac{7}{2}x + 7\frac{3}{8}x^2$$

$$= 1 + \frac{7x}{2} + \frac{59}{8}x^2$$

$$\frac{W^{\frac{1}{2}}\left(1 + \dfrac{1}{100}\right)^{1/2}}{Z^3\left(1 - \dfrac{1}{100}\right)^3} = \frac{W^{\frac{1}{2}}}{Z^3}\left(1 + \frac{1}{100}\right)^{1/2}\left(1 - \frac{1}{100}\right)^{-3}$$

$$= \frac{W^{1/2}}{Z^3}\left(1 + \frac{7}{2}\frac{1}{100} + \frac{59}{8}\frac{1}{100^2}\right)$$

$$= \frac{W^{1/2}}{Z^3}(1 + 0.03574).$$

The percentage change in $\dfrac{W^{\frac{1}{2}}}{Z^3}$ is $+\,3.57\%$.

SOLUTIONS 13

1. (i) $\displaystyle\sum_{r=1}^{n} \sin rx$ (ii) $\displaystyle\sum_{r=1}^{n} \cos rx$

(iii) $\displaystyle\sum_{r=1}^{n} \operatorname{cosec}(2r-1)\,x$ (iv) $\displaystyle\sum_{r=1}^{n} r$

(v) $\displaystyle\sum_{r=1}^{n} r^2$ (vi) $\displaystyle\sum_{r=1}^{n} r(r+1)(r+2)$

(vii) $\displaystyle\sum_{r=1}^{n} 2^r$ (viii) $\displaystyle\sum_{r=1}^{n} \frac{1}{r(r+1)}$

(ix) $\displaystyle\sum_{r=1}^{n} r^3$ (x) $\displaystyle\sum_{r=1}^{n} (r+1)(r+2)(r+3).$

2. (i) $\displaystyle\sum_{r=0}^{\infty} \frac{x^r}{r!} = e^x$ (ii) $\displaystyle\sum_{r=0}^{\infty} \frac{(-1)^r x^{2r+1}}{(2r+1)!} = \sin x$

(iii) $\displaystyle\sum_{r=0}^{\infty} (-1)^r \frac{x^{2r}}{(2r)!} = \cos x$ (iv) $\displaystyle\sum_{r=1}^{\infty} (-1)^{r+1} \frac{x^r}{r} = \ln(1+x)$

(v) $\displaystyle\sum_{r=1}^{\infty} \frac{x^{2r}}{(2r)!} = \cosh x$ (vi) $\displaystyle\sum_{r=0}^{\infty} \frac{x^{2r+1}}{(2r+1)!} = \sinh x.$

3. (i) $\displaystyle\sum_{r=1}^{n} \frac{n(n+1)}{2}$ (ii) $\displaystyle\sum_{r=1}^{n} r^2 = \frac{n(n+1)(2n+1)}{6}$

(iii) $\displaystyle\sum_{r=1}^{n} r^3 = \left(\sum_{r=1}^{n} r\right)^2 = \frac{n^2(n+1)^2}{4}$, for these three, see text.

(iv) $\displaystyle\sum_{r=1}^{n} r^4$

$$n^5 - (n-1)^5 = n^5 - n^5 + 5n^4 - 10n^3 + 10n^2 - 5n + 1$$
$$= 5n^4 - 10n^3 + 10n^2 - 5n + 1$$

$$(n-1)^5 - (n-1)^5 = \qquad = 5(n-1)^4 - 10(n-1)^3 + 10(n-1)^2 - 5(n-1) + 1$$

$$\cdots$$

$$1^5 - 0^5 = \cdots = 5 \times 1^4 - 10 \times 1^3 + 10 \times 1^2 - 5 \times 1 + 1$$

$$n^5 = \qquad = 5 \sum_{r=1}^{n} r^4 - 10 \sum_{r=1}^{n} r^3 + 10 \sum_{r=1}^{n} r^2 - 5 \sum_{r=1}^{n} r + n$$

$$5 \sum_{r=1}^{n} r^4 = 10 \sum_{r=1}^{n} r^3 - 10 \sum_{r=1}^{n} r^2 + 5 \sum_{r=1}^{n} r - n + n^5$$

$$= 10 \frac{n^2 (n+1)^2}{4} - \frac{10}{6} n (n+1)(2n+1) + \frac{5n}{2}(n+1) - n + n^5$$

$$\sum_{r=1}^{n} r^4 = \frac{1}{2} n^2 (n+1)^2 - \frac{1}{3} n(n+1)(2n+1) + \frac{1}{2}n(n+1) + \frac{1}{5} n(n^4 - 1)$$

$$= n(n+1)\left[\frac{1}{2}n(n+1) - \frac{1}{3}(2n+1) + \frac{1}{2} + \frac{1}{5}(n-1)(n^2+1) \right]$$

$$= n(n+1) \frac{1}{30} \left[15n(n+1) - 10(2n+1) + 15 + 6(n-1)(n^2+1) \right]$$

$$= \frac{1}{30} n(n+1)(15n^2 + 15n - 20n - 10 + 15 + 6n - 6 + 6n^3 - 6n^2)$$

$$= \frac{1}{30} n(n+1)(6n^3 + 9n^2 + n - 1).$$

4. (i) $\displaystyle \sum_{r=5}^{25} r = \sum_{r=1}^{25} r - \sum_{r=1}^{4} r = \frac{25 \times 26}{2} - \frac{4 \times 5}{2} = 315$

(ii) $\displaystyle \sum_{r=10}^{50} r^2 = \sum_{r=1}^{50} r^2 - \sum_{r=1}^{9} r^2 = \frac{50 \times 51 \times 101}{6} - \frac{9 \times 10 \times 19}{6} = 42640$

(iii) $\displaystyle \sum_{r=1}^{10} r^3 = \frac{10^2 \times 11^2}{4} = 3025$

(iv) $\displaystyle \sum_{r=1}^{15} r^4 = \frac{1}{30} 15 \times 16 \times (6 \times 15^3 + 9 \times 15^2 + 15 - 1) = 178312$

5. (i) $\displaystyle\sum_{r=1}^{n} r(r+1)(r+2) = \sum_{r=1}^{n}(r^3 + 3r^2 + 2r) = \sum_{r=1}^{n} r^3 + 3\sum_{r=1}^{n} r^2 + 2\sum_{r=1}^{n} r$

$$= \frac{1}{4}n^2(n+1)^2 + \frac{1}{2}n(n+1)(2n+1) + n(n+1)$$

$$= \frac{1}{4}n^4 + \frac{1}{2}n^3 + \frac{1}{4}n^2 + n^3 + \frac{3}{2}n^2 + \frac{1}{2}n + n^2 + n$$

$$= \frac{1}{4}n^4 + \frac{3}{2}n^3 + \frac{11}{4}n^2 + \frac{3}{2}n$$

$$= \frac{n}{4}\left(n^3 + 6n^2 + 11n + 6\right).$$

(ii) $\displaystyle\sum_{r=1}^{n} \frac{1}{r(r+1)(r+2)}$ $\qquad \dfrac{1}{r(r+1)(r+2)} \equiv \dfrac{A}{r} + \dfrac{B}{r+1} + \dfrac{C}{r+2}$

$1 \equiv A(r+1)(r+2) + Br(r+2) + Cr(r+1)$

if $r = -1$, $1 = B(-1)(1)$, $B = -1$, if $r = 0$, $A = \dfrac{1}{2}$ and

if $r = -2$, $C = \dfrac{1}{2}$.

$$\frac{1}{r(r+1)(r+2)} \equiv \frac{1}{2r} - \frac{1}{r+1} + \frac{1}{2(r+2)}$$

$$\sum_{r=1}^{n} \frac{1}{r(r+1)(r+2)} = \frac{1}{2 \times 1} + \frac{1}{2 \times 2} + \frac{1}{2 \times 3} + \ldots + \frac{1}{2 \times n}$$

$$- \left(\frac{1}{2} + \frac{1}{3} + \frac{1}{4} + \ldots + \frac{1}{n+1}\right) + \frac{1}{2}\left(\frac{1}{3} + \frac{1}{4} + \frac{1}{5} + \ldots + \frac{1}{n+2}\right)$$

$$= \frac{1}{2}\left(\frac{1}{1} + \frac{1}{2} + \frac{1}{3} + \ldots + \frac{1}{n}\right) - \frac{1}{2}\left(\frac{1}{2} + \frac{1}{3} + \frac{1}{4} + \ldots + \frac{1}{n+1}\right)$$

$$+ \frac{1}{2}\left(\frac{1}{3} + \frac{1}{4} + \ldots + \frac{1}{n+1} + \frac{1}{n+2}\right) \qquad \text{let } \frac{1}{3} + \frac{1}{4} + \ldots + \frac{1}{n} = S$$

$$\sum_{r=1}^{n} \frac{1}{r\,(r+1)\,(r+2)} = \frac{1}{2}\left(\frac{1}{1} + \frac{1}{2} + S\right) - \left(\frac{1}{2} + S + \frac{1}{n+1}\right)$$

$$+ \frac{1}{2}\left(S + \frac{1}{n+1} + \frac{1}{n+2}\right) = \frac{3}{4} + \frac{1}{2}\,S - \frac{1}{2} - S - \frac{1}{n+1} + \frac{1}{2}\,S$$

$$+ \frac{1}{2\,(n+1)} + \frac{1}{2\,(n+2)}$$

$$= \frac{3}{4} - \frac{1}{2} - \frac{1}{2(n+1)} + \frac{1}{2\,(n+2)} = \frac{1}{4} - \frac{1}{2\,(n+1)} + \frac{1}{2\,(n+2)}$$

(iii) $\displaystyle\sum_{r=1}^{n} \frac{1}{(r+2)\,(r+4)}$ ... (1) $\qquad \dfrac{1}{(r+2)\,(r+4)} \equiv \dfrac{A}{r+2} + \dfrac{B}{r+4}$

$1 \equiv A\,(r+4) + B\,(r+2)$. If $r = -2$, $A = \dfrac{1}{2}$, and if $r = -4$, $B = -\dfrac{1}{2}$

$$\frac{1}{(r+2)\,(r+4)} \equiv \frac{1}{2\,(r+2)} - \frac{1}{2\,(r+4)}, \text{ substituting in (1)}$$

$$\frac{1}{2}\sum_{r=1}^{n}\frac{1}{r+2} - \frac{1}{2}\sum_{r=1}^{n}\frac{1}{r+4} = \frac{1}{2}\left(\frac{1}{3} + \frac{1}{4} + \frac{1}{5} + \dots + \frac{1}{n+2}\right)$$

$$- \frac{1}{2}\left(\frac{1}{5} + \frac{1}{6} + \dots + \frac{1}{n+4}\right) \qquad \text{let } S = \frac{1}{5} + \frac{1}{6} + \dots + \frac{1}{n+2}$$

$$\sum_{r=1}^{n}\frac{1}{(r+2)\,(r+4)} = \frac{1}{2}\left(\frac{1}{3} + \frac{1}{4} + S\right) - \frac{1}{2}\left(S + \frac{1}{n+3} + \frac{1}{n+4}\right)$$

$$= \frac{1}{2}\left(\frac{1}{3} + \frac{1}{4}\right) + \frac{1}{2}\,S - \frac{1}{2}\,S - \frac{1}{2\,(n+3)} - \frac{1}{2\,(n+4)}$$

$$= \frac{7}{24} - \frac{1}{2\,(n+3)} - \frac{1}{2\,(n+4)} = \frac{7}{24} - \frac{1}{2}\frac{n+4+n+3}{(n+3)\,(n+4)}$$

$$= \frac{7}{24} - \frac{1}{2}\frac{2n+7}{(n+3)\,(n+4)}.$$

6. (i) $u_n = \log\left(\dfrac{n}{n+1}\right) = \log\dfrac{1}{1+1/n}$

$\displaystyle\lim_{n\to\infty} u_n = \log 1 = 0$ which may converge

$S_n = \log\dfrac{1}{2} + \log\dfrac{2}{3} + \log\dfrac{3}{4} + \dots + \log\dfrac{n}{n+1}$

$= \log\left(\dfrac{1}{2} \times \dfrac{2}{3} \times \dfrac{3}{4} \times \dots \times \dfrac{n}{n+1}\right) = \log\left(\dfrac{1}{n+1}\right)$

since $\log\dfrac{1}{n+1} \to -\infty$ *as* $n\to\infty$ u_n diverges to $-\infty$.

(ii) $u_n = \dfrac{2n+1}{3n-1} = \dfrac{n(2+1/n)}{n(3-1/n)} = \dfrac{2+1/n}{3-1/n}$ $\displaystyle\lim_{n\to\infty} u_n = \dfrac{2}{3} \neq 0$

therefore $\displaystyle\sum_{r=1}^{\infty} \dfrac{2r+1}{3r-1}$ diverges.

(iii) $u_n = \dfrac{1}{n(n+1)}$

    (a) $\displaystyle\lim_{n\to\infty} u_n = 0$ which may converge.

    (b) $U_n = \dfrac{1}{n} - \dfrac{1}{n+1}$ by partial fractions

$S_n = \left(\dfrac{1}{1} - \dfrac{1}{2}\right) + \left(\dfrac{1}{2} - \dfrac{1}{3}\right) + \left(\dfrac{1}{3} - \dfrac{1}{4}\right) + \dots + \left(\dfrac{1}{n} - \dfrac{1}{n+1}\right)$

$= 1 - \dfrac{1}{n+1} = \dfrac{n+1-1}{n+1} = \dfrac{n}{n+1}$ as $n\to\infty$

$\displaystyle\sum_{r=1}^{\infty} \dfrac{1}{r(r+1)} = 1$, it is covergent.

7. $\displaystyle\sum_{n=1}^{\infty} \left(\frac{1}{n} - \frac{1}{2n^2} - \frac{1}{n+1}\right) = \frac{1}{1} + \frac{1}{2} + \frac{1}{3} + \frac{1}{4} + \ldots + \frac{1}{n} + \frac{1}{n+1} + \ldots -$

$$\frac{1}{2}\left(\frac{1}{1^2} + \frac{1}{2^2} + \frac{1}{3^2} + \ldots + \frac{1}{n^2} + \frac{1}{(n+1)^2} + \ldots\right) -$$

$$\left(\frac{1}{2} + \frac{1}{3} + \frac{1}{4} + \ldots + \frac{1}{n} + \frac{1}{n+1} + \ldots\right)$$

Let $\dfrac{1}{2} + \dfrac{1}{3} + \dfrac{1}{4} + \ldots + \dfrac{1}{n} + \ldots = S$ then

$$\sum_{n=1}^{\infty} \left(\frac{1}{n} - \frac{1}{2\,n^2} - \frac{1}{n+1}\right) = 1 + S - \frac{1}{2}\left(\frac{1}{1^2} + \frac{1}{2^2} + \frac{1}{3^2} + \ldots + \frac{1}{n^2} + \ldots\right)$$

$-\, S = 1 - \dfrac{1}{2}\left(\dfrac{1}{1^2} + \dfrac{1}{2^2} + \dfrac{1}{3^2} + \ldots + \dfrac{1}{n^2} + \ldots\right) = 1 - \dfrac{1}{2} 1 = \dfrac{1}{2}$ convergent

$\left|\dfrac{u_n+1}{u_n}\right| < 1$ for convergency

$u_n = \dfrac{1}{n} - \dfrac{1}{2n^2} - \dfrac{1}{n+1} = \dfrac{2n(n+1) - (n+1) - 2n^2}{2n^2(n+1)}$

$= \dfrac{2n^2 + 2n - n - 1 - 2n^2}{2n^2(n+1)} = \dfrac{n-1}{2n^2(n+1)} \qquad u_{n+1} = \dfrac{n}{2(n+1)^2(n+2)}$

$\dfrac{u_{n+1}}{u_n} = \dfrac{\dfrac{n}{2(n+1)^2(n+2)}}{\dfrac{n-1}{2n^2(n+1)}} = \dfrac{n^3}{(n+1)(n-1)(n+2)}$

$= \dfrac{n^3}{n^3(1+1/n)(1+2/n)} = \dfrac{1}{(1+1/n)(1-1/n)(1+2/n)} \to -1$ if $n \to \infty$.

Inconclusive. If $u_n = 0$, it may be convergent, if $u_n \neq 0$ it is definitely divergent

since the above is of the form $\dfrac{1}{1^k} + \dfrac{1}{2^k} + \dfrac{1}{3^k} + \ldots + \dfrac{1}{n^k} + \ldots$ where $k > 1$ the

series is convergent.

8. $$\sum_{n=1}^{\infty} \frac{1}{n \left(n^2 + 1\right)}$$

$$\frac{u_{n+1}}{u_n} = \frac{n \left(n^2 + 1\right)}{(n + 1) \left[(n + 1)^2 + 1\right]} = \frac{n^3 \left(1 + 1/n^2\right)}{n \left(1 + 1/n\right) n^2 \left(1 + \dfrac{2}{n} + \dfrac{2}{n^2}\right)}$$

$\dfrac{u_{n+1}}{u_n} \rightarrow 1$ as $n \rightarrow \infty$ which inconclusive $u_n = \dfrac{1}{n \left(n^2 + 1\right)} \rightarrow 0$ as $n \rightarrow \infty$ which

may be convergent.

Further investigation $\dfrac{1}{n \left(n^2 + 1\right)} = \dfrac{A}{n} + \dfrac{Bn + C}{n^2 + 1}$

$1 \equiv A \left(n^2 + 1\right) + (Bn + C)\, n$.

If $n = 0$, $A = 1$, if $n = -1$, $B - C = -1$, if $n = 1$, $B + C = -1$ from

which $B = -1$ and $C = 0$ $\dfrac{1}{n \left(n^2 + 1\right)} \equiv \dfrac{1}{n} - \dfrac{n}{n^2 + 1}$ $\displaystyle\sum_{n=0}^{\infty} \dfrac{1}{n}$ is divergent

$\displaystyle\sum_{n^2+1} \dfrac{n}{n^2 + 1}$ is convergent, therefore the series is divergent.

9. $$\frac{u_{n+1}}{u_n} = \frac{n \left(n + 1\right)}{(n + 1) (n + 2)} = \frac{n}{n + 2} = \frac{n}{1 + 2/n} = \frac{1}{1 + 2/n}$$

$\left| \dfrac{u_{n+1}}{u_n} \right| \rightarrow 1$ as $n \rightarrow \infty$ and it is inconclusive

$u_n = \dfrac{1}{n (n + 1)} \rightarrow 0$ as $n \rightarrow \infty$ $\qquad \dfrac{1}{n (n + 1)} \equiv \dfrac{A}{n} + \dfrac{B}{n + 1},$

$1 \equiv A (n + 1) + Bn$, if $n = -1$, $B = -1$, if $n = 0$, $A = 1$.

$$\sum_{n=1}^{\infty} \frac{1}{n (n + 1)} = \sum_{n=1}^{\infty} \frac{1}{n} - \sum_{n=1}^{\infty} \frac{1}{n + 1} = \frac{1}{1} + \frac{1}{2} + \frac{1}{3} + \frac{1}{4} + \dots - \left(\frac{1}{2} + \frac{1}{3} + \frac{1}{4} + \dots\right)$$

$= 1 + S - S = 1$ and the series is convergent.

10. $\displaystyle\sum_{n=1}^{\infty} \frac{1}{n}\left(\frac{1}{3}\right)^n$ $\displaystyle u_n = \frac{1}{n}\left(\frac{1}{3}\right)^n$ $\displaystyle u_{n+1} = \frac{1}{n+1}\left(\frac{1}{3}\right)^{n+1}$

$$\frac{u_{n+1}}{u_n} = \frac{n\,3^n}{(n+1)\,3^{n+1}} = \frac{n}{3(n+1)} = \frac{n}{3n(1+1/n)} = \frac{1}{3(1+1/n)}$$

as $n \to \infty$, $\dfrac{u_{n+1}}{u_n} \to \dfrac{1}{3}$ therefore $\left|\dfrac{u_{n+1}}{u_n}\right| < 1$ and the series is convergent.

11. $\displaystyle\sum_{n=1}^{\infty} \frac{\sin n\theta}{3^n}$ $\displaystyle\frac{u_{n+1}}{u_n} = \frac{\sin(n+1)\theta}{3^{n+1}}\,\frac{3^n}{\sin n\theta}$

$$= \frac{\sin(n+1)\theta}{3\sin n\theta} = \frac{\left[(n+1)\theta - \dfrac{(n+1)^3\theta^3}{3!} + \dfrac{(n+1)^5}{5!} - \cdots\right]}{3\left[n\theta - \dfrac{n^3\theta^3}{3!} + \dfrac{n^5\theta^5}{5!} - \cdots\right]}$$

$$= \frac{\sin n(1+1/n)\theta}{3\sin n\theta} \quad \text{as } n \to \infty \quad \frac{\sin n(1+1/n)\theta)}{\sin n\theta} \to 1 \text{ and } \frac{u_{n+1}}{u_n} \to \frac{1}{3}.$$

The series is convergent θ.

12. $\displaystyle\frac{1}{(2x+1)(2n-1)} \equiv \frac{A}{2n+1} + \frac{B}{2n-1}$ $1 \equiv A(2n-1) + B(2n+1)$

if $n = \dfrac{1}{2}$, $B = \dfrac{1}{2}$, if $n = -\dfrac{1}{2}$, $A = -\dfrac{1}{2}$

$$\frac{1}{(2n+1)(2n-1)} \equiv -\frac{1}{2(2n+1)} + \frac{1}{2(2n-1)}$$

$$\frac{1}{2}\sum_{n=1}^{\infty}\left(-\frac{1}{2n+1} + \frac{1}{2n-1}\right) = \frac{1}{2}\left(\frac{1}{2\times 1-1} + \frac{1}{2\times 2-1} + \frac{1}{2\times 3-1} + \cdots\right) -$$

$$\frac{1}{2}\left(\frac{1}{2\times 1+1} + \frac{1}{2\times 2\times 1} + \frac{1}{2\times 3+1} + \cdots\right)$$

$$= \frac{1}{2}\left(\frac{1}{1} + \frac{1}{3} + \frac{1}{5} + \cdots\right) - \frac{1}{2}\left(\frac{1}{3} + \frac{1}{5} + \frac{1}{7} + \cdots\right) = \frac{1}{2}$$

$$\frac{u_{n+1}}{u_n} = \frac{(2n+1)(2n-1)}{(2n+3)(2n+1)} = \frac{2n-1}{2n+3} = \frac{2n(1-1/2n)}{2n(1+3/2n)} = \frac{1-1/2n}{1+3/2n} \text{ as } n \to \infty,$$

$\dfrac{u_{n+1}}{u_n} \to 1$ inconclusive $u_n \to 0$ as $n \to \infty$ it may be from the above that the series

is convergent $\displaystyle\sum_{n=1}^{\infty} \frac{1}{(2n+1)(2n-1)} = \frac{1}{2}\left(\frac{1}{1} + S\right) - \frac{1}{2}(S) = \frac{1}{2}$

where $S = \dfrac{1}{3} + \dfrac{1}{5} + \dfrac{1}{7} + \dots$

13. $\displaystyle\sum_{n=0}^{\infty} \frac{n^{1/2}}{n+1}$

$$\frac{u_{n+1}}{u_n} = \frac{(n+1)^{1/2}(n+1)}{(n+2)(n^{1/2})} = \frac{n^{1/2}(1+1/n)^{1/2}n(1+1/n)}{n(1+2/n)n^{1/2}} = \frac{(1+1/n)^{1/2}(1+1/n)}{1+2/n}$$

$\dfrac{u_{n+1}}{u_n} \to 1$ as $n \to \infty$ inconclusive

$u_n = \dfrac{n^{1/2}}{n(1+1/n)} = \dfrac{1}{n^{1/2}(1+1/n)}$ $u_n \to 0$ as $n \to \infty$ it may be convergent.

14. $\ln(1+x) = x - \dfrac{x^2}{2} + \dfrac{x^3}{3} - \dfrac{x^4}{4} + \dots + (-1)^r \dfrac{x^r}{r} + \dots$

$\ln(1-x) = -x - \dfrac{x^2}{2} - \dfrac{x^3}{3} - \dfrac{x^4}{4} - \dots - \dfrac{x^r}{r} - \dots$

$\ln \dfrac{1+x}{1-x} = 2x + 2\dfrac{x^3}{3} + 2\dfrac{x^5}{5} + \dots$ $1+x = m \dots$ (1) $1-x = n \dots$ (2)

adding (1) and (2) $m + n = 2$ and subtracting (2) from (1) we have

$2x = m - n, \quad \dfrac{2x}{2} = \dfrac{m-n}{m+n}$ or $x = \dfrac{m-n}{m+n}$

$\ln \dfrac{1+x}{1-x} = 2\left(x + \dfrac{x^3}{3} + \dfrac{x^5}{5} + \dots\right) = 2\left[\dfrac{m-n}{m+n} + \dfrac{1}{3}\left(\dfrac{m-n}{m+n}\right)^3 + \dfrac{1}{5}\left(\dfrac{m-n}{m+n}\right)^5 + \dots\right]$

$$= 2\sum_{r=0}^{\infty}\left(\frac{m-n}{m+n}\right)^{2r+1}\frac{1}{2r+1}.$$

15. $\displaystyle\sum_{r=1}^{\infty} \frac{2r-3}{r^2-5r+2}$ $\qquad u_n = \dfrac{2n-3}{n^2-5n+2} = \dfrac{n\,(2-3/n)}{n^2\,(1-5/n+2/n^2)}$

$\lim\limits_{n\to\infty} u_n \to 0$ and $\displaystyle\sum_{r=1}^{\infty} u_r$ may coverge also

$$\frac{2n-3}{n^2-5n+2} > \frac{2n-3}{n^2+2} > \frac{2n-n}{n^2+n^2} = \frac{1}{2n} \text{ if } n > 3.$$

Therefore from the fourth term on, each term of $\displaystyle\sum_{n=1}^{\infty} \frac{2n-3}{n^2-5n+2}$ is greater

than the corresponding term of $\displaystyle\sum_{n=1}^{\infty} \frac{1}{2}n$ and $\displaystyle\sum_{n=1}^{\infty} \frac{1}{n}$ diverges.

Therefore $\displaystyle\sum_{r=1}^{\infty} \frac{2r-3}{r^2-5r+2}$ diverges.

(ii) $\displaystyle\sum_{r=1}^{\infty} \frac{4\sqrt{r}}{r^2+3r-7}$ $\qquad u_n = \dfrac{4\sqrt{n}}{n^2+3n-7} = \dfrac{4\sqrt{n}}{n^2\,(1+3/n-7/n^2)}$

$\lim\limits_{n\to\infty} u_n \to 0$ and $\displaystyle\sum_{r=1}^{\infty} u_r$ may coverge $n^2+3n-7 > n^2$ for $n \geq 3$

therefore $\dfrac{4\sqrt{n}}{n^2+3n-7} < \dfrac{4\sqrt{n}}{n^2} = \dfrac{4}{n^{3/2}}$

From the third term on, each term of the series is less than the corresponding

term of $4\displaystyle\sum_{r=1}^{\infty} \frac{1}{r^{3/2}}$ which converges therefore $\displaystyle\sum_{r=1}^{\infty} \frac{4\sqrt{r}}{r^2+3r-7}$ converges.

(iii) $u_n = \dfrac{3n^2-5n+4}{2n\sqrt{n}-3} = \dfrac{3-5/n+4/n^2}{2/\sqrt{n}-3/n^2}$

$\lim\limits_{n\to\infty} u_n$ does not exist therefore $\displaystyle\sum_{r=1}^{\infty} \frac{3r^2-5r+4}{2r\sqrt{r}-3}$ diverges.

SOLUTIONS 14

1. (i) $y = ab^x$.

   Taking logarithms to the base ten, we have;

   $\log y = \log ab^x = \log a + \log b^x = \log a + x \log b$

   $\log y = (\log b) x + \log a$ $\log y$ against x is plotted.

   (ii) $T = T_o e^{\mu\Theta}$

   Taking logarithms to the base e, we have;

   $\log_e T = \log_e T_o + \log_e e^{\mu\Theta}$ $\log_e T = \log_e T_o + \mu\Theta \log_e e$

   $\ln T = \mu\Theta + \ln T_o$ $\ln T$ against Θ is plotted.

   (iii) $y = \dfrac{A}{x^n}$ $\log y = \log \dfrac{A}{x^n}$

   $\log y = \log A - \log x^n$ $\log y = -n \log x + \log A$

   $\log y$ against $\log x$ is plotted.

2. $y = ab^x$ $\log y = x \log b + \log a$ $\log y$ is plotted against x, so the
   following table is formed.

x	1.50	2.50	3.15	4.00	4.75
$\log y$	0	0.49	0.80	1.22	1.60

The gradient $= \log b = (1.60 - 0)/(4.75 - 1.5) = 1.60/3.25 = 0.49$.

When $\log y = 0$, $x = 1.5$ $0 = 1.5 \log b + \log a$

$\log a = -1.5 \log b = -1.5 (0.49) = -0.735$ $10^{-0.735} = a = 0.18$.

Therefore $y = 0.18 (0.49)^x$ is the relationship connecting x and y.

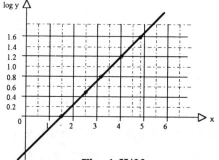

Fig. 1-II/22

3. $T = T_o e^{\mu\Theta}$ $\ln T = \ln Te^{\mu\Theta} = \ln T_o + \ln e^{\mu\Theta} = \mu\Theta + \ln T_o$

Where $\ln e = 1$, $\ln T$ is plotted against Θ from the table.

Θ	5	10	15	20	25
$\ln T$	4.2	5.2	6.2	7.15	8.2

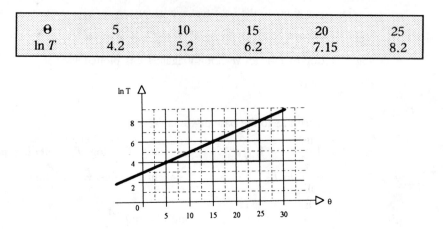

Fig. 1-II/23

The gradient $= (8.2 - 4.2)/(25 - 5) = 4/20 = 1/5 = \mu = 0.2$. When $\Theta = 0$,
$\ln T = \ln T_o$, the intercept on the y-axis; $\ln T_o = 3.2$, $T_o = e^{3.2} = 24.5$.
The law relating T and Θ is: $T = 24.5\, e^{0.2\Theta}$.

4. $V = KI^n$

$\log V$	0.699	1.602	2.130	2.505	2.796
$\log I$	0	0.301	0.477	0.602	0.699

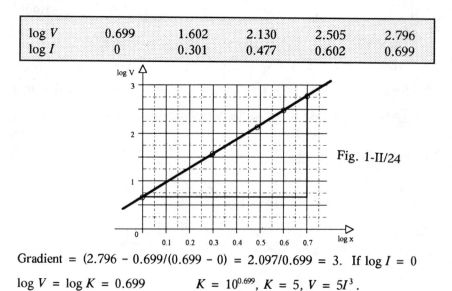

Fig. 1-II/24

Gradient $= (2.796 - 0.699/(0.699 - 0) = 2.097/0.699 = 3$. If $\log I = 0$
$\log V = \log K = 0.699$ $K = 10^{0.699}$, $K = 5$, $V = 5I^3$.

1. ALGEBRA

Miscellaneous

1. (a) Show that $(x - 2)$ is a factor of

$$x^3 - 10x^2 + 28x - 24.$$

Find the set of values of x for which

$$x^3 - 10x^2 + 28x - 24 < 0. \hspace{2cm} \text{(7 marks)}$$

(b) The constants m, n, p and q are chosen so that the identity

$$(mt + n)(t^2 - 4t + 5) \equiv 2t^3 + pt^2 + qt + 5$$

is true for all values of t. Find the values of m, n, p and q.
Prove that the equation $2t^3 + pt^2 + qt + 5 = 0$ has only one real root and state its value.

Deduce that $2e^{3u} + pe^{2u} + qe^u + 5 > 0$ for all $u \in \mathbb{R}$. (9 marks)

Ans. $\left(2e^u + 1\right)\left(e^{2u} - 4e^u + 5\right) = \left(2e^u + 1\right)\left[\left(e^u - 2\right)^2 + 1\right] > 0$

June 90 P1 (13) AEB

2. The quadratic function f is given by

$$f(x) = 2mx^2 + 2(m + 4)x + 9, \; x \in \mathbb{R}, \text{ where } m \neq 0.$$

(a) Find the value of m for which the equation $f(x) = 0$ has equal roots. (4 marks)

(b) When $m = \dfrac{1}{2}$, find the set of values of x for which $\dfrac{f(x)}{x} > -1$. (5 marks)

(c) Form a quadratic equation with coefficients in terms of m whose roots are the squares of the roots of the equation $f(x) = 0$. (7 marks)

Ans. (a) $2, 8$ \hspace{1cm} (b) $-9 < x < -1, x > 0$

(c) $4m^2x^2 - 4(m^2 - m + 10)x + 81 = 0$ \hspace{1cm} **Nov. 89 AEB**

3. The roots of the equation

$$2x^2 + 6x + 3 = 0$$

are α and β.

(a) Show that $\alpha^2 + \beta^2 = 6$.

(b) The roots of the equation
$$2x^2 + px + q = 0$$
are $2\alpha + \beta$ and $\alpha + 2\beta$.

Calculate the value of p and the value of q. **June 90 AEB**

4. Find the set of values of k for which the quadratic equation
$$x^2 + kx + (2k - 3) = 0 \text{ has real roots.}$$

(a) In the case when $k = 4$, find the complex roots of the equation.

(b) In the case when $k = 7$, the roots of the quadratic equation are α and β. Without finding the values of α and β, show that $\alpha^3 + \beta^3 = -112$.

Find a quadratic equation with integer coefficients having roots $\alpha^2 + 3\beta$ and $\beta^2 + 3\alpha$.

Ans. $k \leq 2, k \geq 6; x - 2 \pm i, x^2 - 6x - 116 = 0$. **Nov. 90 AEB**

5. Sketch the graph of the function f defined by
$$f: x \mapsto |2x - 5|, x \in \mathbb{R}.$$

Determine the values of x for which $|2x - 5| = x$.

Using your sketch, or otherwise, find the set of values of x for which $|2x - 5| > x$.

Ans. $x < \dfrac{5}{3}$ and $x > 5$. **June 89 (5) AEB**

6. The first term of a geometric progression is 8 and the sum to infinity is 400.

(a) Find the common ratio. (2 marks)

(b) Determine the least number of terms with a sum greater than 399 (3 marks)

7. Given that $f(x) = 2x^3 - 5x^2 - 4x + 3$, find the stationary values of $f(x)$.

Show that $f(x) = (x + 1)(2x - 1)(x - 3)$.

Hence sketch the curve with equation $y = f(x)$, marking on your sketch the coordinates of the points where the curve crosses the coordinates axes. (5 marks)

(a) Solve the inequalities:-

(i) $2x^3 - 5x^2 - 4x + 3 > 0$ (ii) $2e^{3x} - 5e^{2x} - 4e^x + 3 > 0$.

(b) Express cos $2x$ and cos $3x$ in terms of cos x only, and hence find the general solution in radians, in terms of π, of the equation

$$1 + \cos 3x = 5(\cos 2x + \cos x) \qquad \text{(6 marks)}$$

Ans. $(2, -9); \left(-\dfrac{1}{3}, 3\dfrac{19}{17} \right)$

(a) (i) $-1 < x < \dfrac{1}{2}, \; x > 3$ (ii) $x < -\ln 2, \; x > \ln 3$.

(b) $(2n + 1)\pi, \left(2n \pm \dfrac{1}{3} \right)\pi$, n any integer.   **June 87 AEB**

8. Find the complete solution set of each of the inequalities.

(a) $| 3x - 2 | < 4$.   (2 marks)

(b) $y^3 + 7y^2 - y - 7 \geq 0$.   (4 marks)

Ans. (a) $-\dfrac{2}{3} < x < 2$ (b) $-7 \leq y \leq -1, \; y \geq 1$.   **June 88 AEB**

9. (a) The functions f and g are defined by

$$f: x \mapsto e^x, \; x \in \mathbb{R} \text{ and}$$
$$g: x \mapsto x + 2, \; x \in \mathbb{R}.$$

(i) Express in a similar form the composite functions f o g and g o f.

(ii) Show that g o f (0) – f o g (– 2) = 2.

(iii) Sketch on the same axes the graphs of the functions f and f o g indicating clearly which specify a simple transformation which maps the graph of f onto the graph of f o g.

(b) The function h is defined by h: $x \mapsto 2 + e^x, \; x \in \mathbb{R}$.

Express in a similar form h^{-1}, the inverse function of h.
State the domain of h^{-1}. Sketch h^{-1}.

Ans. (a) (i) $e^{x + 2}, \; e^x + 2$ (ii) $y = af(x)$ where $a = e^2$

(b) $2 + e^x, x \in \mathbb{R}$, $\ln (x - 2), x > 2$ **June 89 (11) AEB**

10. The function f is defined by

$$f: x \mapsto \frac{x + 1}{x - 2}, x \in \mathbb{R}, x \neq 2.$$

Find the inverse function f^{-1}, writing your answer in a similar form, stating clearly the domain of f^{-1}.

There are two values, of x for which $f(x) = f^{-1}(x)$.

Find the sum of these values. (6 marks)

June 90 AEB

11. The functions f and g are defined by

$$f: x \mapsto 1 + e^{-x}, x \in \mathbb{R}$$

$$g: x \mapsto \ln (3x - 5), x \geq 2.$$

(a) Show that the range of f is $\{y : y > 1\}$ and find the range of g.

(b) State all the values of x for which $g(f(x))$ is not defined.

(c) Show that $fog(x) = \dfrac{3x - 4}{3x - 5}, x \geq 2.$

(d) By considering the graph of $y = 1 + e^{-x}$, or otherwise, show that the inverse function f^{-1} exists.

Find $f^{-1}(x)$ and states the domain of f^{-1}. **Nov. 90 AEB**

12. The functions f and g are defined by $f: x \mapsto x^2 - 2$, where $x \in \mathbb{R}$,

$$g: x \mapsto e^x, \text{ where } x \in \mathbb{R}.$$

Write down the composite function f o g and the inverse function g^{-1}, stating the domain of each. Sketch in separate diagrams, the graphs of f o g and g^{-1}, showing the general shape of each graph and writing on your sketches the coordinates of points where the curves cross the coordinate axes.

$fog: x \mapsto e^x - 2, x \in \mathbb{R}; g^{-1}: x \mapsto \ln x, x \in \mathbb{R} + ..$ **June 86 AEB**

13. A quadratic function f, defined by $f: x \mapsto x^2 + bx + c, x \in \mathbb{R}$, has the following properties:-

$$f(3) = -17$$

$$f'(3) = 0.$$

Find the value of b and the value of c and state the range of f.

Sketch the graph of f: (6 marks)

A second quadratic function g has the same rule as f and has domain for all real $x \geq 3$. Find the inverse function g^{-1} of g in the form $g^{-1}: x \mapsto g^{-1}(x)$, stating clearly $g^{-1}(x)$ in terms of x and stating the domain of this inverse function.

Sketch in the same diagram the graphs of g and g^{-1} and by observing the symmetry of your graphs, or otherwise, calculate the value of x for which

$$g(x) = g^{-1}(x)$$ (10 marks)

Ans. $-6, -8, \geq -17$; $g^{-1}: x \mapsto 3 + (x + 17)^{1/2}$

   $x \geq -17$; $x = 8$. **June 88 AEB**

14.   Functions f and g are defined as follows:-

$$f: x \mapsto \frac{1}{x}, \qquad x \in \mathbb{R} \;\; x \neq 0,$$

$$g: x \mapsto -x, x \in \mathbb{R}.$$

Write down expressions for $f\,g(x)$ and $g\,f(x)$, where $x \neq 0$, $x \neq 1$, and hence show that $gfg(x) = fgf(x)$ for all such x. (4 marks)

The function h is defined by h: $x \mapsto e^x$, $x \in \mathbb{R}$.

On a single, clearly labelled diagram, sketch the graphs of fhand hg, and describe a single transformation which maps the graph of f h onto the graph of hg.
(4 marks)

Show that $h^{-1} f(x) = (fh)^{-1}(x)$ for all $x > 0$. (4 marks)

June 1990 (4) C

15.   The function f is defined by f: $x \mapsto (x - 1)^2 + 2, x \in \mathbb{R}, x \geq 1$.

On a single clearly labelled diagram, sketch the graphs of $y = f(x)$ $y = f^{-1}(x)$ and $y = ff^{-1}(x)$. (5 marks)

The function g is defined by g: $x \mapsto 3x + 1, x \in \mathbb{R}$.

Find gf(x), for $x \geq 1$. The function h is defined by h: $x \mapsto ax + b, x \in \mathbb{R}$, where a and b are constants. Find values of a and b such that fh : $x \mapsto 4x^2 + 16x + 18, x \in \mathbb{R}, x \geq 1$.

Ans. $f^{-1}(x) = \sqrt{x - 2} + 1$, $ff^{-1}(x) = x$; $gf(x) = 3x^2 - 6x + 10$

   $a = 2, b = 5$; $a = 2, b = -3$. **Nov. 89 (5) C**

16.   Sketch in separate diagrams the curves whose equations are

$$y = \ln x, x > 0$$
$$y = |\ln x| . x > 0.$$ (2 marks)

1-M/5

Calculate, correct to two decimal places, the values of x for which $|\ln x| = 2$.

(2 marks)

Giving a reason, state the number of real roots, of the equation

$$|\ln x| + x = 3$$

(2 marks)

Ans. 7.39, 0.14; 2 roots.

Nov. 89 AEB

17. Solve these equations giving your answers to two significant figures:-

(a) $2\log_x 6 = 7$,

(b) $2^{2y+1} = 3^{y-2}$

Ans. (a) $x = 1.7$ (b) $y = -10$ June 89 AEB

18. Given that $\log_4 xy = 6$, prove that $\log_2 x + \log_2 y = 12$. Hence solve for x and y the simultaneous equations

$$\log_4 xy = 6,$$
$$\log_2 x \, \log_2 y = 32$$

Ans. $x = 2^8, y = 2^4$ or $x = 2^4, y = 2^8$.   Nov. 85 AEB

19. (a) The variables p and q are related by the law $q = ap^b$ where a and b are constants. Given that $\ln p = 1.32$ when $\ln q = 1.73$, and $\ln p = 0.44$ when $\ln q = 1.95$, find the values of b and $\ln a$.   (5 marks)

(b) Given that $y = \log_2 x$ and that $\log_2 x - \log_x 8 + \log_2 2^k + k\log_x 4 = 0$, prove that $y^2 + ky + (2k - 3) = 0$.   (4 marks)

(i) Hence deduce the set of values of k for which y is real.   (4 marks)

(ii) Find the values of x when $k = 1.5$.   (3 marks)

Ans. (a) $\ln a = 2.06, b = -0.25$

(b) (i) $k \leq 2, k \geq 6$, (ii) $1, \frac{1}{4}\sqrt{2}$.   Nov. 86 (13) AEB

20. The sum of the first and second terms of a geometric progression is 108 and the sum of the third and fourth terms is 12. Find the two possible values of the common ratio and the corresponding values of the first term.   (6 marks)

Ans. $r = \frac{1}{3}$, $a = 81$; $r = \frac{1}{3}$, $a = 162$.   June 89 (1) AEB

21. A geometric series has first term 4 and common ratio r, where $0 < r < 1$. Given that the first, second and fourth terms of this geometric series form three successive terms of an arithmetic series, show that

$$r^3 - 2r + 1 = 0.$$

Find the value of r. (6 marks)

Ans. $\dfrac{1}{2}\left(\sqrt{5} - 1\right)$ **Nov. 89 AEB**

22. A geometric series has first term 4 and second term 7.

Giving your answer to 3 significant figures find the sum of the first 20 terms of the series. **June 90 AEB**

23. Express $\log_9 x$ in the form $k \log_3 x$ stating the value of k. Show that the sum to infinity of the geometric series $\log_3 x + \log_9 x + \log_{81} x + \ldots$ is $\log_3 x^2$.

Find, in terms of $\log_2 y$, the sum of the first 20 terms of the arithmetic series

$$\frac{1}{\log_2 y} + \frac{1}{\log_8 y} + \frac{1}{\log_{32} y} + \ldots$$

Given that this sum equals 100, find the value of y. **June 85 AEB**

24. The 4th term of a geometric series is 7 and the 7th term is 4. Find the sum to infinity of this series, giving your answer to the nearest integer.
Nov. 85 AEB

25. The ninth term of an arithmetic progression is 52 and the sum of the first twelve terms is 414.

Find the first term and the common difference.

The rth term of an arithmetic progression is $(1 + 4r)$. Find, in terms of n, the sum of the first n terms of the progression. **Nov. 90 AEB**

26. The 4th term of an arithmetic series is 7 and the 7th term is 4. Find the sum of the first 29 terms of this series. **Nov. 85 AEB**

27. The first term of an arithmetic progression is -13 and the last term is 99. The sum of the progression is 1419. Find the number of terms and the common difference. (4 marks)

Find also the sum of all the positive terms of the progression. (2 marks)

Ans. 33, $3\dfrac{1}{2}$; 1450. **June 87 AEB**

28. All the terms of a certain geometric series are positive.

The first term is a and the second term is $a^2 - a$. Find the set of values of a for which the series converges.

Given that $a = \dfrac{5}{3}$

(a) find the sum of the first 10 terms of the series, giving your answer to 2 decimal places, (4 marks)

(b) show that the sum to infinity of the series is 5, (2 marks)

(c) find the least number of terms of the series required to make their sum exceed 4.999. (5 marks)

Ans. $1 < a < 2$, (a) 4.91; (c) 22. **Nov. 87 AEB**

29. Express $2 \cos \left(x - \dfrac{\pi}{3} \right)$ in the form $a \cos x + b \sin x$.

Using the small angle approximations for $\sin x$ and $\cos x$, show that, if x is small enough for x^3 and higher powers to be ignored.

$$\sqrt{\left(2 \cos \left(x - \frac{\pi}{3} \right) \right)} = 1 + \frac{\sqrt{3}}{2} x + k x^2,$$

where k is a constant. State the value of k.

Ans. $a = 1, \ b = \sqrt{3}; \ k = -\dfrac{5}{8}$ **June 89 AEB**

30. (a) Write down and simplify binomial series in ascending powers of x up to and including the terms in x^3 for

$$(1 + x)^{-1}, \ (1 - 2x)^{-1} \text{ and } (1 - 2x)^{-2}.$$ (5 marks)

(b) Express $\dfrac{6 - 11x + 10x^2}{(1 + x)(1 - 2x)^2}$ in partial fractions. (3 marks)

(c) Using your series from (a) expand $\dfrac{6 - 11x + 10x^2}{(1 + x)(1 - 2x)^2}$ in

ascending powers of x up to and including the term in x^3. (3 marks)

(d) State the set of values of x for which your series in (c) is valid. (1 mark)

(e) Using the properties of logarithms and the series for $\ln(1 + y)$ in ascending powers of y, show that

$$\ln\left(\frac{6 - 11x + 10x^2}{(1 + x)(1 - 2x)^2}\right) = \ln 6 + Ax + Bx^2,$$

provided that terms in x^3 and higher powers of x can be neglected. Find the values of A and B. (4 marks)

Ans. (a) $1 - x + x^2 - x^3 \ldots,$ $\qquad\qquad 1 + 2x + 4x^2 + 8x^3 \ldots,$

$1 + 4x + 12x^2 + 32x^3 \ldots$ (b) $\dfrac{3}{1 + x} + \dfrac{1}{1 - 2x} + \dfrac{2}{(1 - x)^2}$

(c) $6 + 7x + 31x^2 + 69x^3 \ldots$ (d) $|x| < \dfrac{1}{2};$

(e) $A = \dfrac{7}{6}, B = \dfrac{323}{72}.$ $\qquad\qquad$ **Nov. 89 AEB**

31. Use the method of mathematical induction to show that

$$\sum_{r=1}^{n} r^2 = \frac{1}{6} n(n + 1)(2n + 1). \qquad \text{(5 marks)}$$

Hence find $\displaystyle\sum_{r=1}^{n} (n + r - 1)(n + r)$, giving your answer in terms of n.

(5 marks)

Find also $\displaystyle\sum_{r=1}^{n} \frac{1}{(n + r - 1)(n + r)}$, giving your answer in terms of n.

(5 marks)

Ans. $\dfrac{n}{3}(7n^2 - 1); \dfrac{1}{2n}.$ $\qquad\qquad$ **Nov. 89 P2 (2) AEB**

32. Verify that $4r^3 = r^2(r + 1)^2 - (r - 1)^2 r^2.$ (1 mark)

Deduce that $\displaystyle\sum_{r=1}^{n} r^3 = \frac{1}{4} n^2(n + 1)^2$, where n is a positive integer. (4 marks)

Hence find $\displaystyle\sum_{r=10}^{20} r^3$, expressing your answer in the form $p^2 - q^2$,

where p and q are integers whose values are to be stated. (4 marks)

By using the above formula for $\sum_{r=1}^{n} r^3$, or otherwise, prove that for each positive integer n.

$$1^3 + 3^3 + 5^3 + \ldots + (2n - 1)^3 = n^2 (2n^2 - 1).$$ (6 marks)

June 90 AEB

33. (a) Prove the identity

$$\frac{2r + 3}{r (r + 1)} - \frac{2r + 5}{(r + 1) (r + 2)} \equiv \frac{2 (r + 3)}{r (r + 1) (r + 2)}.$$ (2 marks)

Hence, or otherwise, find the sum of the series:-

$$S_n = \frac{8}{1 \times 2 \times 3} + \frac{10}{2 \times 3 \times 4} + \ldots + \frac{2 (n + 3)}{n (n + 1) (n + 2)}.$$ (4 marks)

Find $\lim_{x \to 0} S_n$. (2 marks)

(b) Given than $n > 1$, evaluate $I (n) = \int_{1}^{n} \frac{2 (x + 3)}{x (x + 1)(x + 2)} \, dx$ (5 marks)

Find $\lim_{x \to \infty} I (n)$. (2 marks)

Nov. 90 P2 (4) AEB

34. (a) Prove by mathematical induction that $\sum_{r=1}^{n} r \, 2^{r-1} = (n - 1) \, 2^n + 1$ (4 marks)

(b) By considering the expansion of $\ln (1 - x)$ find the sum of the infinite series $\sum_{r=1}^{\infty} \frac{1}{r \, 2^{r-1}}$. (5 marks)

(c) Write down the first four terms and the general term of the expansion in ascending powers of x of $(1 - x)^{-1}$. Hence, by differentiation, obtain the first 3 terms and the general term in the expansion of $(1 - x)^{-2}$.

Hence find the sum of the infinite series $\sum_{r=1}^{\infty} \frac{r}{2^{r-1}}$. (6 marks)

Ans. (b) 2 ln 2;   (c) $1 + x + x^2 + x^3 + \ldots + x^n + \ldots$;

$1 + 2x + 3x^2 + \ldots + nx^{n-1} + \ldots$; 4   **June 87 AEB**

35. (a) Use the method of mathematical induction to prove that

$$\sum_{r=1}^{n} r(2^r) = 2^{n+1}(n-1) + 2$$

for each positive integer n.   (4 marks)

(b) Write down in ascending powers of x the series for $\ln(1-x)$, where $|x| < 1$.

Hence find $\displaystyle\sum_{r=1}^{\infty} \frac{1}{r\,(2^r)}$, giving your answer in the form $\ln p$, for some number p.   (5 marks)

(c) Find $\displaystyle\sum_{r=1}^{\infty} \frac{1}{(r+1)!\ 2^r}$ (6 marks)

Ans. (b) $\ln 2$; (c) $2e^{\frac{1}{2}} - 3$.   **June 88 AEB**

36. The population p, in millions, of a small country was recorded in the January of various years and the results are shown in the table below.

Year	1968	1974	1980	1985
p	12.3	13.4	15.1	17.1

Given that $p = 10 + ab^t$ where t is the time measured in years from January 1965 and a and b are constants, express $\log_{10}(p-10)$ as a linear function of t. Draw a suitable straight line graph for $0 \le t \le 25$.   (4 marks)

Use your graph to estimate:-   (a)   the values of a and b,

                                  (b)   the year in which the population will
                                         reach 19.4 million.   (1 mark)

Ans. (a) $a = 1.86$, $b = 1.07$ (b) 1989   **June 85 AEB**

37. An infinite geometric series has first term a and common ratio r, where $a > 0$ and $0 < r < 1$. Show that D, the difference between the sum to infinity of the series and the sum of the first n terms of the series, is given by

$$D = \frac{ar^n}{1-r}$$ (3 marks)

Deduce that $\log_{10} D = n \log_{10} r + \log_{10}\left(\dfrac{a}{1-r}\right)$. (3 marks)

The following table gives values of D, rounded for the nearest 100, corresponding to some values of n.

n	4	6	10	14	16
D	4200	3000	1000	800	600

By drawing an appropriate linear graph, estimate to 2 significant figures, a value for r and a value for a.

An. $r = 0.85$, $a = 1200$. **June 86 AEB**

38. For a given mass of gas, the volume, V cm^3, and pressure, p cm of mercury, are related by $p = kV^n$ where k and n are constants.

(a) Prove that $\dfrac{dp}{dV} = \dfrac{np}{V}$. (2 marks)

(b) For a particular mass of gas $n = -1.4$. At the instant when the volume is 20 cm^3, the pressure is 150 cm of mercury and the volume is decreasing at a rate of 0.5 cm^3 s^{-1}. Calculate the rate of change of pressure at this instant, in cm of mercury per second. (5 marks)

(c) The following measurements of the volume, V cm^3, and the pressure, p cm of mercury, of a given mass of gas were taken.

V	10	50	110	170	230
p	1412.5	151.4	50.3	27.4	18.6

By plotting values of $\log_{10} p$ against $\log_{10} V$, verify graphically the relationship $p = kV^n$ where k and n are constants.

Use your graph to find approximate values of k and n, giving your answers to two significant figures. (9 marks)

Ans. 5.25 cm s^{-1}; 33000, -1.4. **June 87 AEB**

39. (a) When an employee retires from a particular firm, a lump-sum payment is made depending on the number of years of full-time employment with the firm. At the end of the first year of employment £300 is set aside towards this lump-sum. At the end of the second year another £300 is added and interest at 6% is added to the first year's £300. At the end of the third year another £300 is added and interest at 6% is added to the total sum of money which had accrued by the end of the second year. This process continues for the number of completed years of employment. By forming and summing a series, prove that an employee would receive $5000 [(1.06)^n - 1]$ pounds as the lump-sum payment for n years of employment with this firm. (4 marks)

Hence find the least number of years required for a lump-sum to exceed £15,000. (3 marks)

(b) Another employee retired with savings of just under £10,000. He records the value of these savings (S pounds) at the end of t years after retirement. The results are shown in the following table.

t	3	5	8	12
S	5100	3100	1700	700

The value of his savings is believed to follow a law of the form

$S = A(B^t)$, where A and B are constants. By drawing an appropriate

linear graph, verify that this belief is approximately valid and use your graph to estimate values for A and B. (9 marks)

Ans. (a)   24, 9600, 0.8   **June 88 AEB (9)**

40. Given that $y = (1 + 2x)^{-3}$ and that $|x| < \dfrac{1}{2}$, find and simplify a series in

ascending powers of x up to and including the term in x^3 for

(a) y,   (b) $\ln y$ **June 90 AEB**

41. Given that $-1 < x < 1$, find the expansion of $\dfrac{3 - 2x}{(1 + x)(4 + x^2)}$ in ascending

powers of x up to and including the term in x^3.   **Nov. 90 AEB**

42. Expand $(1 + 2x)^{-3}$ as a series of ascending powers of x, where $|x| < \dfrac{1}{2}$, up to and including the term in x^3, expressing the coefficients in their simplest form. **June 90 C**

43. Find the first three terms in the series expansion, in ascending powers of x, of $(1 + x)^{-2}$, where $|x| < 1$.

Hence, or otherwise, show that, when x is small

$$\left(\frac{1 - x}{1 + x}\right)^2 \approx 1 - 4x + 8\,x^2.$$ **June 89 C**

44. The function g is defined by g: $x \mapsto e^{-x} \cos x$, $x \in \mathbb{R}$.

Find and classify the stationary points of g in the interval $0 \leq x \leq 2\pi$. Show that $g(x + 2\pi) = kg(x)$, where k is a constant. Sketch the graph of the function g in the interval $0 \leq x \leq 4\pi$, giving the coordinates of the points of intersection with the coordinate, axes and of all the turning points.

$$\left[\text{Ans. } \frac{3\pi}{4} \text{ (minimum)}, \ x = \frac{7\pi}{4} \text{ (maximum)}: \ k = e^{-2\pi} \right]$$

Jan. 86 P2 (12) U.L.

45. (i)   Investigate the convergence or divergence of the series

(a) $\displaystyle\sum_{n=1}^{\infty} \frac{1}{2\,(1 + 2^{n+1})}$ (b) $\displaystyle\sum_{n=1}^{\infty} \frac{1}{1 + 2\sqrt{n}}$

(ii)   Using the expansion of $\sin x$ and $\cos x$ in series of ascending powers of x, prove that the first two non-zero terms in the series expansion of $\tan x$ are x and $+ x^3$. Given that the series expansion of $e^{\tan x}$ in ascending powers of x is $1 + ax + bx^2 + cx^3 + \ldots$, find the values of the constants a, b, and c.

Ans. (i) (a) Convergent,   (b) Divergent, (ii) $a = 1$, $b = c = \dfrac{1}{2}$.

June 86 P2 (5) U.L.

46. (i)   Sketch the curve $y = x^2 - 1$. Hence sketch the curve $y = |x^2 - 1|$.

Find the points of intersection of the curves $y = |x^2 - 7|$ and $y = |x^2 - 1|$. Hence, or otherwise, solve the inequality

$$|x^2 - 7| > |x^2 - 1|.$$

(ii) Show that the function f, where

$$f: x \to \frac{4x^2 + 8}{2x + 1}, \ x \in \mathbf{R} \ \ x \neq -\frac{1}{2} \ \text{ has range } \{x : x \leq -8\} \cup \{x : x \geq 4\}.$$

Ans. (i) (2, 3) (− 2, 3), − 2 < x < 2.   (ii) $x = -\frac{1}{2}, y = 2x - 1$

June 86 P2 (8) U.L.

47.   The quadratic function $q\ (x)$ is given by $q\ (x) = x^2 + 2kx + k + 2, \ x \in \mathbf{R}$, where k is a constant. Given that the roots of the equation $q\ (x) = 0$ are α and ß, show that $(\alpha - ß)^2 = 4(k^2 - k - 2)$

(a)   Find the values of k for which the roots of the equation $q\ (x) = 0$ differ by 4.

(b)   Given that $k \neq -2$ form a quadratic equation, with coefficients in terms of k, whose roots are $\left(1 + \dfrac{\alpha}{ß}\right)$ and $\left(1 + \dfrac{ß}{\alpha}\right)$.

Jan. 87 P2 (13) U.L.

48.   (i)   Find the sum of the series

$$\ln\left(\frac{1}{2}\right) + \ln\left(\frac{2}{3}\right) + \ln\left(\frac{3}{4}\right) + \ldots + \ln\left(\frac{n}{n+1}\right).$$

Hence determine whether or not the series $\displaystyle\sum_{r=1}^{\infty} \ln\left(\frac{r}{r+1}\right)$ converges.

(ii)   Investigate the convergence or divergence of the series

(a) $\displaystyle\sum_{r=1}^{\infty} \left(\frac{\sqrt{r}}{r^2 + 1}\right),$ (b) $\displaystyle\sum_{2^{r-1}}^{\infty} \left(\frac{3^r + 1}{2^r - 1}\right)$

(iii)   Obtain the expansion of $f(x) = e^x \ln (1 + 2x)$ in ascending powers of x, up to and including the terms in x^3. Hence find

$$\lim_{x \to 0} \frac{e^x \ln (1 + 2x) - \sin 2x}{x^3}.$$

June 87 U.L.

1. ALGEBRA

ANSWERS

EXERCISES 1

1. (i) $-x^3 - x - 4, 10;$ (ii) $x^2 + 3x + 7, 15;$ (iii) $-x^2 - x - 3; -5.$

2. (i)   10;   (ii)   15;   (iii) $-5.$

3. (i) $x = 2, x = -1$ (ii) $x = 2; x = -2, x = 3;$ (iii) $\pm a;$

   (iv)   2   (v) $0, -\dfrac{1}{2}, \dfrac{1}{3}.$

4. 2.   5.   0.   6. $-\dfrac{43}{3}.$

7. $a = \dfrac{28}{3}, b = \dfrac{34}{3}$ 8. $a = -\dfrac{3}{4}, b = \dfrac{7}{3}, c = 1$ 9. $4x - 1.$

10. $\pm i$, complex.   11. $a = \dfrac{17}{2}, b = -\dfrac{3}{2}.$

12. $a = \dfrac{121}{6}, b = \dfrac{203}{6}.$ 13. $a = \dfrac{25}{6}, b = \dfrac{5}{2}, c = -\dfrac{8}{3}.$

14. $a = -\dfrac{3}{2}, b = -\dfrac{5}{2}, c = 4, d = 4$ or $d = -3$

15. $a = -\dfrac{331}{180}, b = \dfrac{413}{30}, c = \dfrac{649}{180}.$ 16. $a = 4, b = -11$

17. $a = 4, b = 6, c = 3.$

19. $a = -20, b = -4, c = 50.$ 20. $a = \dfrac{33}{7}, b = -9, c = -\dfrac{297}{7}.$

EXERCISES 2

1. $\dfrac{6(2 - x)}{9 - x^2}.$ 2. $\dfrac{4}{5}.$ 3. $\dfrac{8x + 3}{(x + 3)(x + 4)}.$

4. $\dfrac{6 - x}{x(x + 3)}$.

5. $\dfrac{2 + x - x^2}{x^2(x + 2)}$.

6. $\dfrac{6x^2 + 13x + 3}{x(x + 1)(x + 3)}$.

7. $\dfrac{11}{30}$.

8. $\dfrac{x^3 - 4x^2 - 18x + 23}{(x + 2)(x - 3)(x - 5)}$.

9. $\dfrac{x}{x + 1}$.

10. $\dfrac{2x + 2}{x + 2}$.

11. $\dfrac{x^2 + 4x - 3}{x(x - 1)}$.

12. $\dfrac{3x^3 + 6x^2 + 6x + 2}{(x + 1)^3(2x + 1)}$.

13. $\dfrac{x(x + 1)}{(x^2 + 1)(x - 1)}$.

14. $\dfrac{2x^2 - 2x - 2}{(2x - 1)(2x^2 - 3)}$.

15. $\dfrac{x^3 + 2x^2 - 9x - 19}{(x + 2)^2(x^2 - 5)}$.

16. $\dfrac{10}{7(x - 3)} - \dfrac{3}{7(x + 4)}$.

17. $\dfrac{1}{x - 1} + \dfrac{1}{x + 2}$.

18. $-\dfrac{8}{5(2x + 1)} + \dfrac{17}{5(3x - 1)}$.

19. $1 - \dfrac{3}{x + 2} - \dfrac{1}{x + 3}$.

20. $3 - \dfrac{5}{4(x - 1)} - \dfrac{23}{4(x + 3)}$.

21. $x + 1 + \dfrac{64}{9(x + 4)} + \dfrac{125}{9(x - 5)}$.

22. $\dfrac{5}{7(x - 7)} + \dfrac{2}{7(x + 7)}$.

23. $\dfrac{17}{18(9 - x)} - \dfrac{19}{18(9 + x)}$.

24. $\dfrac{25}{12(x - 6)} + \dfrac{11}{12(x + 6)}$.

25. $-\dfrac{3}{2(x + 1)} + \dfrac{1}{5(x - 2)} + \dfrac{23}{10(x + 3)}$.

26. $\dfrac{37}{20(x + 3)} - \dfrac{7}{24(x + 5)} + \dfrac{413}{120(x - 7)}$.

27. $-\dfrac{1}{3 - x} + \dfrac{5}{3 + x}$.

28. $\dfrac{2}{x} - \dfrac{3}{x + 3}$.

29. $\dfrac{1}{x} + \dfrac{2}{x + 1} + \dfrac{3}{x + 3}$.

30. $1 + \dfrac{32}{35(x + 2)} + \dfrac{3}{10(x - 3)} + \dfrac{25}{14(x - 5)}$.

31. $1 - \dfrac{1}{x + 1}$.

32. $2 - \dfrac{2}{x + 2}$.

EXERCISES 3

1. (i) $a < 0$ (ii) $a > 0$ 2. $x = -\dfrac{b}{2a}$ 3. --   4. --

5. (a) $a = 1, b = 4, c = 7;$ (b) $a = \dfrac{7}{9}, b = \dfrac{14}{3}, c = 2$

    (c) $a = \dfrac{4}{9}, b = -\dfrac{8}{3}, c = 5;$ (d) $a = -\dfrac{9}{25}, b = \dfrac{90}{25}, c = 10.$

13. $k = 1.14$ (i) $D = 0$ (ii) $D < 0$ (iii) $D > 0$

EXERCISES 4

1. (i) $\dfrac{c}{a}$ (ii) $\sqrt{\dfrac{b^2 - 4ac}{a^2}}$ (iii) $\dfrac{b^2 - 4ac}{a^2}$

   (iv) $\dfrac{b^2}{a^2}$ (v) $\dfrac{b^2 + 2ba}{a^2}$ (vi) $\dfrac{3abc - b^3}{a^3}$

   (vii) $\sqrt{\dfrac{b^2 - 4ac}{a^2}} \left[\dfrac{b^2 + 2ab}{a^2} - \dfrac{c}{a} \right]$ (viii) $\sqrt{\dfrac{b^2 - 4ac}{a^2}} \left(-\dfrac{b}{a} \right)$

   (ix) $\left(\dfrac{b^2 + 2ab}{a^2} \right)^2 - \dfrac{2c^2}{a^2}$ (x) $\dfrac{b(b + 2a)}{c^2}.$

2. (i) $\dfrac{5}{7}$ (ii) $\pm 0.09i$ 3. $c = a, b^2 \geq 4a^2$

4. $7x^2 + 49x + 156 = 0$ 5. $3b^2 = 16ac$ 6. (i) $-\dfrac{17}{49}$ (ii) $-\dfrac{4513}{2401}$

7. 0.342 and 0.684 or 13.158 and 26.316 8. $k < 0.003$ and $k > 33.97$

9. $\dfrac{1}{\sqrt{3}}$ or $\dfrac{4}{\sqrt{3}}$, and $-\dfrac{1}{\sqrt{3}}$ and $-\dfrac{4}{\sqrt{3}}$; $5\sqrt{3}$ or $-5\sqrt{3}$.

10. (i) $S = -\dfrac{1}{2}, P = \dfrac{1}{2}$ (ii) $S = -\dfrac{5}{3}, P = 3$ (iii) 2, 7

    (iv) 4, -2 (v) $1, -\dfrac{1}{5}$

11. (i) $x^2 + 3x + 5 = 0$ (ii) $x^2 - 25x - 39 = 0$

    (iii) $x^2 - 37x + 2 = 0$

12. (i) $-\dfrac{b}{a}$ (ii) $-\dfrac{d}{a}$ (iii) $\dfrac{c}{a}$.

EXERCISES 5

1. (i) $x < 1$ (ii) $x > -\dfrac{8}{5}$ (iii) $x \leq 0$ (iv) $1 < x < 4$ (v) $1 < x < \dfrac{4}{3}$

    (vi) $x > 5$ and $x < 0$ (vii) $x < -1, x > 0$ (viii) $x > 0$

2. (i) $x \neq 1$ (ii) $x > 4, x < -1$

3. (i) $x < -1, x > 0$ (ii) $1 \leq x \leq 3$ (iii) $x < \dfrac{3}{2}$.

4. $0 < x < 1$ and $x < -1$

5. (i) $x < -2$ and $1 < x < 3$ (ii) $-1 < x < 0$ and $x > 2$

6. (i) $\dfrac{1}{2} < x < 5$ (ii) $-5 < x < \dfrac{1}{2}$ (iii) $\dfrac{1}{4} < x < 1$

7. (i) $-1 < x < 5$ (ii) $-7 \leq x \leq 4$ (iii) $-1 < x < 4$

8. $\dfrac{7}{10} < x < \dfrac{8}{5}$.

EXERCISES 6

4. (i) One-to-one function   (ii) & (iii) are not functions.

5. (i) $g\left(-\dfrac{2}{5}\right) = 0$ (ii) $g\left(\dfrac{1}{2}\right) = 4.5$;

    (iii) $k = -\dfrac{2}{5}$;   (iv) $\{-13, -8, -3, 2, 7, 12, 17\}$.

6. $\{0, 7, 18, 33, 52\}$.   7. $\left\{0, \dfrac{1}{25}, \dfrac{4}{25}, \dfrac{9}{25}\right\}$.

8. $h(-2) = -1$; $x = 0$, $x = 0.443$, $x = -1.69$.

9. (b) $\dfrac{1 - x}{x}$

    (c) $-\infty < x < 0$ and $0 < x < 0$; $-\infty < y < -1$ and $-1 < y < \infty$.

    (d) (i) -2;   (ii) $\dfrac{1}{3}$;   (iii) $\dfrac{5}{9}$;   (iv) $-\dfrac{1}{2}$ (e) one-to-one functions.

EXERCISES 7

1. (i) $\dfrac{1}{64}$ (ii) 9   (iii) $\dfrac{1}{8}$ (iv) $\dfrac{1}{8}$ (v) $\dfrac{1}{5^9}$

    (vi) $675\sqrt{5}$ (vii) 8   (viii) 8   (ix) $3^{24/5}$ (x) 8.

2. (i) -6 (ii) $\dfrac{1}{3}$ (iii) $\dfrac{1}{2}$.

3. (i) $\left(\dfrac{12}{25}\right)^{5/3}$ (ii) $\dfrac{13}{27}$ (iii) $\dfrac{49}{125}$ (iv) $\dfrac{1}{10}$ (v) 5.

4. (i) 0.693 (ii) -1.19 (iii) $x = 0$.

5. $8 \times 5^{6x + 8}$.   6. 1.11.

7. (i) -5 (ii) $-\dfrac{1}{9}$ (iii) $-\dfrac{41}{22}$ (iv) 3.26×10^{-3} (v) $-\dfrac{5}{3}$.

8. (i) $\dfrac{3^{3x + 2}}{2^{3x + 6}}$;   (ii) $2^{x + 4}$ (iii) $6^{4x - 1}$.

9. (i) $\dfrac{xy(x + y)}{(x^2 + y^2)}$ (ii) $\dfrac{1}{x} + x + 2$ (iii) $\dfrac{x^2 + y^2}{xy(x^3 - y^3)}$

10. (i) $x = \dfrac{3}{2}, y = -\dfrac{3}{2}$ (ii) $x = \dfrac{3}{2}, y = -\dfrac{3}{4}$.

EXERCISES 8

1. (i) $5^4 = 625$ (ii) $144 = 12^2$ (iii) $2^7 = 128$

   (iv) $13^2 = 169$ (v) $\left(\dfrac{1}{5}\right)^{-2} = 25$ (vi) $\left(\dfrac{1}{7}\right)^{-2} = 49$

   (vii) $\left(\dfrac{1}{11}\right)^{-2} = 121$ (viii) $M^p = N$ (ix) $y^2 = x^2$

   (x) $B^C = A$ (xi) $y^w = x^z$ (xii) $5^4 = 625$.

2. (i) $\log_2 1024 = 10$ (ii) $\log_3 243 = 5$ (iii) $10 \log_{1024} 2 = 1$

   (iv) $5 \log_{243} 3 = 1$ (v) $\dfrac{t}{T} = \log_e \dfrac{I}{i}$ (vi) $\dfrac{t}{T} = \ln \dfrac{V}{v}$

   (vii) $\dfrac{t}{T} = \ln \dfrac{Q}{q}$ (viii) $\log_{24} 576 = 2$ (ix) $\log_{143} 20449 = 2$

   (x) $\log_8 4094 = 4$.

3. (i) $\log 1024 = 10 \log 2$ (ii) $\log_{10} 243 = 5 \log_{10} 3$

   (iii) $\log 1024 = 10 \log 2$ (iv) $\log 243 = 5 \log 3$

   (v) $\dfrac{t}{T} \log e = \log \dfrac{I}{i}$ (vi) $\dfrac{t}{T} \log e = \log \dfrac{V}{v}$

   (vii) $\dfrac{t}{T} \log e = \log \dfrac{Q}{q}$ (viii) $\log 576 = 2 \log 24$

   (ix) $\log 20449 = 2 \log 143$ (x) $\log 4096 = 4 \log 8$.

1. ALGEBRA

INDEX